Pharmaco-Genomics Handbook

2nd Edition

Larisa M. Cavallari, PharmD, BCPS
Vicki L. Ellingrod, PharmD, BCPP
Jill M. Kolesar, PharmD, FCCP, BCPS

LEXI-COMP'S

Pharmaco-Genomics Handbook

2nd Edition

Larisa H. Cavallari, PharmD, BCPS
Assistant Professor, Section of Cardiology
University of Illinois at Chicago
Chicago, IL

Vicki L. Ellingrod, PharmD, BCPP
Associate Professor
University of Iowa
Iowa City, IA

Jill M. Kolesar, PharmD, FCCP, BCPS
Associate Professor of Pharmacy
University of Wisconsin
Madison, WI

LEXI-COMP, INC

NOTICE

This handbook is intended to serve as a useful reference and not as a complete resource. The explosion of information in many directions, in multiple scientific disciplines, with advances in techniques, and continuing evolution of knowledge requires constant scholarship. The authors, editors, reviewers, contributors, and publishers cannot be responsible for the continued currency of the information or for any errors or omissions in this manual or for any consequences arising therefrom. Because of the dynamic nature of medicine as a discipline, readers are advised that decisions regarding diagnosis and treatment must be based on the independent judgment of the clinician. The editors are not responsible for any inaccuracy of quotation or for any false or misleading implication that may arise due to the text.

The editors, authors, and contributors have written this book in their private capacities. No official support or endorsement by any federal or state agency or pharmaceutical company is intended or inferred.

The publishers have made every effort to trace the copyright holders for borrowed material. If they have inadvertently overlooked any, they will be pleased to make the necessary arrangements at the first opportunity.

If you have any suggestions or questions regarding any information presented in this handbook, please contact our drug information pharmacist at (330) 650-6506.

This manual was produced using the FormuLex™ Program — a complete publishing service of Lexi-Comp, Inc.

1100 Terex Road
Hudson, Ohio 44236
(330) 650-6506

ISBN 1-59195-124-0

TABLE OF CONTENTS

ABOUT THE AUTHORS

Larisa H. Cavallari, PharmD, BCPS

Dr Cavallari received her Bachelor of Science in Pharmacy and Doctor of Pharmacy degrees from the University of Georgia, College of Pharmacy. She then completed a one-year pharmacy practice residency with an emphasis in cardiology at the VA Medical Center in Memphis. Dr Cavallari subsequently completed a two-year fellowship in cardiovascular pharmacogenomics at the University of Florida, where she was awarded the 1999-2001 American Foundation for Pharmaceutical Education Clinical Pharmacy Post-PharmD Fellowship in the Biomedical Research Sciences. Dr Cavallari is presently an Assistant Professor of Pharmacy Practice at the University of Illinois at Chicago and a clinical pharmacist at the University of Illinois Medical Center. Dr Cavallari is a Board-Certified Pharmacotherapy Specialist (BCPS) and taught the cardiology and critical care sections of the American College of Clinical Pharmacy-Sponsored Pharmacotherapy Preparatory Course from 2001-2003.

In her current position, Dr Cavallari teaches in the cardiovascular section and is actively involved in clinical and basic science research focusing on genetic contributions to cardiovascular drug therapy response. Her research is funded by the American Heart Association Midwest Affilliate and the National Heart Foundation, a division of the American Health Assistance Foundation. She also participates in the student experiential program, serves on several departmental and college committees, serves as a Senator for the College of Pharmacy, and remains actively involved in the care of patients in the Antithrombosis Clinic. Dr Cavallari has authored several original research articles, review articles, and book chapters and has given a number of presentations on the subject of pharmacogenomics at both the state and national levels. Dr Cavallari is currently a reviewer for the *Annals of Pharmacotherapy* and the 5th edition of the *Pharmacotherapy Self-Assessment Program (PSAP).*

Dr Cavallari is an active member of the American College of Clinical Pharmacy (ACCP), where she has served on several committees, the American Heart Association, the Heart Failure Society of America (HFSA), and American Association of Colleges of Pharmacy (AACP).

Vicki L. Ellingrod, PharmD, BCPP

Vicki L. Ellingrod received her bachelor's degree and Doctor of Pharmacy degree from the University of Minnesota. She completed a two-year fellowship in psychopharmacology and pharmacogenetics at the University of Iowa. Currently, Dr Ellingrod is an Associate Professor at the University of Iowa and Director of the Pharmacogenetics Laboratory at the University of Iowa College of Pharmacy. Her research interests include the genetics behind the metabolism of psychiatric medications, as well as the pharmacogenetics of the adverse drug reactions seen with antipsychotics. Currently, her research is primarily funded by the National Institutes of Mental Health through a career development award entitled "The

Genetics of Antipsychotic Metabolism." In addition to her research in schizophrenia, Dr Ellingrod is also actively involved in studies involving antipsychotic use in dementia, as well as serving as a co-investigator on several other projects involving pharmacogenetics and drug metabolism. Dr Ellingrod has authored numerous journal articles and lectures locally, as well as nationally, on pharmacogenomics in psychiatry.

In her capacity as director of the Pharmacogenetics Laboratory, Dr Ellingrod is also involved in patient care and is board certified in psychiatric pharmacy. She serves as a reviewer for many psychiatric publications including the *American Journal of Psychiatry*, the *American Journal of Geriatric Psychiatry*, *PharmacoGenomics*, and *Journal of the American Geriatrics Society*. She is actively involved in many pharmacy organizations including the American College of Clinical Pharmacy and the College of Psychiatric and Neurologic Pharmacists. Recently, Dr Ellingrod was awarded the "Young Investigator Award" by the American College of Clinical Pharmacy for her work in pharmacogenomics.

Jill M. Kolesar, PharmD, FCCP, BCPS

Jill M. Kolesar, Pharm D, FCCP, BCPS, received a Doctor of Pharmacy and completed a specialty practice residency in oncology/hematology and a two-year fellowship in molecular oncology pharmacotherapy at the University of Texas Health Science Center in San Antonio, Texas. She is currently an Associate Professor of Pharmacy at the University of Wisconsin School of Pharmacy and the Director of Analytical Instrumentation Laboratory for Pharmacokinetics, Pharmacogenetics, and Pharmacodynamics (3P) at the University of Wisconsin Comprehensive Cancer Center.

Dr Kolesar practices in the Hematology and Oncology Clinics at the William S. Middleton VA Hospital in Madison, Wisconsin, managing the pharmacotherapy of ambulatory patients. Her research in pharmacogenomics includes the use of molecular markers to predict response and monitor efficacy of cancer chemotherapy, population genotyping for cancer susceptibility, and the regulation of gene expression of the two electron reductases. She has authored more than 100 abstracts, research articles, and book chapters, and as a principal investigator, she has received more than $500,000 in research funding from the NCI, ACS, and other sources. In addition, she holds two U.S. patents for novel assay methodologies for gene expression and mutation analysis. She has received several research awards from local, national, and international pharmacy organizations and a Merit Award from the American Society of Clinical Oncology (ASCO). She also received the "Innovations in Teaching Award" from the American Association of Colleges of Pharmacy.

CONTRIBUTING AUTHORS

Mark F. Bonfiglio, BS, PharmD, RPh

Dr Bonfiglio received his bachelor's degrees and undergraduate training from the University of Toledo (BA in Biology/BS in Pharmacy) and his PharmD from the Ohio State University. He completed a residency in Critical Care Pharmacy at University Hospitals in Columbus, Ohio. On completion of his training, he worked for several years as a Clinical Specialist in Critical Care in the SUMMA Health System, followed by a position as Pharmacotherapy Specialist in Internal Medicine at Akron General Medical Center. In both of these positions he was concurrently employed by the College of Pharmacy at Ohio Northern University where he attained the rank of Associate Clinical Professor. He currently coordinates the Advanced Pharmacology course for the College of Nursing at Malone College, and serves as a Part-Time Faculty in the Department of Biological Sciences at Kent State University, serving as the primary lecturer for the Department's course in Immunology.

Dr Bonfiglio is currently the Director of the Medical Science Division of Lexi-Comp, Inc. He coordinates the development and maintenance of the core pharmacology database and serves as an author for several printed titles, including the *Drug Information Handbook for Advanced Practice Nursing* and *Drug Interactions Handbook*. Dr Bonfiglio maintains memberships in the Society for Critical Care Medicine (SCCM), the American Pharmacists Association (APhA), the American Society of Health-System Pharmacists (ASHP), the Ohio College of Clinical Pharmacy (OCCP), the American Society for Automation in Pharmacy (ASAP), and the American Association for the Advancement of Science (AAAS).

Matthew A. Fuller, PharmD, BCPS, BCPP, FASHP

Dr Fuller received his Bachelor of Science in Pharmacy from Ohio Northern University and then earned a Doctor of Pharmacy degree from the University of Cincinnati. A residency in hospital pharmacy was completed at Bethesda hospital in Zanesville, Ohio. After completion of his training, Dr Fuller accepted a position at the Veterans Affairs Medical Center in Cleveland, Ohio.

Dr Fuller has over 20 years of experience in psychiatric psychopharmacology in a variety of clinical settings including acute care and ambulatory care. Dr Fuller is currently a Clinical Pharmacy Specialist in Psychiatry at the Veterans Affairs Medical Center in Cleveland, Ohio. He is also an Associate Clinical Professor of Psychiatry and Clinical Instructor of Psychology at Case Western Reserve University in Cleveland, Ohio and Adjunct Associate Professor of Clinical Pharmacy at the University of Toledo in Toledo, Ohio. In this position, Dr Fuller is responsible for providing service, education, and research. He is also the Director of an ASHP accredited Psychiatric Pharmacy Practice Residency Program.

Dr Fuller has received several awards including the Upjohn Excellence in Research Award and the OSHP Hospital Pharmacist of the Year Award in 1994. In 1996, he received the CSHP Evelyn Gray Scott Award (Pharmacist of the Year). In 2001, he received the OSHP Pharmacy Practice Research Award.

Dr Fuller is Board Certified by the Board of Pharmaceutical Specialties in both Pharmacotherapy and Psychiatric Pharmacy. He speaks regularly on the topic of psychotropic use and has published articles and abstracts on various issues in psychiatric psychopharmacology. His research interests include the psychopharmacologic treatment of schizophrenia and bipolar disorder.

Dr Fuller is a member of numerous professional organizations, including the College of Psychiatric and Neurologic Pharmacists (CPNP) where he was recently elected president-elect, the American Society of Health-System Pharmacists (ASHP), where he was recently designated as a fellow. He completed his term as a member of the Commission on Therapeutics and is a member of the Clinical Specialist Section; Ohio Society of Health-System Pharmacists (OSHP) where he has served as an Educational Affairs Division member and a House of Delegates member; American College of Clinical Pharmacy (ACCP); Ohio College of Clinical Pharmacy where he served as secretary/treasurer; and Cleveland Society of Health-System Pharmacist (CSHP) where he has served as the education chair and treasurer. He is a member of the National Alliance for the Mentally Ill (NAMI) and also serves as a reviewer for pharmacy and psychiatric journals. He is also a member of the psychiatry editorial board for the *Annals of Pharmacotherapy*.

David M. Weinstein, PhD, RPh

After receiving his BS in Pharmacy from the Ohio State University, Dr Weinstein earned a Doctorate of Pharmacology from Ohio State, specializing in the area of neuropharmacology. He then completed a 2-year postdoctoral fellowship in cardiovascular therapeutics, focusing on understanding mechanisms of nitric oxide signaling and myocardial oxidative injury. While at Ohio State, Dr Weinstein also served as coinstructor for several pharmacology courses, and as adjunct faculty for molecular biology at Ohio Dominican College. Dr. Weinstein subsequently held positions within the pharmaceutical industry, including Assistant Director of Scientific Communications for Bayer Pharmaceuticals and Project Manager for Pro-ED COMMUNICATIONS, Inc. In these roles, he managed scientific publication and continuing education efforts for various anti-infective, oncology, and rheumatology products. He has also served for the past 4 years as a clinical staff pharmacist at South Pointe Hospital, within the Cleveland Clinic Health System. Currently, as a Pharmacotherapy Specialist for Lexi-Comp, Inc., Dr Weinsteins primary responsibility is coordinating the continued development and integration of the company's proprietary pharmacogenomics database. Additional responsibilities include maintaining updates to the core pharmacology database,

CONTRIBUTING AUTHORS *(Continued)*

with particular emphasis in the areas of infectious disease and neurology. Dr Weinstein remains committed to teaching and publication opportunities and maintains professional affiliations with the American Society of Health-System Pharmacists (ASHP), its Cleveland chapter (CSHP), and adjunct faculty appointment to Cuyahoga Community College.

ACKNOWLEDGMENTS

The *Pharmacogenomics Handbook* exists in its present form as the result of the concerted efforts of the following individuals: Robert D. Kerscher, publisher and president of Lexi-Comp Inc; Mark Bonfiglio, PharmD, director of pharmacotherapy resources; Stacy S. Robinson, editorial manager; Barbara F. Kerscher, production manager; Robin L. Farabee, project manager; David C. Marcus, director of information systems; Dave Weinstein, PhD, pharmacotherapy specialist; Leslie J. Hoppes, pharmacology database manager; Tracey J. Henterly, graphic designer; Alexandra Hart, composition specialist; Darik Warnke, product manager.

Special acknowledgment goes to all Lexi-Comp staff for their contributions to this handbook.

In addition, the authors wish to thank their families, friends, and collegues who supported them in their efforts to complete this handbook.

PREFACE

The potential for successful drug therapy outcomes may be enhanced by tailoring dosage to the unique requirements of the individual. For many years, the application of pharmacokinetic principles, coupled with information concerning major organ function, has facilitated the design of dosing regimens to achieve desired serum drug concentrations. However, many of the pharmacokinetic and pharmacodynamic factors responsible for drug response are not addressed by these efforts. The potential to adjust drug selection and/or regimen design to address individual variation in the rate of and/or capacity for drug metabolism, sensitivity to untoward effects, or response at a given serum concentration has been limited.

Recognition of patient factors, such as acetylator status and glucose-6-phosphate dehydrogenase deficiency, provided early evidence of genetic traits which could explain adverse reactions which would otherwise be characterized as "idiosyncratic." Advancing molecular biology techniques, as well as the recent completion of the Human Genome Project, have provided a wealth of information concerning genetic variability. Many of these variations are being examined as predisposing factors for disease, as well as their influence on drug response.

A number of significant advances in our understanding of genetic influences on drug therapy has been made in recent years. As differences in the genes which encode cellular processes are explored, it is hoped that the ability to tailor dosing regimens to individual characteristics will be dramatically expanded.

This book presents information concerning key genetic variations that appear to influence drug disposition and/or sensitivity. Because of the rapidly-changing nature of this field, no static effort to encapsulate the literature will ever be sufficient. However, we believe it is reasonable to provide a snapshot of current knowledge, and attempt to equip the reader with a fundamental understanding of genomic issues. In the process, we hope to establish a paradigm for the incorporation of new information as it unfolds. We look forward to participating in the collection and dissemination of information as we enter the genomic age.

DESCRIPTION OF SECTIONS AND FIELDS IN THIS HANDBOOK

Lexi-Comp's Pharmacogenomics Handbook is divided into five sections: Introductory information, drug information, potential polymorphisms, index of polymorhpisms and drugs potentially affected, and alphabetical index.

Alphabetical Listing of Drugs

The drug information section of the handbook provides a comprehensive listing of selected and pertinent drug monographs.

Individual monographs contain most or all of the following fields of information:

Generic Name	U.S. adopted name
Pronunciation	Phonetic pronunciation
Genes of Interest	Listing and cross-reference to the polymorphism affected by the drug
U.S. Brand Names	Trade names (manufacturer-specific) found in the United States. The symbol [DSC] appears after trade names that have been recently discontinued.
Canadian Brand Names	Trade names found in Canada (if different from the U.S.)
Synonyms	Other names or accepted abbreviations for the generic drug
Pharmacologic Class	Unique systematic classification of medications

Alphabetical Listing of Potential Polymorphisms

Individual monographs contain most or all of the following fields of information:

Name	Common name
Related Information	Cross-reference to other pertinent drug information found in the handbook
Synonyms	Other names or accepted abbreviations of the polymorphism
Chromosome Location	Nomenclature which identifies the location on the human chromosome
Clinically-Important Polymorphisms	Known gene variance with clinical implications
Discussion	Description of the normal gene function and studies related to effect on individual drugs

DESCRIPTION OF SECTIONS AND FIELDS IN THIS HANDBOOK *(Continued)*

May Alter Pharmacokinetics of	Lists drugs for which kinetics may be affected
May Alter Pharmacodynamics of	Lists drugs for which dynamics may be affected
May Affect Disease Predisposition of	Comments on the influence of gene polymorphism on disease risk
Laboratory Evaluation	Comments on laboratory testing when known
Clinical Recommendations	Summary of significance in current clinical practice
Counseling Points	Information for individuals who carry a polymorphism
References	

Polymorphisms and Drugs Potentially Affected Index

This index provides a useful listing of drugs by their potential polymorphism.

Alphabetical Index

A listing of all polymorphism names, drug names, synonyms, U.S. brand names, and Canadian brand names found in this handbook.

FDA NAME DIFFERENTIATION PROJECT THE USE OF TALL-MAN LETTERS

Confusion between similar drug names is an important cause of medication errors. For years, The Institute For Safe Medication Practices (ISMP), has urged generic manufacturers use a combination of large and small letters as well as bolding (ie, chlorpro**MAZINE** and chlorpro**PAMIDE**) to help distinguish drugs with look-alike names, especially when they share similar strengths. Recently the FDA's Division of Generic Drugs began to issue recommendation letters to manufacturers suggesting this novel way to label their products to help reduce this drug name confusion. Although this project has had marginal success, the method has successfully eliminated problems with products such as diphenhydr**AMINE** and dimenhy**DRINATE**. Hospitals should also follow suit by making similar changes in their own labels, preprinted order forms, computer screens and printouts, and drug storage location labels.

Lexi-Comp Medical Publishing has adopted the use of these "Tall-Man" letters for the drugs suggested by the FDA.

The following is a list of product names and recommended FDA revisions:

Drug Product	Recommended Revision
acetazolamide	aceta**ZOLAMIDE**
acetohexamide	aceto**HEXAMIDE**
bupropion	bu**PROP**ion
buspirone	bus**PIR**one
chlorpromazine	chlorpro**MAZINE**
chlorpropamide	chlorpro**PAMIDE**
clomiphene	clomi**PHENE**
clomipramine	clomi**PRAMINE**
cycloserine	cyclo**SERINE**
cyclosporine	cyclo**SPORINE**
daunorubicin	**DAUNO**rubicin
dimenhydrinate	dimenhy**DRINATE**
diphenhydramine	diphenhydr**AMINE**
dobutamine	**DOBUT**amine
dopamine	**DOP**amine
doxorubicin	**DOXO**rubicin
glipizide	glipi**ZIDE**
glyburide	gly**BURIDE**
hydralazine	hydr**ALAZINE**
hydroxyzine	hydr**OXY**zine

FDA NAME DIFFERENTIATION PROJECT THE USE OF TALL-MAN LETTERS *(Continued)*

Drug Product	Recommended Revision
medroxyprogesterone	medroxy**PROGESTER**one
methylprednisolone	methyl**PREDNIS**olone
methyltestosterone	methyl**TESTOSTER**one
nicardipine	ni**CAR**dipine
nifedipine	**NIFE**dipine
prednisolone	predniso**LONE**
prednisone	predni**SONE**
sulfadiazine	sulfa**DIAZINE**
sulfisoxazole	sulfi**SOXAZOLE**
tolazamide	**TOLAZ**amide
tolbutamide	**TOLBUT**amide
vinblastine	vin**BLAS**tine
vincristine	vin**CRIS**tine

Institute for Safe Medication Practices. "New Tall-Man Lettering Will Reduce Mix-Ups Due to Generic Drug Name Confusion," *ISMP Medication Safety Alert*, September 19, 2001. Available at: http://www.ismp.org.

Institute for Safe Medication Practices. "Prescription Mapping, Can Improve Efficiency While Minimizing Errors With Look-Alike Products," *ISMP Medication Safety Alert*, October 6, 1999. Available at: http://www.ismp.org.

U.S. Pharmacopeia, "USP Quality Review: Use Caution-Avoid Confusion," March 2001, No. 76. Available at: http://www.usp.org.

DEFINITIONS / GLOSSARY

Allele: Single copy of a gene (in most cases, everybody has 2 alleles for a given gene). Genes may be polyallelic. For example, the genes for blood type (A, B, and O) are triallelic.

Chromosome: The self-replicating genetic structure of cells containing the cellular DNA that bears in its nucleotide sequence the linear array of genes.

Codon: Three consecutive nucleotides in the mRNA molecule to which the "anti-codon" region (of complimentary nucleotides) of a transfer RNA (tRNA) molecule binds. The amino acid carried by the tRNA molecule is added to the growing peptide chain during the translation process.

Deletion: Loss of a section of DNA from a gene.

DNA sequencing: Molecular biology technique used to determine the identity and exact pattern of nucleotides in a segment of DNA.

Electrophoresis: Involves the process of separating molecules based on their size and electrical charge, based on passing an electrical current through a gel or similar material with a known pore size.

Gene: The fundamental physical and functional unit of heredity. A gene is an ordered sequence of nucleotides located in a particular position on a particular chromosome that encodes a specific functional product (ie, a protein or RNA molecule).

Gene cloning: Restriction endonucleases are capable of cutting DNA at specific sequences, which may be joined with another fragment of DNA which has been cleaved by a similar process. In this way, DNA fragments can be introduced into systems which allow transcription and analysis of the gene product. The fundamental underpinning of DNA-recombinant technology and the production of insulin, growth factors, and erythropoietin.

Gene frequencies: Frequency of a specific allele in a population.

Genotype: Description of the inherited genes (eg, XY).

Heterozygous: The two copies (alleles) of a gene are different.

Haplotypes: Expression of a set of alleles, signifies one-half of the genetic information for the gene.

Homozygous: Both copies (alleles) of a gene are identical.

Insertion: Addition of a segment of DNA into a gene.

Linkage disequilibrium: Closely-spaced alleles tend to be inherited together. However, when alleles at two distinct loci occur together more frequently than expected based on the known allele frequencies and recombination fraction, the alleles are said to be in linkage disequilibrium. Evidence for linkage disequilibrium is often used to map genes.

Loci: Discrete location or portion of a chromosome where a gene is located.

Messenger RNA (mRNA): RNA that serves as a template for protein synthesis (see Codon).

DEFINITIONS / GLOSSARY *(Continued)*

Microarray: The basic principle of microarray analysis relies on base pairing, or hybridization between strands of nucleotides (between A-T and G-C for DNA and A-U and G-C for RNA). DNA which is complementary to the gene of interest is created and placed in microscopic quantities on solid surfaces. DNA is eluted over the surface, leading to binding of complementary strands. Presence of bound DNA is detected electronically (by fluorescence following laser excitation). Microarrays are often referred to as genome "chips," and are remarkable for the ability to screen large quantities of DNA (high-throughput). Microarrays require specialized robotics and imaging equipment. An experiment with a single DNA chip can provide researchers information on thousands of genes simultaneously. DNA-microarray technology may be used to identify DNA sequences (identify mutation), and to determine the level of expression of specific genes. Gene expression signatures for molecular diagnosis of leukemias is not currently employed in routine clinical practice.

Mutation or mutant: Copy of a gene which differs from the "wild type"; often assigned a numerical designation (*2, *3, etc). The "mutant" allele may be a misnomer as the allele generally occurs commonly in the human population, and in some instances, occurs more commonly than the "wild-type" allele.

Nonsynonymous: A single nucleotide polymorphism occurring anywhere in the codon which generates either a missense or nonsense codon. A missense codon results in a change of the encoded amino acid, leading to an alteration of protein sequence. A nonsense codon may function as a premature stop codon, leading to protein truncation. In either case, a change of protein function or stability may be expected.

Nucleotide: A subunit of DNA or RNA consisting of a nitrogenous base (adenine, guanine, thymine, or cytosine in DNA; adenine, guanine, uracil, or cytosine in RNA), a phosphate molecule, and a sugar molecule (deoxyribose in DNA and ribose in RNA). Thousands of nucleotides are linked to form a DNA or RNA molecule.

Open reading frame (ORF): A stretch of DNA that has the potential to encode a protein. To qualify, it must begin with a start codon and terminate with one of the three "stop" codons. An ORF is not usually considered equivalent to a gene until a phenotype has been associated with a mutation in the ORF or a specific gene product has been identified.

Phenotype: Expression of the genotype/genome, appearance or metabolism (eg, male).

Polymerase chain reaction (PCR): A method of creating multiple copies of specific fragments of DNA. PCR rapidly amplifies a single DNA molecule into many billions of molecules. In a typical application, small samples of DNA, such as those found in a strand of hair at a crime scene, can produce sufficient copies to carry out forensic tests.

Polymorphism: Difference in DNA sequence among individuals that may underlie differences in health. Genetic variations occurring in more than 1% of a population would be considered useful polymorphisms for genetic linkage analysis.

Restriction fragment: The result of enzymatic digestion by an enzyme capable of cleaving DNA based on the recognition of a specific nucleic acid sequence. Digestion produces a reproducible group of DNA fragments. A number of restriction enzymes are available, with unique recognition sequences, resulting in a distinct pattern of fragments. The fragments are detected by electrophoresis/Southern blotting of a gene of interest.

Restriction fragment length polymorphism (RFLP): Variation in DNA sequence which introduces a new site for the activity of a restriction enzyme (or removes a site); this variation results in a change in the banding pattern seen on electrophoresis and subsequent Southern blotting. For a given gene, different restriction enzymes may be tested to identify an enzyme which results in a different pattern between two individuals (an RFLP).

RNA (Ribonucleic acid): A molecule found in the nucleus and cytoplasm of cells; it plays an important role in protein synthesis and other chemical activities of the cell. The structure of RNA is similar to that of DNA. There are several classes of RNA molecules, including messenger RNA, transfer RNA, ribosomal RNA, and other small RNAs, each serving a different purpose.

"**Signatures:**" Groupings of genes of interest. Identifies the notion that many genes may group together to create phenotypes which dictate response. This may be the most clinically-relevant term.

SNP: Single Nucleotide Polymorphism or "Snips" - changes in a gene involving the substitution of one nucleotide base for another. Often designated as the normal base, location of exchange, and secondary base (C825T).

Synonymous: Refers to a single nucleotide polymorphism that usually occurs in the third (or "wobble") position of the codon. This mutation frequently does not lead to a change in the assignment of amino acid and therefore would not be expected to alter protein sequence.

"**Wild-type:**" Refers to an allele or genotype that was either the first described or that occurs in the majority of the population (often designated as *1). It is important to note that in some cases, the "wild-type" occurs at a lower frequency than the "mutant." Also, given that the frequency of genetic polymorphisms often varies among racial groups, the most commonly occurring allele/genotype in one racial group may be the least commonly occurring allele/genotype in another group.

INTRODUCTION TO GENETICS

Structure of DNA

The central dogma of molecular genetics states that genes encoded in DNA are transcribed to RNA and translated into protein products. Therefore, all potential products of the genome are encoded on DNA, located in the nucleus of a cell. Despite its complex functions, the molecular structure of DNA is based on only four nucleic acid molecules, or nucleotides. In humans, these four nucleotide bases are adenine, cytosine, guanine, and thymidine. Each base binds preferentially to one complementary nucleotide, leading to two fundamental associations: Guanine with cytosine (G-C pairs) and adenine with thymidine (A-T pairs). These associations are illustrated in Figure 1.

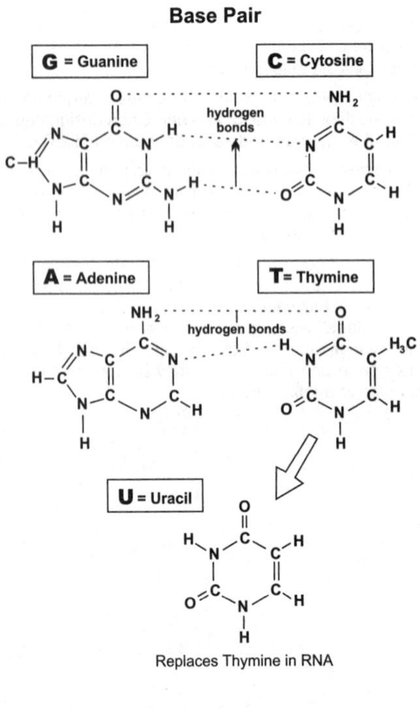

Base Pair

G = Guanine

C = Cytosine

hydrogen bonds

A = Adenine

T = Thymine

hydrogen bonds

U = Uracil

Replaces Thymine in RNA

Figure 1. Base pairs of nucleic acids. Adenine pairs with thymidine by hydrogen bonding in DNA. Thymidine is replaced by uracil in the RNA transcript.

DNA is arranged in a double helix. The helix is formed by two strands of nucleotide bases, linked to each other by bonds between complementary pairs of nucleotides. A strand of nucleotides, associated with its complementary strand, forms a structure which may be likened to a twisted ladder, with the "rungs" of the ladder corresponding to the linkage between bases of opposite strands. One side of the DNA encodes the sequence for a protein (sense strand) while the opposite mirror-image strand does not encode protein (anti-sense strand). The length of a DNA segment is often described by the number of base pairs in the segment (ie, 1600 bp for a segment consisting of 1600 sequential nucleotide bases).

Genetic Code Showing How Nucleotide Combinations Determine the Amino Acid Encoded

1st Position	2nd Position				3rd Position
	U	C	A	G	
U	Phe	Ser	Tyr	Cys	U
	Phe	Ser	Tyr	Cys	C
	Leu	Ser	STOP	STOP	A
	Leu	Ser	STOP	Trp	G
C	Leu	Pro	His	Arg	U
	Leu	Pro	His	Arg	C
	Leu	Pro	Gln	Arg	A
	Leu	Pro	Gln	Arg	G
A	Ile	Thr	Asn	Ser	U
	Ile	Thr	Asn	Ser	C
	Ile	Thr	Lys	Arg	A
	Met	Thr	Lys	Arg	G
G	Val	Ala	Asp	Gly	U
	Val	Ala	Asp	Gly	C
	Val	Ala	Glu	Gly	A
	Val	Ala	Glu	Gly	G

Inheritance: Dominant / Recessive Genes

The human genome contains 46 chromosomes (23 pairs). The Human Genome Project is an international research effort to determine the DNA sequence of the entire human genome. The complete genome has been sequenced with remarkable implications for health and disease.

The inheritance of genetic information depends on the segregation of chromosomes as individual gametes are formed. This results in one-half of the genetic information needed by the individual's progeny. A haplotype refers to the pattern of single nucleotide polymorphisms on a chromosome in a block. Since the ultimate human genome results from the contribution of two copies of each chromosome (with the exception of the X and Y chromosomes), each individual inherits two copies of each gene.

INTRODUCTION TO GENETICS *(Continued)*

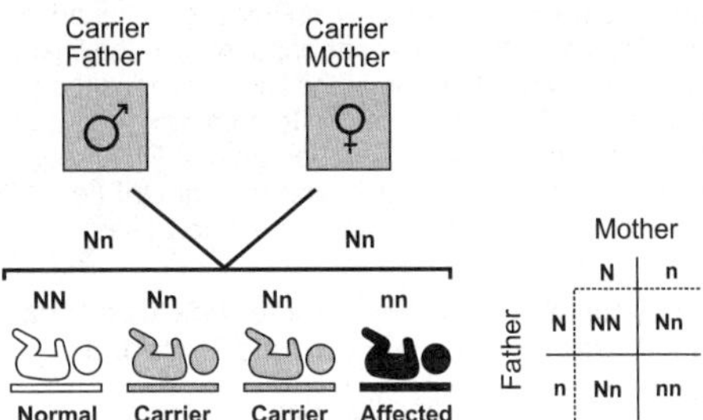

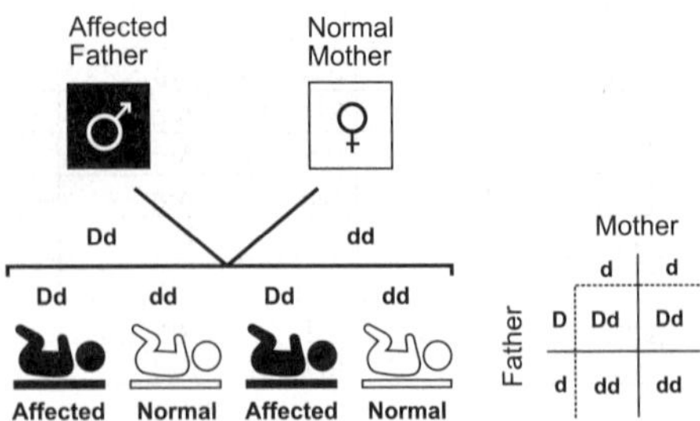

Figure 2. Examples of dominant and recessive single-gene inheritance. A gene which is inherited as a recessive trait requires both alleles to encode this trait (small letter "n" in the first example) before the trait will be expressed. In dominant inheritance, any combination in which the dominant allele ("D" in the second example) is included will result in expression of the trait.

In some cases, one gene is described as being expressed in preference over another. This concept of "dominant" and "recessive" genes is a useful illustration of simple inheritance patterns, and correlates with many physical traits such as eye and hair pigmentation. Dominant and recessive genes are often further identified as being autosomal or sex-linked (residing on the X or Y chromosome). Basic education in genetics frequently focuses on this simple pattern of inheritance, which is illustrated in Figure 2.

However, in many cases, simple dominant and recessive concepts do not adequately characterize gene expression. In some cases, genes exhibit codominance, in which both alleles are expressed. Many genes are polyallelic (for example, blood type is determined by A, B, and O gene products). In addition, many cellular processes are the result of multiple gene products, and it is difficult to predict an individual phenotype based on a change in only one of the involved genes.

Additional factors that moderate the phenotype include variable expression and incomplete penetrance. Variable expression of either allele results in intermediate expression of the individual genes. In some cases, this expression may be complex, and may relate to developmental stage or other cellular conditions. The term "penetrance" describes the degree to which a specific gene is expressed in the phenotype of the individual. As an extension of the concept of penetrance, if an individual carries the gene for a specific disease, and the disease usually develops in these patients, the gene is said to exhibit a high phenotypic penetrance.

Genes and Proteins

Genetic material contains the code for sequences of amino acids. The amino acid sequence determines the production of functional proteins. To translate from code to protein, two distinct steps must occur. First, the code must be transferred from the nucleic acids within the nucleus to the "machinery" of protein synthesis within the cytoplasm, the ribosome. Second, the code must be interpreted to allow assembly of the appropriate amino acids from the nucleic acid template. These two processes are known as transcription and translation. Figure 3 illustrates the steps of transcription and translation.

All cellular processes are determined by the activity of specific proteins. The individual's genotype is a representation of the inherited set of genes that provides the "code" for these proteins. Each individual inherits a pair of alleles, or forms of the gene, one from each parent. An allele is defined as the amino acid sequence at a given chromosomal locus. The phenotype of an individual refers to the actual physical or metabolic traits that result from expression of the inherited genes. Since a variety of processes regulate expression of a particular gene, the relationship between genotype and phenotype may be complex. For example, the genetic regulation of blood pressure involves a large number of physiologic processes, and other physiologic regulatory processes may compensate for a polymorphism in any single gene.

Transcription

During transcription, DNA segments are used to prepare complementary strands of RNA, that are later used as a template for protein synthesis (messenger RNA or mRNA). As encoded on DNA, individual genes have characteristics that regulate their transcription. For example, the segment of the DNA that encodes the information to "switch" the gene from active transcription to suppression is known as the promoter region.

Transcription is accomplished by specific proteins within the nucleus. The key transcriptional protein is RNA polymerase, that "reads" the DNA code and translates it into corresponding mRNA sequences. RNA polymerase requires several other proteins, called transcription factors, to initiate this

INTRODUCTION TO GENETICS *(Continued)*

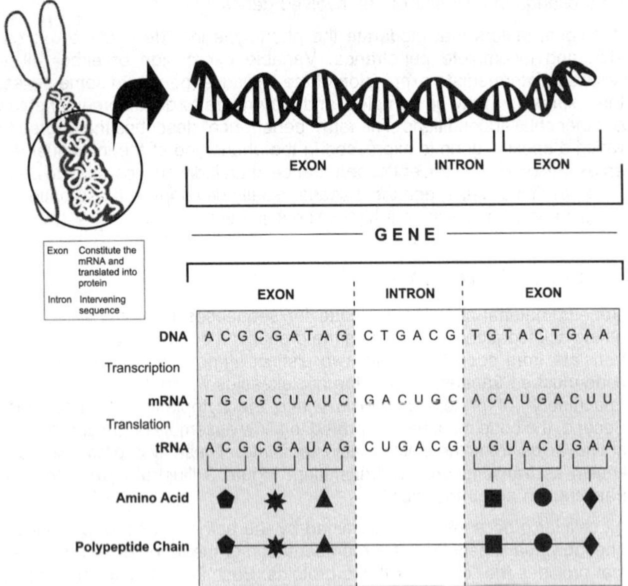

Figure 3. Gene expression: Transcription from DNA to mRNA within nucleus, transport to cytoplasmic ribosome for translation by tRNA + amino acids. Exon translation occurs within the ribosome.

process. These proteins assemble in the promoter region of the gene, and recognize a specific DNA sequence called the TATA box. With remarkable consistency, this sequence is located 25 nucleotides away from the site where transcription will be initiated.

When transcription terminates, the mRNA contains segments that encode the final protein (exons) as well as segments that do not encode protein (introns). Prior to being translocated to the cytoplasm, introns are spliced out of the mRNA to yield a strand that will correspond to the amino acid sequence the ribosome will assemble. It is important to note that the splicing process may introduce additional complexity into the gene expression process. Alternative splicing, in which one or more exons are shared among multiple transcripts, may lead to the production of different proteins from the same DNA sequence. Sometimes, the two products are very similar in terms of activities but, in other cases, the activities of the two proteins have no clear association.

Translation

In the translation process, the nucleic acid code is used to guide the assembly of amino acids to yield protein products. The translation process occurs on ribosomes, within the cytoplasm of the cell. Transfer RNA (tRNA) shuttles a specific amino acid to the ribosome. Sequences on the tRNA portion of an amino-acid-containing complex correspond to the complementary base pairs of the mRNA.

Translation is initiated at the start codon, AUG. Translation requires the recognition of discrete sequences of three nucleic acids (codons) that determine a "vocabulary" of amino acids. The corresponding tRNA is called the anticodon. Since there are 4 nucleic acids, the requirement that these be arranged in triplets, the potential number of codons is 64 (4 x 4 x 4). However, only 20 amino acids are used in human protein synthesis, so a single amino acid may be encoded by more than one codon (therefore, the code is referred to as "degenerate"). Some codons do not correspond to an amino acid, and terminate protein synthesis ("stop" codons). The string of amino acids is manufactured by joining amino acids from their carboxy-terminus to the amino terminal. Figure 4 illustrates the relationship between RNA sequence and amino acid codons.

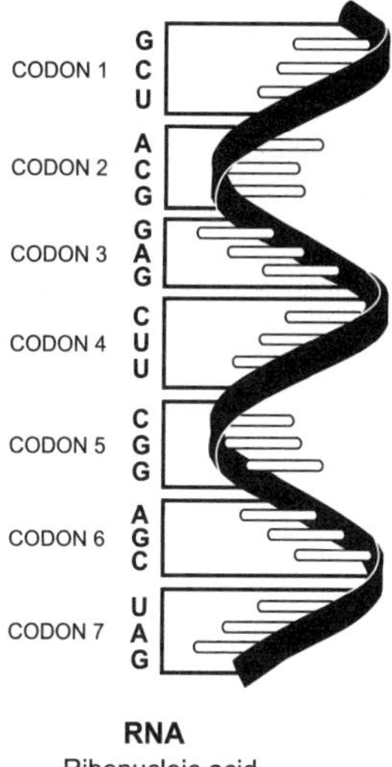

Figure 4. Organization of nucleic acid triplets into codons.

If an alteration occurs in the DNA, the triad of nucleic acids is disturbed. In some cases, there is no change because of the redundancy of the genetic code. In some cases, this leads to the coding of one amino acid rather than another during protein synthesis. This may result in altered activity of

INTRODUCTION TO GENETICS *(Continued)*

the synthesized protein. In other cases, the substitution results in a triad that cannot be recognized (as stop codon), and synthesis of the protein terminates (non-sense mutation). Mutations are genetic variations which occur in <1% of the population. A polymorphism refers to a genetic variation present in ≥1% of a population. Variation may also occur within the regions of DNA that regulate the production or processing of mRNA.

Post-Translational Modification

Following synthesis of the initial polypeptide chain, a number of modifications may be required before the amino acid sequence becomes a functional protein. For example, insulin is only active following the removal of C-peptide (this is often used as a marker of endogenous synthesis). The two-dimensional polypeptide folds into a three-dimensional structure, as determined by hydrophobic/hydrophilic characteristics, as well as the formation of stabilizing bonds within the internal structure. In many cases, enzymes within the cell assist in modification by cleaving segments of the amino acid chain, assisting in the formation of bonds (for example, disulfide bonds between cysteine groups), and the addition of polysaccharide groups to the initial chain.

Learning More

This brief introduction is intended to review basic principles of genetics and inheritance. Interested readers are encouraged to access additional resources, including the National Human Genome Research Institute (www.genome.gov) and Access Excellence, a project of the National Health Museum (www.nationalhealthmuseum.org).

INTRODUCTION TO PHARMACOGENOMICS

Genetic Variation: Polymorphisms

Each gene is encoded in a sequence of nucleic acid bases (see "Introduction to Genetics"). Common variations in the genome are termed polymorphisms. Polymorphisms are mutations which occur in >1% of the population. It is important to note that polymorphisms may occur in any segment of the gene, including exon regions, which encode the final protein, noncoding intron sequences, and gene promoter regions, which regulate gene transcription. The variability may result in a change in the final protein, altered mRNA processing, or a difference in the regulation of gene expression. Some of the more common types of polymorphisms include single nucleotide changes (SNP or "snips"), insertions, deletions, or tandem repeats.

Single nucleotide polymorphisms occur when one nucleotide is replaced by another. Over 1.4 million SNPs have been identified in the human genome, and it has been estimated that as many as 3 million SNPs may be present. This yields a frequency of as many as 1 SNP per every 1000 base pairs. A SNP may result in a change in the amino acid sequence of the final protein product. However, given the redundancy in the human genetic code (one codon may code for more than one amino acid, as discussed in the "Introduction to Genetics") some SNPs may not result in an amino acid change. Single nucleotide polymorphisms that result in amino acid changes are termed nonsynonymous. Those that do not result in an amino acid change are called synonymous. For example, in the sequence CCA and CCG, adenine has been replaced by guanine; however, both triads encode the amino acid proline, and no overall change in the encoded protein would result from this substitution.

Specific mutations are frequently assigned "shorthand" designations. Single nucleotide pairs, for example, are often identified by the two bases which are exchanged, along with a designation of the position on the gene where the substitution occurs. An example of this is C825T, where thymidine is substituted for cytosine at nucleotide position 825. This may also be designated as C825→T. Nonsynonymous SNPs are usually designated by the usual amino acid, codon (amino acid) position, and substituted amino acid (eg, Arg389Gly or Arg389→Gly indicates that glycine replaces arginine at codon 389), and may be represented by the amino acid symbol (eg, Arg389Gly may be abbreviated as R389G); see table of abbreviations below.

A	Ala	G	Gly	M	Met	S	Ser
C	Cys	H	His	N	Asn	T	Thr
D	Asp	I	Ile	P	Pro	V	Val
E	Glu	K	Lys	Q	Gln	W	Trp
F	Phe	L	Leu	R	Arg	Y	Tyr

INTRODUCTION TO PHARMACOGENOMICS *(Continued)*

Insertions and deletions refer to changes of greater than one base pair, in which a section of DNA is either added or deleted. These may be designated by the I or D alleles. For insertions and deletions, the typical nomenclature specifies the I (insertion) allele or the D (deletion) allele. The total genotype may be expressed as I/I or D/D for homozygotes (those who carry two I or D alleles) or I/D for heterozygotes (those who carry one I allele and one D allele) of the gene of interest. Tandem repeats are segments of DNA in which the same nucleotide sequence is repeated multiple times.

In some cases, insertion of a segment of DNA which is not divisible by three will lead to a frameshift mutation, since the codon:anticodon pattern will be disturbed for all DNA which lies downstream from the insertion. Some polymorphisms alter the stability of mRNA, which may result in the synthesis of a reduced number of proteins. In addition, differences may result in changes in post-translational modifications of the final protein product, yielding a protein with altered functionality. Finally, polymorphisms may lead to the creation of stop codons, which would terminate translation prior to formation of the final gene product.

In addition to the nomenclature mentioned above for SNPs and insertion/deletions, mutations may be expressed in a manner which relates to their discovery and/or naming. In these cases, the first form of the gene (usually, but not always, the most common, or "wild-type"), is designated as the *1 genotype (CYP3A4*1). Subsequent mutations may be designated numerically (CYP3A4*2, CYP3A4*3, etc).

Pharmacokinetic and Pharmacodynamic Consequences

Since proteins may participate as enzymes, transporters, receptors, or structural elements of the cell, the final expression of the polymorphism may take a variety of forms. Specific effects on pharmacologic activities may result from altered metabolism of a drug (pharmacokinetic differences), or changes in sensitivity to a drug's action at any given concentration (pharmacodynamic differences).

An example of pharmacokinetic consequences is the relationship between mercaptopurine and the enzyme thiopurine methyltransferase (TPMT). This enzyme has a number of polymorphisms, which lead to the expression of three basic phenotypes. Approximately 89% to 94% of the population demonstrate "high activity" of this enzyme, while 6% to 11% display "intermediate activity." Importantly, a segment of the population, approximately 0.3%, displays very low activity. In a single study of 147 patients receiving mercaptopurine for the treatment of ALL, homozygotes for the low metabolic activity demonstrated severe hematologic toxicity despite a 50% reduction in dose. Formerly, this type of observation would be idiotypic, without sufficient explanation. With the advent of pharmacogenomic analysis, it is possible to identify patients at risk of this reaction prior to administration of mercaptopurine, as well as other drugs metabolized by this enzyme.

Other polymorphisms which may result in pronounced pharmacokinetic variability include polymorphisms of cytochrome P450 enzymes (CYP isoenzyme variants), drug transporters (such as P-glycoprotein), and various activating enzymes, such as DPD (required to activate fluorouracil).

Several pharmacodynamic consequences of drug polymorphisms are also well documented. For example, specific alleles of the β_2-adrenergic receptor may alter receptor sensitivity and response to β_2-receptor agonists.

Pharmacogenomic Testing

The recognition of specific genetic mutations which significantly influence drug response and/or toxicity is fueling an aggressive effort by many companies to develop suitable in vitro diagnostic tests. The intention is for these diagnostic tests to be readily available for use in the clinical setting (without the need to send to remote laboratories) to quickly evaluate/assess a patient's genotype in order to guide the most appropriate pharmacotherapy for that patient. The challenge for this industry, of course, is correctly identifying which of the estimated 30,000 genes (and/or combinations of) are appropriate markers for influencing the physiologic response to drug therapy. However, as evidenced by this publication, advances in molecular genetics are occurring on a daily basis and leading to much greater insight regarding the pharmacogenetic impact on drug therapy. As such, the emergence of clinically accepted, FDA-approved diagnostics is expected to grow substantially in the coming years. One can anticipate that these advances are sure to intensify questions regarding the legal and ethical ramifications of who and when to test and how best to interpret or utilize this information, issues which are beyond the scope of this publication. However, it should be recognized that from an ethical standpoint, the implications of genetic testing are likely to be far more profound with respect to disease assessment and/or prediction. Application of genetic information for the purposes of rational drug selection and dosing should be much less controversial. Nevertheless, there is clear enthusiasm within the healthcare community regarding the potential for genetic diagnostics to advance the strategic and individualized treatment of disease, ultimately leading to improved clinical outcomes.

At the time of this publication, only a handful of pharmacogenetic designated diagnostic tests are available for clinical use. Only two are specifically approved by the FDA for this purpose. A sample of tests which are in use, or are in late-stage development is shown in the following table.

INTRODUCTION TO PHARMACOGENOMICS
(Continued)

Diagnostic Test or Device	Company or Laboratory	Status	Function
AmpliChip™	Roche Diagnostics	Available; FDA approved	Microarray-based screen for 27 SNPs in CYP2D6 and 2C19
Invader® UGT1A1 Molecular Assay	Third Wave technologies	Available; FDA approved	Screen for presence of variant *UGT1A1*28* allele associated with irinotecan toxicity
PRO-PredictRx TPMT®	Prometheus Laboratories	Available	Screen for *TPMT*2*, *TPMT*3A*, and *TPMT*3C* alleles associated increased immunosuppressive toxicity with azathioprine and 6-mercaptopurine
DrugMEt™	Jurilab/ Nanogen	Investigational use only; 510K application submitted[1]	Microarray-based slide which tests for 29 SNPs in 8 enzymes: CYP2D6, 2C9, 2C19, 3A5, and 2B6; NAT2, MDR1, and CYP2D6 (deletion/ duplication)
MegAllele™ DME-T	ParAllele/ Affymetrix	Investigational use only; 510K application pending[1]	Microarray-based screen for approximately 170 SNPs across 29 genes

[1]*Pharmacogenomics Reporter*, July 28, 2005, Genome Web News, LLC, http://www.pgxreporter.com; last accessed 8/12/05.

In addition, a large number of genetic tests in routine clinical use are focused on the diagnosis and/or prediction of disease. However, it is currently beyond the scope of this publication to adequately address these services.

Ultimately, we hope and anticipate that future editions of this publication, as well as our online Pharmacogenomics database resource will publish the specifics of available pharmacogenomic tests, as they relate to clearly identified polymorphisms of interest. An additional aim will be to profile the specifications of these diagnostic devices/assays to aid the clinician in defining expectations and interpretation of the test results.

Web Sites

http://www.fda.gov/cder/genomics/default.htm

http://www.gene.ucl.ac.uk/nomenclature/

http://www.genomica.net/RICERCA/HAPMAP/HAPMAP_consorzio.htm

http://www.ncbi.nlm.nih.gov/entrez/query.fcgi (Gene database)

http://snp500cancer.nci.nih.gov/snp.cfm

http://snp.cshl.org

CYTOCHROME P450 NOMENCLATURE

Cytochrome P450 refers to an important group of enzymes responsible for a variety of Phase I reactions including epoxidation, N-dealkylation, O-dealkylation, S-oxidation, and hydroxylation. The designation "P450" refers to the original identification of these enzymes as a pigment (P) with a characteristic absorption of light at a wavelength of 450 nm.

A large portion of cytochrome P450 enzymes exist in the liver and small intestine. They are also found in the skin, kidneys, lungs, and brain. CYP enzymes are localized in the microsomal portion of the cytoplasm, which includes the endoplasmic reticulum. CYP enzymes are responsible for the metabolism of xenobiotics, but are also involved in the formation of steroidal compounds, cholesterol, and arachadonic acid metabolites.

After its original identification, it became clear that "Cytochrome P450" actually consisted of a large number of enzymes with individual substrate specificity and separate genetic coding. These are referred to as isoforms, or variants. Isoforms are classified according to the similarities within their amino-acid sequences.

CYP isoforms are divided into families which contain substantial homology in their genetic sequence (at least 40% homology). At least 18 families have been identified in humans, and a total of over 70 families have been identified across various animal species. Families are assigned a numerical designation, such as CYP3. Isoenzyme families are further divided into subfamilies, which have at least 60% sequence homology. Subfamilies are designated by a letter after the specific CYP numerical designation. Finally, an individual gene is designated by an additional Arabic numeral. The following example illustrates the increasing specificity of these designations.

Family: CYP3

Subfamily: CYP3A

Genetic designation: CYP3A4

Individual isoforms may also have allelic variants, which are designated by an additional * symbol (CYP3A*2). The ability to classify CYP isoenzymes has been an important advance in terms of the ability to predict drug interactions between inhibitors, inducers, and substrates of this enzyme system. Additional investigation and potential profiling may allow more sophisticated analysis of drug metabolism, yielding greater accuracy in the prediction of interactions, and the tailoring of a dosing regimen to the specific capabilities of individual patients.

CYTOCHROME P450 ENZYMES: SUBSTRATES, INHIBITORS, AND INDUCERS

INTRODUCTION

Most drugs are eliminated from the body, at least in part, by being chemically altered to less lipid-soluble products (ie, metabolized), and thus are more likely to be excreted via the kidneys or the bile. Phase I metabolism includes drug hydrolysis, oxidation, and reduction, and results in drugs that are more polar in their chemical structure, while Phase II metabolism involves the attachment of an additional molecule onto the drug (or partially metabolized drug) in order to create an inactive and/or more water soluble compound. Phase II processes include (primarily) glucuronidation, sulfation, glutathione conjugation, acetylation, and methylation.

Virtually any of the Phase I and II enzymes can be inhibited by some xenobiotic or drug. Some of the Phase I and II enzymes can be induced. Inhibition of the activity of metabolic enzymes will result in increased concentrations of the substrate (drug), whereas induction of the activity of metabolic enzymes will result in decreased concentrations of the substrate. For example, the well-documented enzyme-inducing effects of phenobarbital may include a combination of Phase I and II enzymes. Phase II glucuronidation may be increased via induced UDP-glucuronosyltransferase (UGT) activity, whereas Phase I oxidation may be increased via induced cytochrome P450 (CYP) activity. However, for most drugs, the primary route of metabolism (and the primary focus of drug-drug interaction) is Phase I oxidation, and specifically, metabolism.

CYP enzymes may be responsible for the metabolism (at least partial metabolism) of approximately 75% of all drugs, with the CYP3A subfamily responsible for nearly half of this activity. Found throughout plant, animal, and bacterial species, CYP enzymes represent a superfamily of xenobiotic metabolizing proteins. There have been several hundred CYP enzymes identified in nature, each of which has been assigned to a family (1, 2, 3, etc), subfamily (A, B, C, etc), and given a specific enzyme number (1, 2, 3, etc) according to the similarity in amino acid sequence that it shares with other enzymes. Of these many enzymes, only a few are found in humans, and even fewer appear to be involved in the metabolism of xenobiotics (eg, drugs). The key human enzyme subfamilies include CYP1A, CYP2A, CYP2B, CYP2C, CYP2D, CYP2E, and CYP3A.

CYP enzymes are found in the endoplasmic reticulum of cells in a variety of human tissues (eg, skin, kidneys, brain, lungs), but their predominant sites of concentration and activity are the liver and intestine. Though the abundance of CYP enzymes throughout the body is relatively equally distributed among the various subfamilies, the relative contribution to drug metabolism is (in decreasing order of magnitude) CYP3A4 (nearly 50%), CYP2D6 (nearly 25%), CYP2C8/9 (nearly 15%), then CYP1A2, CYP2C19, CYP2A6, and CYP2E1. Owing to their potential for numerous drug-drug interactions, those drugs that are identified in preclinical studies as substrates of CYP3A enzymes are often given a lower priority for

CYTOCHROME P450 ENZYMES: SUBSTRATES, INHIBITORS, AND INDUCERS *(Continued)*

continued research and development in favor of drugs that appear to be less affected by (or less likely to affect) this enzyme subfamily.

Each enzyme subfamily possesses unique selectivity toward potential substrates. For example, CYP1A2 preferentially binds medium-sized, planar, lipophilic molecules, while CYP2D6 preferentially binds molecules that possess a basic nitrogen atom. Some CYP subfamilies exhibit polymorphism (ie, multiple allelic variants that manifest differing catalytic properties). The best described polymorphisms involve CYP2C9, CYP2C19, and CYP2D6. Individuals possessing "wild type" gene alleles exhibit normal functioning CYP capacity. Others, however, possess allelic variants that leave the person with a subnormal level of catalytic potential (so called "poor metabolizers"). Poor metabolizers would be more likely to experience toxicity from drugs metabolized by the affected enzymes (or less effects if the enzyme is responsible for converting a prodrug to it's active form as in the case of codeine). The percentage of people classified as poor metabolizers varies by enzyme and population group. As an example, approximately 7% of Caucasians and only about 1% of Orientals appear to be CYP2D6 poor metabolizers.

CYP enzymes can be both inhibited and induced by other drugs, leading to increased or decreased serum concentrations (along with the associated effects), respectively. Induction occurs when a drug causes an increase in the amount of smooth endoplasmic reticulum, secondary to increasing the amount of the affected CYP enzymes in the tissues. This "revving up" of the CYP enzyme system may take several days to reach peak activity, and likewise, may take several days, even months, to return to normal following discontinuation of the inducing agent.

CYP inhibition occurs via several potential mechanisms. Most commonly, a CYP inhibitor competitively (and reversibly) binds to the active site on the enzyme, thus preventing the substrate from binding to the same site, and preventing the substrate from being metabolized. The affinity of an inhibitor for an enzyme may be expressed by an inhibition constant (Ki) or IC50 (defined as the concentration of the inhibitor required to cause 50% inhibition under a given set of conditions). In addition to reversible competition for an enzyme site, drugs may inhibit enzyme activity by binding to sites on the enzyme other than that to which the substrate would bind, and thereby cause a change in the functionality or physical structure of the enzyme. A drug may also bind to the enzyme in an irreversible (ie, "suicide") fashion. In such a case, it is not the concentration of drug at the enzyme site that is important (constantly binding and releasing), but the number of molecules available for binding (once bound, always bound).

Although an inhibitor or inducer may be known to affect a variety of CYP subfamilies, it may only inhibit one or two in a clinically important fashion. Likewise, although a substrate is known to be at least partially metabolized by a variety of CYP enzymes, only one or two enzymes may contribute significantly enough to its overall metabolism to warrant concern when used with potential inducers or inhibitors. Therefore, when attempting to predict the level of risk of using two drugs that may affect each other via altered CYP function, it is important to identify the relative effectiveness of the inhibiting/inducing drug on the CYP subfamilies that significantly contribute to the metabolism of the substrate. The contribution of a specific CYP pathway to substrate metabolism should be considered not only in light of other known CYP pathways, but also other nonoxidative pathways for substrate metabolism (eg, glucuronidation) and transporter proteins (eg, P-glycoprotein) that may affect the presentation of a substrate to a metabolic pathway.

HOW TO USE THE TABLES

The following CYP SUBSTRATES, INHIBITORS, and INDUCERS tables provide a clinically relevant perspective on drugs that are affected by, or affect, cytochrome P450 (CYP) enzymes. Not all human, drug-metabolizing CYP enzymes are specifically (or separately) included in the tables. Some enzymes have been excluded because they do not appear to significantly contribute to the metabolism of marketed drugs (eg, CYP2C18). Others have been combined in recognition of the difficulty in distinguishing their metabolic activity one from another, or the clinical practicality of doing so (eg, CYP2C8/9, CYP3A4). In the case of CYP3A4, the industry routinely uses this single enzyme designation to represent all enzymes in the CYP3A subfamily. CYP3A7 is present in fetal livers. It is effectively absent from adult livers. CYP3A4 (adult) and CYP3A7 (fetal) appear to share similar properties in their respective hosts. The impact of CYP3A7 in fetal and neonatal drug interactions has not been investigated.

The **CYP Substrates table** contains a list of drugs reported to be metabolized, at least in part, by one or more CYP enzymes. An enzyme that appears to play a clinically significant (major) role in a drug's metabolism is indicated by "●", and an enzyme whose role appears to be clinically insignificant (minor) is indicated by "○". A clinically significant designation is the result of a two-phase review. The first phase considered the contribution of each CYP enzyme to the overall metabolism of the drug. The enzyme pathway was considered potentially clinically relevant if it was responsible for at least 30% of the metabolism of the drug. If so, the drug was subjected to a second phase. The second phase considered the clinical relevance of a substrate's concentration being increased twofold, or decreased by one-half (such as might be observed if combined with an effective CYP inhibitor or inducer, respectively). If either of these changes was considered to present a clinically significant concern, the CYP pathway for the drug was designated "major." If neither change would appear to present a clinically significant concern, or if the CYP enzyme was responsible for a smaller portion of the overall metabolism (ie, <30%), the pathway was designated "minor."

The **CYP Inhibitors table** contains a list of drugs that are reported to inhibit one or more CYP enzymes. Enzymes that are strongly inhibited by a drug are indicated by "●". Enzymes that are moderately inhibited are indicated by "◑". Enzymes that are weakly inhibited are indicated by "○". The designations are the result of a review of published clinical reports, available Ki data, and assessments published by other experts in the field. As it pertains to Ki values set in a ratio with achievable serum drug concentrations ([I]) under normal dosing conditions, the following parameters were employed: [I]/Ki ≥1 = strong; [I]/Ki 0.1-1 = moderate; [I]/Ki <0.1 = weak.

CYTOCHROME P450 ENZYMES: SUBSTRATES, INHIBITORS, AND INDUCERS *(Continued)*

The **CYP Inducers table** contains a list of drugs that are reported to induce one or more CYP enzymes. Enzymes that appear to be effectively induced by a drug are indicated by "●", and enzymes that do not appear to be effectively induced are indicated by "○". The designations are the result of a review of published clinical reports and assessments published by experts in the field.

In general, clinically significant interactions are more likely to occur between substrates and either inhibitors or inducers of the same enzyme(s), all of which have been indicated by "●". However, these assessments possess a degree of subjectivity, at times based on limited indications regarding the significance of CYP effects of particular agents. An attempt has been made to balance a conservative, clinically-sensitive presentation of the data with a desire to avoid the numbing effect of a "beware of everything" approach. Even so, other potential interactions (ie, those involving enzymes indicated by "○") may warrant consideration in some cases. It is important to note that information related to CYP metabolism of drugs is expanding at a rapid pace, and thus, the contents of this table should only be considered to represent a "snapshot" of the information available at the time of publication.

Selected Readings

Bjornsson TD, Callaghan JT, Einolf HJ, et al, "The Conduct of *in vitro* and *in vivo* Drug-Drug Interaction Studies: A PhRMA Perspective," *J Clin Pharmacol*, 2003, 43(5):443-69.

Drug-Drug Interactions, Rodrigues AD, ed, New York, NY: Marcel Dekker, Inc, 2002.

Levy RH, Thummel KE, Trager WF, et al, eds, *Metabolic Drug Interactions*, Philadelphia, PA: Lippincott Williams & Wilkins, 2000.

Michalets EL, "Update: Clinically Significant Cytochrome P-450 Drug Interactions," *Pharmacotherapy*, 1998, 18(1):84-112.

Thummel KE and Wilkinson GR, "*In vitro* and *in vivo* Drug Interactions Involving Human CYP3A," *Annu Rev Pharmacol Toxicol*, 1998, 38:389-430.

Zhang Y and Benet LZ, "The Gut as a Barrier to Drug Absorption: Combined Role of Cytochrome P450 3A and P-Glycoprotein," *Clin Pharmacokinet*, 2001, 40(3):159-68.

Selected Websites

http://www.gentest.com
http://www.imm.ki.se/CYPalleles
http://medicine.iupui.edu/flockhart
http://www.mhc.com/Cytochromes

CYP Substrates

● = major substrate
○ = minor substrate

Drug	1A2	2A6	2B6	2C8/9	2C19	2D6	2E1	3A4
Acenocoumarol	●			●	○			
Acetaminophen	○	○		○		○	○	○
Albendazole	○							○
Albuterol								●
Alfentanil								●
Almotriptan						○		○

CYP Substrates *(continued)*

Drug	1A2	2A6	2B6	2C8/9	2C19	2D6	2E1	3A4
Alosetron	●			○				○
Alprazolam								●
Aminophylline	●						○	○
Amiodarone	○			●	○	○		●
Amitriptyline	○		○	○	○	●		○
Amlodipine								●
Amoxapine						●		
Amphetamine						○		
Amprenavir				○				●
Aprepitant	○				○			●
Argatroban								○
Aripiprazole						●		●
Aspirin				○				
Atazanavir								●
Atomoxetine					○	●		
Atorvastatin								●
Azelastine	○				○	○		○
Azithromycin								○
Benzphetamine			○					●
Benztropine						○		
Betaxolol	●					●		
Bexarotene								○
Bezafibrate								○
Bisoprolol						○		●
Bortezomib	○			○	○	○		●
Bosentan				●				●
Brinzolamide								○
Bromazepam								●
Bromocriptine								●
Budesonide								●
Bupivacaine	○				○	○		○
Buprenorphine								●
BuPROPion	○	○	●	○		○	○	○
BusPIRone						○		●
Busulfan								●
Caffeine	●			○		○	○	○
Candesartan				○				
Capsaicin							○	
Captopril						●		
Carbamazepine				○				●
Carisoprodol					●			
Carteolol						○		
Carvedilol	○			●		●	○	○
Celecoxib				○				○
Cerivastatin								●
Cetirizine								○

CYTOCHROME P450 ENZYMES: SUBSTRATES, INHIBITORS, AND INDUCERS *(Continued)*

CYP Substrates *(continued)*

Drug	1A2	2A6	2B6	2C8/9	2C19	2D6	2E1	3A4
Cevimeline						○		○
Chlordiazepoxide								●
Chloroquine						●		●
Chlorpheniramine						○		●
ChlorproMAZINE	○					●		○
ChlorproPAMIDE				○				
Chlorzoxazone	○	○				○	●	○
Cilostazol	○				○	○		●
Cinacalcet	○					○		○
Cisapride	○	○	○	○	○			●
Citalopram					●	○		●
Clarithromycin								●
Clobazam					●			●
Clofibrate								○
ClomiPRAMINE	●				●	●		○
Clonazepam								●
Clopidogrel	○							○
Clorazepate								●
Clozapine	●	○		○	○	○		○
Cocaine								●
Codeine[1]						●		○
Colchicine								●
Cyclobenzaprine	●					○		○
Cyclophosphamide[2]		○	●	○	○			●
CycloSPORINE								●
Dacarbazine	●						●	
Dantrolene								●
Dapsone				○	○		○	●
Delavirdine						○		●
Desipramine	○					●		
Desogestrel					●			
Dexamethasone								○
Dexmedetomidine		●						
Dextroamphetamine						●		
Dextromethorphan		○		○	○	●	○	○
Diazepam	○		○	○	●			●
Diclofenac	○		○	○	○	○		○
Digitoxin								●
Digoxin								○
Dihydrocodeine[1]						●		
Dihydroergotamine								●
Diltiazem				○		○		●
Dirithromycin								○

CYP Substrates *(continued)*

Drug	1A2	2A6	2B6	2C8/9	2C19	2D6	2E1	3A4
Disopyramide								●
Disulfiram	○	○	○			○	○	○
Docetaxel								●
Dofetilide								○
Dolasetron				○				○
Domperidone								○
Donepezil						○		○
Dorzolamide				○				○
Doxepin	●					●		●
DOXOrubicin						●		●
Doxycycline								●
Drospirenone								○
Duloxetine	●					●		
Dutasteride								○
Efavirenz			●					●
Eletriptan								●
Enalapril								●
Enflurane							●	
Eplerenone								●
Ergoloid mesylates								●
Ergonovine								●
Ergotamine								●
Erythromycin			○					●
Escitalopram					●			●
Esomeprazole					●			○
Estazolam								○
Estradiol	●	○	○	○	○	○	○	●
Estrogens, conjugated A/synthetic	●	○	○	○	○	○	○	●
Estrogens, conjugated equine	●	○	○	○	○	○	○	●
Estrogens, conjugated esterified	●		○	○			○	●
Estrone	●		○	○			○	●
Estropipate	●		○	○			○	●
Ethinyl estradiol				○				●
Ethosuximide								●
Etonogestrel								○
Etoposide	○						○	●
Exemestane								●
Felbamate							○	●
Felodipine								●
Fenofibrate								○
Fentanyl								●
Fexofenadine								○
Finasteride								○
Flecainide	○					●		

CYTOCHROME P450 ENZYMES: SUBSTRATES, INHIBITORS, AND INDUCERS *(Continued)*

CYP Substrates *(continued)*

Drug	1A2	2A6	2B6	2C8/9	2C19	2D6	2E1	3A4
Fluoxetine	○		○	●	○	●	○	○
Fluphenazine						●		
Flurazepam								●
Flurbiprofen				○				
Flutamide	●							●
Fluticasone								●
Fluvastatin				○		○		○
Fluvoxamine	●					●		
Formoterol		○		○	○	○		
Fosamprenavir (as amprenavir)				○				●
Fosphenytoin (as phenytoin)				●	●			○
Frovatriptan	○							
Fulvestrant								○
Galantamine						○		○
Gefitinib								●
Gemfibrozil								○
Glimepiride				●				
GlipiZIDE				●				
Granisetron								○
Guanabenz	●							
Halazepam								○
Halofantrine				○		○		●
Haloperidol	○					●		●
Halothane		○	○	○		○	●	○
Hydrocodone[1]						●		
Hydrocortisone								○
Ibuprofen				○	○			
Ifosfamide[3]		○	○	○	○			●
Imatinib	○			○	○	○		●
Imipramine	○		○		●	●		○
Imiquimod	○							○
Indinavir						○		●
Indomethacin				○	○			
Irbesartan				○				
Irinotecan			●					●
Isoflurane							●	
Isoniazid							●	
Isosorbide								●
Isosorbide dinitrate								●
Isosorbide mononitrate								●
Isradipine								●

CYP Substrates *(continued)*

Drug	1A2	2A6	2B6	2C8/9	2C19	2D6	2E1	3A4
Itraconazole								●
Ivermectin								○
Ketamine			●	●				●
Ketoconazole								●
Labetalol						●		
Lansoprazole				○	●			●
Letrozole		○						●
Levobupivacaine	○							○
Levonorgestrel								●
Lidocaine	○	○	○	○		●		●
Lomustine						●		
Lopinavir								○
Loratadine						○		○
Losartan				●				●
Lovastatin								●
Maprotiline						●		
MedroxyPROGESTERone								●
Mefenamic acid				○				
Mefloquine								●
Meloxicam				○				○
Meperidine			○		○			○
Mephenytoin			○	●	●			
Mephobarbital			○	○	●			
Mestranol[4]				●				●
Methadone				○	○	○		●
Methamphetamine						●		
Methoxsalen		○						
Methsuximide					●			
Methylergonovine								●
Methylphenidate						●		
MethylPREDNISolone								○
Metoclopramide	○					○		
Metoprolol					○	●		
Mexiletine	●					●		
Miconazole								●
Midazolam			○					●
Mifepristone								○
Miglustat								●
Mirtazapine	●			○		●		●
Moclobemide					●	●		
Modafinil								●
Mometasone furoate								○
Montelukast				●				●
Moricizine								●
Morphine sulfate						○		
Naproxen	○			○				

CYTOCHROME P450 ENZYMES: SUBSTRATES, INHIBITORS, AND INDUCERS *(Continued)*

CYP Substrates *(continued)*

Drug	1A2	2A6	2B6	2C8/9	2C19	2D6	2E1	3A4
Nateglinide				●				●
Nefazodone						●		●
Nelfinavir				○	●	○		●
Nevirapine			○			○		●
NiCARdipine	○			○		○	○	●
Nicotine	○	○	○	○	○	○	○	○
NIFEdipine						○		●
Nilutamide					●			
Nimodipine								●
Nisoldipine								●
Nitrendipine								●
Norelgestromin								○
Norethindrone								●
Norgestrel								●
Nortriptyline	○				○	●		○
Olanzapine	○					○		
Omeprazole		○		○	●	○		○
Ondansetron	○			○		○	○	●
Orphenadrine	○		○			○		○
Oxybutynin								○
Oxycodone[1]						●		
Paclitaxel				●				●
Palonosetron	○					○		○
Pantoprazole					●			○
Paroxetine						●		
Pentamidine					●			
Pergolide								●
Perphenazine	○			○	○	●		○
Phencyclidine								●
Phenobarbital				○	●		○	
Phenytoin				●	●			○
Pimecrolimus								○
Pimozide	●							●
Pindolol						●		
Pioglitazone				●				●
Pipecuronium				○				
Pipotiazine						●		●
Piroxicam				○				
Pravastatin								○
Prazepam								○
PrednisoLONE								○
PredniSONE								○
Primaquine								●

CYP Substrates *(continued)*

Drug	1A2	2A6	2B6	2C8/9	2C19	2D6	2E1	3A4
Procainamide						●		
Progesterone	○	○		○	●	○		●
Proguanil	○				○			○
Promethazine			●			●		
Propafenone	○					●		○
Propofol	○	○	●	●	○	○	○	○
Propranolol	●				○	●		○
Protriptyline						●		
Quazepam								○
Quetiapine						○		●
Quinidine				○			○	●
Quinine	○				○			○
Rabeprazole					●			●
Ranitidine	○				○	○		
Repaglinide				●				●
Rifabutin	●							●
Rifampin		●		●				●
Riluzole	●							
Risperidone						●		○
Ritonavir	○		○			○		●
Rofecoxib				○				
Ropinirole	●							○
Ropivacaine	○		○			○		○
Rosiglitazone				●				
Rosuvastatin				○				○
Saquinavir						○		●
Selegiline	○	○	●	●		○		○
Sertraline			○	○	●	●		○
Sevoflurane		○	○				●	○
Sibutramine								●
Sildenafil				○				●
Simvastatin								●
Sirolimus								●
Spiramycin								●
Sufentanil								●
SulfaDIAZINE				●			○	○
Sulfamethoxazole				●				○
Sulfinpyrazone				●				○
SulfiSOXAZOLE				●				
Suprofen				○				
Tacrine	●							
Tacrolimus								●
Tamoxifen		○	○	●		●	○	●
Tamsulosin						●		●
Telithromycin	○							●
Temazepam			○	○	○			○

CYTOCHROME P450 ENZYMES: SUBSTRATES, INHIBITORS, AND INDUCERS *(Continued)*

CYP Substrates *(continued)*

Drug	1A2	2A6	2B6	2C8/9	2C19	2D6	2E1	3A4
Teniposide								●
Terbinafine	○			○	○			○
Testosterone			○	○	○			○
Tetracycline								●
Theophylline	●			○		○	●	●
Thiabendazole	○							
Thioridazine					○	●		
Thiothixene	●							
Tiagabine								●
Ticlopidine								●
Timolol						●		
Tinidazole								○
Tiotropium						○		○
Tipranavir								●
Tizanidine	●							
TOLBUTamide				●	○			
Tolcapone		○						○
Tolterodine				○	○	●		●
Toremifene	○							●
Torsemide				●				
Tramadol[1]						●		○
Trazodone						○		●
Tretinoin		○	○	○				
Triazolam								●
Trifluoperazine	●							
Trimethadione				○	○		●	○
Trimethoprim				●				●
Trimipramine					●	●		●
Troleandomycin								●
Valdecoxib				○				○
Valproic acid		○	○	○	○		○	
Vardenafil								●
Venlafaxine				○	○	●		●
Verapamil	○		○	○			○	●
VinBLAStine						○		●
VinCRIStine								●
Vinorelbine						○		●
Voriconazole				●	●			○
Warfarin	○			●	○			○
Yohimbine						○		
Zafirlukast				●				
Zaleplon								○
Zidovudine		○		○	○			○

CYP Substrates *(continued)*

Drug	1A2	2A6	2B6	2C8/9	2C19	2D6	2E1	3A4
Zileuton	○			○				○
Ziprasidone	○							○
Zolmitriptan	○							
Zolpidem	○			○	○	○		●
Zonisamide					○			●
Zopiclone				●				●
Zuclopenthixol						●		

[1]This opioid analgesic is bioactivated *in vivo* via CYP2D6. Inhibiting this enzyme would decrease the effects of the analgesic. The active metabolite might also affect, or be affected by, CYP enzymes.

[2]Cyclophosphamide is bioactivated *in vivo* to acrolein via CYP2B6 and 3A4. Inhibiting these enzymes would decrease the effects of cyclophosphamide.

[3]Ifosfamide is bioactivated *in vivo* to acrolein via CYP3A4. Inhibiting this enzyme would decrease the effects of ifosfamide.

[4]Mestranol is bioactivated *in vivo* to ethinyl estradiol via CYP2C8/9. See Ethinyl Estradiol for additional CYP information.

CYTOCHROME P450 ENZYMES: SUBSTRATES, INHIBITORS, AND INDUCERS *(Continued)*

CYP Inhibitors

● = strong inhibitor
◑ = moderate inhibitor
○ = weak inhibitor

Drug	1A2	2A6	2B6	2C8/9	2C19	2D6	2E1	3A4
Acebutolol						○		
Acetaminophen								○
AcetaZOLAMIDE								○
Albendazole	○							
Alosetron	○						○	
Amiodarone	●	◑	○	◑	○	◑		◑
Amitriptyline	○			○	○	○	○	
Amlodipine	◑	○	○	○		○		○
Amphetamine						○		
Amprenavir					○			●
Anastrozole	○			○				○
Aprepitant				○	○			◑
Atazanavir	○			○				●
Atorvastatin								○
Azelastine			○	○	○	○		○
Azithromycin								○
Bepridil						○		
Betamethasone								○
Betaxolol						○		
Biperiden						○		
Bortezomib	○			○	◑	○		○
Bromazepam							○	
Bromocriptine	○							○
Buprenorphine	○	○			○	○		
BuPROPion						○		
Caffeine	●							◑
Candesartan				○				
Celecoxib						○		
Cerivastatin								○
Chloramphenicol				○				○
Chloroquine						◑		
Chlorpheniramine						○		
ChlorproMAZINE						●	○	
Chlorzoxazone							○	○
Cholecalciferol				○	○	○		
Cimetidine	◑			○	◑	◑	○	◑

CYP Inhibitors *(continued)*

Drug	1A2	2A6	2B6	2C8/9	2C19	2D6	2E1	3A4
Cinacalcet						○		
Ciprofloxacin	●							○
Cisapride						○		○
Citalopram	○		○		○	○		
Clarithromycin	○							●
Clemastine						○		○
Clofazimine								○
Clofibrate		○						
ClomiPRAMINE						◑		
Clopidogrel				○				
Clotrimazole	○	○	○	○	○	○	○	◑
Clozapine	○			○	○	◑	○	○
Cocaine						●		○
Codeine						○		
Cyclophosphamide								○
CycloSPORINE				○				◑
Danazol								○
Delavirdine	○			●	●	●		●
Desipramine		◑	◑			◑	○	◑
Dexmedetomidine	○			○		●		○
Dextromethorphan						○		
Diazepam					○			○
Diclofenac	◑			○			○	●
Dihydroergotamine								○
Diltiazem				○		○		◑
Dimethyl sulfoxide				○	○			
DiphenhydrAMINE						◑		
Disulfiram	○	○	○	○		○	●	○
Docetaxel								○
Dolasetron						○		
DOXOrubicin			◑			○		○
Doxycycline								◑
Drospirenone	○			○	○			○
Duloxetine						◑		
Econazole							○	
Efavirenz				◑	◑			◑
Enoxacin	●							●
Entacapone	○	○		○	○	○	○	○
Eprosartan				○				
Ergotamine								○
Erythromycin	○							◑
Escitalopram						○		
Estradiol	○							

CYTOCHROME P450 ENZYMES: SUBSTRATES, INHIBITORS, AND INDUCERS *(Continued)*

CYP Inhibitors *(continued)*

Drug	1A2	2A6	2B6	2C8/9	2C19	2D6	2E1	3A4
Estrogens, conjugated A/synthetic	○							
Estrogens, conjugated equine	○							
Ethinyl estradiol	○		○		○			○
Ethotoin					○			
Etoposide				○				○
Felbamate					○			
Felodipine				○		○		○
Fenofibrate		○		○	○			
Fentanyl								○
Fexofenadine						○		
Flecainide						○		
Fluconazole	○			●	●			◑
Fluoxetine	◑		○	○	◑	●		○
Fluphenazine	○			○		○	○	
Flurazepam							○	
Flurbiprofen				●				
Flutamide	○							
Fluvastatin	○			◑		○		○
Fluvoxamine	●		○	○	●	○		○
Fosamprenavir (as amprenavir)					○			●
Gefitinib					○	○		
Gemfibrozil	◑			●	●			
Glyburide								○
Grapefruit juice								◑
Halofantrine						○		
Haloperidol						◑		◑
HydrALAZINE								○
HydrOXYzine						○		
Ibuprofen				●				
Ifosfamide								○
Imatinib				○		○		●
Imipramine	○				○	◑	○	
Indinavir				○	○	○		●
Indomethacin				●	○			
Interferon alfa-2a	○							
Interferon alfa-2b	○							
Interferon gamma-1b	○						○	
Irbesartan				◑		○		○

CYP Inhibitors *(continued)*

Drug	1A2	2A6	2B6	2C8/9	2C19	2D6	2E1	3A4
Isoflurane			○					
Isoniazid	○	◑		◑	●	◑	◑	●
Isradipine								○
Itraconazole								●
Ketoconazole	●	◑	○	●	◑	◑		●
Ketoprofen				○				
Labetalol						○		
Lansoprazole				○	◑	○		○
Leflunomide				○				
Letrozole		●			○			
Lidocaine	●					◑		◑
Lomefloxacin	○							
Lomustine						○		○
Loratadine					◑	○		
Losartan	○			◑	○			○
Lovastatin				○		○		○
Mefenamic acid				●				
Mefloquine						○		○
Meloxicam				○				
Mephobarbital					○			
Mestranol	○		○		○			○
Methadone						◑		○
Methimazole	○	○	○	○	○	◑	○	○
Methotrimeprazine						○		
Methoxsalen	●	●		○	○	○	○	○
Methsuximide					○			
Methylphenidate						○		
MethylPREDNISolone								○
Metoclopramide						○		
Metoprolol						○		
Metronidazole				○				◑
Metyrapone		○						
Mexiletine	●							
Miconazole	◑	●	○	●	●	●	◑	●
Midazolam				○				○
Mifepristone						○		○
Mirtazapine	○							○
Mitoxantrone								○
Moclobemide	○				○	○		
Modafinil	○	○		○	●		○	○
Montelukast				○				
Nalidixic acid	○							
Nateglinide				○				

CYTOCHROME P450 ENZYMES: SUBSTRATES, INHIBITORS, AND INDUCERS *(Continued)*

CYP Inhibitors *(continued)*

Drug	1A2	2A6	2B6	2C8/9	2C19	2D6	2E1	3A4
Nefazodone	○		○			○		●
Nelfinavir	○		○	○	○	○		●
Nevirapine	○					○		○
NiCARdipine				●	◑	◑		●
Nicotine		○					○	
NIFEdipine	◑			○		○		○
Nilutamide					○			
Nisoldipine	○							○
Nitrendipine								○
Nizatidine								○
Norfloxacin	●							◑
Nortriptyline						○	○	
Ofloxacin	●							
Olanzapine	○			○	○	○		○
Omeprazole	○			◑	●	○		○
Ondansetron	○			○		○		
Orphenadrine	○	○	○	○	○	○	○	○
Oxcarbazepine					○			
Oxprenolol						○		
Oxybutynin						○		○
Pantoprazole				◑				
Paroxetine	○		◑	○	○	●		○
Peginterferon alfa-2a	○							
Peginterferon alfa-2b	○							
Pentamidine				○	○	○		○
Pentoxifylline	○							
Pergolide						●		○
Perphenazine	○					○		
Phencyclidine								○
Pilocarpine		○					○	○
Pimozide					○	○	○	○
Pindolol						○		
Pioglitazone				●	○	◑		
Piroxicam				●				
Pravastatin				○		○		○
Praziquantel						○		
PrednisoLONE								○
Primaquine	●					○		○
Probenecid					○			
Progesterone				○	○			○

CYP Inhibitors *(continued)*

Drug	1A2	2A6	2B6	2C8/9	2C19	2D6	2E1	3A4
Promethazine						○		
Propafenone	○			○		○		
Propofol	◑			○	◑	○	○	●
Propoxyphene				○		○		○
Propranolol	○					○		
Pyrimethamine				◑		◑		
Quinidine				○		●		●
Quinine				◑		●		○
Quinupristin								○
Rabeprazole					◑	○		○
Ranitidine	○					○		
Risperidone						○		○
Ritonavir				○	○	●	○	●
Rofecoxib	○							
Ropinirole	○					●		
Rosiglitazone				◑	○	○		
Saquinavir				○	○	○		◑
Selegiline	○	○		○	○	○	○	○
Sertraline	○		◑	○	◑	◑		◑
Sildenafil	○			○	○	○	○	○
Simvastatin				○		○		
Sirolimus								○
Sulconazole	○	○		○	○	○	○	○
SulfaDIAZINE				●				
Sulfamethoxazole				◑				
Sulfinpyrazone				◑				
SulfiSOXAZOLE				●				
Tacrine	○							
Tacrolimus								○
Tamoxifen			○	○				○
Telithromycin						○		●
Telmisartan					○			
Teniposide				○				○
Tenofovir	○							
Terbinafine						●		
Testosterone								○
Tetracycline								◑
Theophylline	○							
Thiabendazole	●							
Thioridazine	○			○		◑	○	
Thiotepa			●					
Thiothixene						○		
Ticlopidine	○			○	●	◑	○	○

CYTOCHROME P450 ENZYMES: SUBSTRATES, INHIBITORS, AND INDUCERS *(Continued)*

CYP Inhibitors *(continued)*

Drug	1A2	2A6	2B6	2C8/9	2C19	2D6	2E1	3A4
Timolol						○		
Tioconazole	○	○		○	○	○	○	
Tocainide	○							
TOLBUTamide				●				
Tolcapone				○				
Topiramate					○			
Torsemide					○			
Tranylcypromine	◑	●		○	◑	◑	○	○
Trazodone						◑		○
Tretinoin				○				
Triazolam				○				
Trimethoprim				◑				
Tripelennamine						◑		
Triprolidine						○		
Troleandomycin								◑
Valdecoxib				○	○			
Valproic acid				○	○	○		○
Valsartan				○				
Venlafaxine			○			○		○
Verapamil	○			○		○		◑
VinBLAStine						○		○
VinCRIStine								○
Vinorelbine						○		○
Voriconazole				○	○			◑
Warfarin				◑	○			
Yohimbine						○		
Zafirlukast	○			◑	○	○		○
Zileuton	○							
Ziprasidone						○		○

CYP Inducers

● = effectively induced
○ = not effectively induced

Drug	1A2	2A6	2B6	2C8/9	2C19	2D6	2E1	3A4
Aminoglutethimide	●				●			●
Amobarbital		●						
Aprepitant				○				○
Bexarotene								○
Bosentan				●				●
Calcitriol								○
Carbamazepine	●		●	●	●			●
Clofibrate			○				○	○
Colchicine				○			○	○
Cyclophosphamide			○	○				
Dexamethasone		○	○	○				○
Dicloxacillin								○
Efavirenz (in liver only)			○					●
Estradiol								○
Estrogens, conjugated A/synthetic								○
Estrogens, conjugated equine								○
Exemestane								○
Felbamate								○
Fosphenytoin (as phenytoin)			●	●	●			●
Griseofulvin	○			○				○
Hydrocortisone								○
Ifosfamide				○				
Insulin preparations	○							
Isoniazid (after D/C)							○	
Lansoprazole	○							
MedroxyPROGESTERone								○
Mephobarbital		○						
Metyrapone								○
Modafinil	○		○					○
Moricizine	○							○
Nafcillin								●
Nevirapine			●					●
Norethindrone					○			
Omeprazole	○							
Oxcarbazepine								●
Paclitaxel								○
Pantoprazole	○							○
Pentobarbital		●						●

CYTOCHROME P450 ENZYMES: SUBSTRATES, INHIBITORS, AND INDUCERS *(Continued)*

CYP Inducers *(continued)*

Drug	1A2	2A6	2B6	2C8/9	2C19	2D6	2E1	3A4
Phenobarbital	●	●	●	●				●
Phenytoin			●	●	●			●
Pioglitazone								○
PredniSONE					○			○
Primaquine	○							
Primidone[1]	●		●	●				●
Rifabutin								●
Rifampin	●	●	●	●	●			●
Rifapentine				●				●
Ritonavir (long-term)	○			○				○
Rofecoxib								○
Secobarbital		●		●				
Sulfinpyrazone								○
Terbinafine								○
Topiramate								○
Tretinoin							○	
Troglitazone								○
Valproic acid		○						

[1]Primidone is partially metabolized to phenobarbital. See Phenobarbital for additional CYP information.

ALPHABETICAL LISTING OF DRUGS

Abacavir (a BAK a veer)

Genes of Interest

Human Leukocyte Antigen *on page 301*

U.S. Brand Names Ziagen®

Canadian Brand Names Ziagen®

Synonyms ABC; Abacavir Sulfate

Pharmacologic Class Antiretroviral Agent, Reverse Transcriptase Inhibitor (Nucleoside)

- ♦ **Abacavir Sulfate** *see* Abacavir *on page 52*
- ♦ **ABC** *see* Abacavir *on page 52*

Abciximab (ab SIK si mab)

Genes of Interest

Glycoprotein IIIa Receptor *on page 285*

U.S. Brand Names ReoPro®

Canadian Brand Names Reopro®

Synonyms 7E3; C7E3

Pharmacologic Class Antiplatelet Agent, Glycoprotein IIb/IIIa Inhibitor

- ♦ **Abilify®** *see* Aripiprazole *on page 64*
- ♦ **Accolate®** *see* Zafirlukast *on page 204*
- ♦ **AccuNeb™** *see* Albuterol *on page 54*
- ♦ **Accupril®** *see* Quinapril *on page 174*
- ♦ **ACE** *see* Captopril *on page 75*

Acebutolol (a se BYOO toe lole)

Genes of Interest

Angiotensin-Converting Enzyme *on page 214*
Beta$_1$-Adrenergic Receptor *on page 230*
Gs Protein Alpha-Subunit *on page 288*

U.S. Brand Names Sectral®

Canadian Brand Names Apo-Acebutolol®; Gen-Acebutolol; Monitan®; Novo-Acebutolol; Nu-Acebutolol; Rhotral; Rhoxal-acebutolol; Sectral®

Synonyms Acebutolol Hydrochloride

Pharmacologic Class Antiarrhythmic Agent, Class II; Beta Blocker With Intrinsic Sympathomimetic Activity

- ♦ **Acebutolol Hydrochloride** *see* Acebutolol *on page 52*
- ♦ **Aceon®** *see* Perindopril Erbumine *on page 164*

Acetaminophen and Codeine

(a seet a MIN oh fen & KOE deen)

Genes of Interest

COMT *on page 244*
CYP2D6 *on page 254*

U.S. Brand Names Capital® and Codeine; Tylenol® With Codeine

Canadian Brand Names Triatec-30; Triatec-8 Strong; Triatec-8; Tylenol Elixir with Codeine; Tylenol No. 1 Forte; Tylenol No. 1; Tylenol

No. 2 with Codeine; Tylenol No. 3 with Codeine; Tylenol No. 4 with Codeine; ratio-Emtec; ratio-Lenoltec

Synonyms Codeine and Acetaminophen

Pharmacologic Class Analgesic, Narcotic

- **Acetaminophen and Hydrocodone** *see* Hydrocodone and Acetaminophen *on page 120*
- **Acetaminophen and Oxycodone** *see* Oxycodone and Acetaminophen *on page 161*

Acetaminophen and Phenyltoloxamine

(a seet a MIN oh fen & fen il to LOKS a meen)

Genes of Interest

COMT *on page 244*

U.S. Brand Names Genesec® [OTC]; Percogesic® [OTC]; Phenylgesic® [OTC]

Synonyms Phenyltoloxamine and Acetaminophen

Pharmacologic Class Analgesic, Non-narcotic

Acetaminophen and Tramadol

(a seet a MIN oh fen & TRA ma dole)

Genes of Interest

COMT *on page 244*

CYP2D6 *on page 254*

U.S. Brand Names Ultracet™

Synonyms APAP and Tramadol; Tramadol Hydrochloride and Acetaminophen

Pharmacologic Class Analgesic, Miscellaneous; Analgesic, Non-narcotic

- **Acetaminophen, Caffeine, Codeine, and Butalbital** *see* Butalbital, Acetaminophen, Caffeine, and Codeine *on page 73*

Acetophenazine (a set oh FEN a zeen)

Genes of Interest

$Alpha_1$-Adrenergic Receptor *on page 210*

D_2 Receptor *on page 263*

Synonyms Acetophenazine Maleate

Pharmacologic Class Antipsychotic Agent, Typical, Phenothiazine

- **Acetophenazine Maleate** *see* Acetophenazine *on page 53*
- **Acetoxymethylprogesterone** *see* MedroxyPROGESTERone *on page 137*
- **Acetylsalicylic Acid** *see* Aspirin *on page 65*
- **Achromycin** *see* Tetracycline *on page 192*
- **Aciclovir** *see* Acyclovir *on page 54*
- **AcipHex®** *see* Rabeprazole *on page 175*
- **Actiq®** *see* Fentanyl *on page 107*
- **Actonel®** *see* Risedronate *on page 179*
- **Actos®** *see* Pioglitazone *on page 166*
- **Acular®** *see* Ketorolac *on page 129*
- **Acular LS™** *see* Ketorolac *on page 129*

♦ **Acular® PF** *see* Ketorolac *on page 129*
♦ **ACV** *see* Acyclovir *on page 54*
♦ **Acycloguanosine** *see* Acyclovir *on page 54*

Acyclovir (ay SYE kloe veer)

Genes of Interest None known
U.S. Brand Names Zovirax®
Canadian Brand Names Apo-Acyclovir®; Gen-Acyclovir; Nu-Acyclovir; Zovirax®; ratio-Acyclovir
Synonyms ACV; Aciclovir; Acycloguanosine
Pharmacologic Class Antiviral Agent

♦ **Aczone™** *see* Dapsone *on page 88*
♦ **Adalat® XL® (Can)** *see* NIFEdipine *on page 150*
♦ **Adalat® CC** *see* NIFEdipine *on page 150*
♦ **Adderall®** *see* Dextroamphetamine and Amphetamine *on page 90*
♦ **Adderall XR®** *see* Dextroamphetamine and Amphetamine *on page 90*
♦ **Adoxa™** *see* Doxycycline *on page 96*
♦ **ADR (error-prone abbreviation)** *see* DOXOrubicin *on page 95*
♦ **Adria** *see* DOXOrubicin *on page 95*
♦ **Adriamycin® (Can)** *see* DOXOrubicin *on page 95*
♦ **Adriamycin PFS®** *see* DOXOrubicin *on page 95*
♦ **Adriamycin RDF®** *see* DOXOrubicin *on page 95*
♦ **Adrucil®** *see* Fluorouracil *on page 109*
♦ **Advair Diskus®** *see* Fluticasone and Salmeterol *on page 111*
♦ **Advil® [OTC]** *see* Ibuprofen *on page 123*
♦ **Advil® Children's [OTC]** *see* Ibuprofen *on page 123*
♦ **Advil® Infants' [OTC]** *see* Ibuprofen *on page 123*
♦ **Advil® Junior [OTC]** *see* Ibuprofen *on page 123*
♦ **Advil® Migraine [OTC]** *see* Ibuprofen *on page 123*
♦ **Aerius® (Can)** *see* Desloratadine *on page 89*
♦ **Afeditab™ CR** *see* NIFEdipine *on page 150*
♦ **Aggrastat®** *see* Tirofiban *on page 195*
♦ **Aggrenox®** *see* Aspirin and Dipyridamole *on page 66*
♦ **A-hydroCort** *see* Hydrocortisone *on page 121*
♦ **Airomir (Can)** *see* Albuterol *on page 54*
♦ **Akne-Mycin®** *see* Erythromycin *on page 99*
♦ **Alavert™ [OTC]** *see* Loratadine *on page 133*
♦ **Albert® Glyburide (Can)** *see* GlyBURIDE *on page 117*
♦ **Albert® Tiafen (Can)** *see* Tiaprofenic Acid *on page 194*

Albuterol (al BYOO ter ole)

Genes of Interest
Beta$_2$-Adrenergic Receptor *on page 233*
U.S. Brand Names AccuNeb™; Proventil® HFA; Proventil® Repetabs®; Proventil®; Ventolin® HFA; VoSpire ER™; Volmax® [DSC]

Canadian Brand Names Airomir; Alti-Salbutamol; Apo-Salvent®; Gen-Salbutamol; PMS-Salbutamol; Rhoxal-salbutamol; Salbu-2; Salbu-4; Ventolin® Diskus; Ventolin® HFA; Ventolin®; Ventrodisk; ratio-Inspra-Sal; ratio-Salbutamol

Synonyms Albuterol Sulfate; Salbutamol

Pharmacologic Class $Beta_2$-Adrenergic Agonist

- **Albuterol and Ipratropium** *see* Ipratropium and Albuterol *on page 125*
- **Albuterol Sulfate** *see* Albuterol *on page 54*
- **Aldactone®** *see* Spironolactone *on page 186*

Alendronate (a LEN droe nate)

Genes of Interest None known

U.S. Brand Names Fosamax®

Canadian Brand Names Apo-Alendronate®; Fosamax®; Novo-Alendronate

Synonyms Alendronate Sodium

Pharmacologic Class Bisphosphonate Derivative

- **Alendronate Sodium** *see* Alendronate *on page 55*
- **Alertec® (Can)** *see* Modafinil *on page 145*
- **Alesse®** *see* Ethinyl Estradiol and Levonorgestrel *on page 104*
- **Aleve® [OTC]** *see* Naproxen *on page 148*
- **Alfenta®** *see* Alfentanil *on page 55*

Alfentanil (al FEN ta nil)

Genes of Interest

COMT *on page 244*

CYP3A4 *on page 260*

U.S. Brand Names Alfenta®

Canadian Brand Names Alfenta®

Synonyms Alfentanil Hydrochloride

Pharmacologic Class Analgesic, Narcotic

- **Alfentanil Hydrochloride** *see* Alfentanil *on page 55*
- **Allegra®** *see* Fexofenadine *on page 108*
- **Aller-Chlor® [OTC]** *see* Chlorpheniramine *on page 79*

Allopurinol (al oh PURE i nole)

Genes of Interest None known

U.S. Brand Names Aloprim™; Zyloprim®

Canadian Brand Names Apo-Allopurinol®; Novo-Purol; Zyloprim®

Synonyms Allopurinol Sodium

Pharmacologic Class Xanthine Oxidase Inhibitor

- **Allopurinol Sodium** *see* Allopurinol *on page 55*
- **Aloprim™** *see* Allopurinol *on page 55*
- **Alora®** *see* Estradiol *on page 101*

Alosetron (a LOE se tron)

Genes of Interest

CYP2C8 *on page 248*

U.S. Brand Names Lotronex®

Pharmacologic Class Selective 5-HT_3 Receptor Antagonist

Alprazolam (al PRAY zoe lam)

Genes of Interest

CYP3A4 *on page 260*

U.S. Brand Names Alprazolam Intensol®; Niravam™; Xanax XR®; Xanax®

Canadian Brand Names Alti-Alprazolam; Apo-Alpraz®; Gen-Alprazolam; Novo-Alprazol; Nu-Alprax; Xanax TS™; Xanax®

Pharmacologic Class Benzodiazepine

- **Alprazolam Intensol®** *see* Alprazolam *on page 56*
- **Altace®** *see* Ramipril *on page 176*
- **Alti-Alprazolam (Can)** *see* Alprazolam *on page 56*
- **Alti-Amiodarone (Can)** *see* Amiodarone *on page 57*
- **Alti-Amoxi-Clav (Can)** *see* Amoxicillin and Clavulanate Potassium *on page 59*
- **Alti-Azathioprine (Can)** *see* Azathioprine *on page 67*
- **Alti-Captopril (Can)** *see* Captopril *on page 75*
- **Alti-Clindamycin (Can)** *see* Clindamycin *on page 82*
- **Alti-Clobazam (Can)** *see* Clobazam *on page 83*
- **Alti-Clonazepam (Can)** *see* Clonazepam *on page 83*
- **Alti-Desipramine (Can)** *see* Desipramine *on page 89*
- **Alti-Diltiazem CD (Can)** *see* Diltiazem *on page 93*
- **Alti-Divalproex (Can)** *see* Valproic Acid and Derivatives *on page 201*
- **Alti-Domperidone (Can)** *see* Domperidone *on page 94*
- **Alti-Doxazosin (Can)** *see* Doxazosin *on page 95*
- **Alti-Fluoxetine (Can)** *see* Fluoxetine *on page 109*
- **Alti-Flurbiprofen (Can)** *see* Flurbiprofen *on page 111*
- **Alti-Fluvoxamine (Can)** *see* Fluvoxamine *on page 112*
- **Alti-Metformin (Can)** *see* Metformin *on page 139*
- **Alti-Minocycline (Can)** *see* Minocycline *on page 144*
- **Alti-Moclobemide (Can)** *see* Moclobemide *on page 144*
- **Alti-MPA (Can)** *see* MedroxyPROGESTERone *on page 137*
- **Alti-Nadolol (Can)** *see* Nadolol *on page 147*
- **Alti-Nortriptyline (Can)** *see* Nortriptyline *on page 152*
- **Alti-Ranitidine (Can)** *see* Ranitidine *on page 176*
- **Alti-Salbutamol (Can)** *see* Albuterol *on page 54*
- **Alti-Sotalol (Can)** *see* Sotalol *on page 185*
- **Alti-Sulfasalazine (Can)** *see* Sulfasalazine *on page 188*
- **Alti-Terazosin (Can)** *see* Terazosin *on page 191*
- **Alti-Ticlopidine (Can)** *see* Ticlopidine *on page 194*
- **Alti-Timolol (Can)** *see* Timolol *on page 195*

♦ **Alti-Trazodone (Can)** *see* Trazodone *on page 197*
♦ **Alti-Verapamil (Can)** *see* Verapamil *on page 201*
♦ **Alti-Zopiclone (Can)** *see* Zopiclone *on page 206*
♦ **Altoprev™** *see* Lovastatin *on page 135*
♦ **Alupent®** *see* Metaproterenol *on page 139*
♦ **Amaryl®** *see* Glimepiride *on page 117*
♦ **Ambien®** *see* Zolpidem *on page 205*
♦ **A-Methapred** *see* MethylPREDNISolone *on page 141*

Amiloride (a MIL oh ride)

Genes of Interest

Epithelial Sodium Channel Beta-Subunit *on page 273*

U.S. Brand Names Midamor® [DSC]

Canadian Brand Names Apo-Amiloride®

Synonyms Amiloride Hydrochloride

Pharmacologic Class Diuretic, Potassium-Sparing

♦ **Amiloride Hydrochloride** *see* Amiloride *on page 57*
♦ **2-Amino-6-Mercaptopurine** *see* Thioguanine *on page 193*
♦ **2-Amino-6-Trifluoromethoxy-benzothiazole** *see* Riluzole *on page 179*

Aminophylline (am in OFF i lin)

Genes of Interest

CYP1A2 *on page 246*

Canadian Brand Names Phyllocontin®-350; Phyllocontin®

Synonyms Theophylline Ethylenediamine

Pharmacologic Class Theophylline Derivative

Amiodarone (a MEE oh da rone)

Genes of Interest

ATP-Binding Cassette, Sub-Family B, Member 1 *on page 224*
Cardiac Potassium Ion Channel *on page 241*
Cardiac Sodium Channel *on page 242*
CYP2C8 *on page 248*
CYP2C9 *on page 248*
CYP2D6 *on page 254*

U.S. Brand Names Cordarone®; Pacerone®

Canadian Brand Names Alti-Amiodarone; Apo-Amiodarone®; Cordarone®; Gen-Amiodarone; Novo-Amiodarone; Rhoxal-amiodarone

Synonyms Amiodarone Hydrochloride

Pharmacologic Class Antiarrhythmic Agent, Class III

♦ **Amiodarone Hydrochloride** *see* Amiodarone *on page 57*

Amitriptyline (a mee TRIP ti leen)

Genes of Interest

$Alpha_1$-Adrenergic Receptor *on page 210*
ATP-Binding Cassette, Sub-Family B, Member 1 *on page 224*
Cardiac Potassium Ion Channel *on page 241*
(Continued)

Amitriptyline *(Continued)*

Cardiac Sodium Channel *on page 242*
G-Protein $Beta_3$ Subunit *on page 286*
Gs Protein Alpha-Subunit *on page 288*
TNF-Alpha *on page 319*

U.S. Brand Names Elavil® [DSC]

Canadian Brand Names Apo-Amitriptyline®; Levate®; Novo-Triptyn; PMS-Amitriptyline

Synonyms Amitriptyline Hydrochloride

Pharmacologic Class Antidepressant, Tricyclic (Tertiary Amine)

Amitriptyline and Chlordiazepoxide

(a mee TRIP ti leen & klor dye az e POKS ide)

Genes of Interest

$Alpha_1$-Adrenergic Receptor *on page 210*
ATP-Binding Cassette, Sub-Family B, Member 1 *on page 224*
Cardiac Potassium Ion Channel *on page 241*
Cardiac Sodium Channel *on page 242*
CYP3A4 *on page 260*
G-Protein $Beta_3$ Subunit *on page 286*
Gs Protein Alpha-Subunit *on page 288*
TNF-Alpha *on page 319*

U.S. Brand Names Limbitrol® DS; Limbitrol®

Canadian Brand Names Limbitrol®

Synonyms Chlordiazepoxide and Amitriptyline

Pharmacologic Class Antidepressant, Tricyclic (Tertiary Amine); Benzodiazepine

Amitriptyline and Perphenazine

(a mee TRIP ti leen & per FEN a zeen)

Genes of Interest

$Alpha_1$-Adrenergic Receptor *on page 210*
ATP-Binding Cassette, Sub-Family B, Member 1 *on page 224*
Cardiac Potassium Ion Channel *on page 241*
Cardiac Sodium Channel *on page 242*
CYP2D6 *on page 254*
D_2 Receptor *on page 263*
G-Protein $Beta_3$ Subunit *on page 286*
Gs Protein Alpha-Subunit *on page 288*
TNF-Alpha *on page 319*

U.S. Brand Names Triavil®

Canadian Brand Names Etrafon®

Synonyms Perphenazine and Amitriptyline

Pharmacologic Class Antidepressant, Tricyclic (Tertiary Amine); Antipsychotic Agent, Typical, Phenothiazine

♦ **Amitriptyline Hydrochloride** *see* Amitriptyline *on page 57*

Amlodipine (am LOE di peen)

Genes of Interest

CYP3A4 *on page 260*

U.S. Brand Names Norvasc®
Canadian Brand Names Norvasc®
Synonyms Amlodipine Besylate
Pharmacologic Class Calcium Channel Blocker

Amlodipine and Benazepril

(am LOE di peen & ben AY ze pril)

Genes of Interest

Aldosterone Synthase *on page 208*
Angiotensin II Type 1 Receptor *on page 213*
Angiotensin-Converting Enzyme *on page 214*
Angiotensinogen *on page 219*
Bradykinin B_2-Receptor *on page 237*
CYP3A4 *on page 260*

U.S. Brand Names Lotrel®
Synonyms Benazepril and Amlodipine
Pharmacologic Class Antihypertensive Agent, Combination

- **Amlodipine Besylate** *see* Amlodipine *on page 58*

Amoxapine (a MOKS a peen)

Genes of Interest

Alpha$_1$-Adrenergic Receptor *on page 210*
G-Protein Beta$_3$ Subunit *on page 286*
Gs Protein Alpha-Subunit *on page 288*

Synonyms Asendin [DSC]
Pharmacologic Class Antidepressant, Tricyclic (Secondary Amine)

Amoxicillin (a moks i SIL in)

Genes of Interest None known
U.S. Brand Names Amoxil®; DisperMox™; Moxilin®; Trimox®
Canadian Brand Names Apo-Amoxi®; Gen-Amoxicillin; Lin-Amox; Novamoxin®; Nu-Amoxi; PMS-Amoxicillin
Synonyms *p*-Hydroxyampicillin; Amoxicillin Trihydrate; Amoxycillin
Pharmacologic Class Antibiotic, Penicillin

Amoxicillin and Clavulanate Potassium

(a moks i SIL in & klav yoo LAN ate poe TASS ee um)

Genes of Interest None known
U.S. Brand Names Augmentin ES-600®; Augmentin XR™; Augmentin®
Canadian Brand Names Alti-Amoxi-Clav; Apo-Amoxi-Clav®; Augmentin®; Clavulin®; Novo-Clavamoxin; ratio-Aclavulanate
Synonyms Amoxicillin and Clavulanic Acid
Pharmacologic Class Antibiotic, Penicillin

- **Amoxicillin and Clavulanic Acid** *see* Amoxicillin and Clavulanate Potassium *on page 59*
- **Amoxicillin Trihydrate** *see* Amoxicillin *on page 59*
- **Amoxil®** *see* Amoxicillin *on page 59*
- **Amoxycillin** *see* Amoxicillin *on page 59*

- **Amphetamine and Dextroamphetamine** *see* Dextroamphetamine and Amphetamine *on page 90*
- **Anafranil®** *see* ClomiPRAMINE *on page 83*
- **Anandron® (Can)** *see* Nilutamide *on page 150*
- **Anaprox®** *see* Naproxen *on page 148*
- **Anaprox® DS** *see* Naproxen *on page 148*
- **Andriol® (Can)** *see* Testosterone *on page 192*
- **Androderm®** *see* Testosterone *on page 192*
- **AndroGel®** *see* Testosterone *on page 192*
- **Andropository (Can)** *see* Testosterone *on page 192*
- **Anestacon®** *see* Lidocaine *on page 131*
- **Anexsia®** *see* Hydrocodone and Acetaminophen *on page 120*
- **Ansaid®** *see* Flurbiprofen *on page 111*
- **Ansamycin** *see* Rifabutin *on page 179*
- **Antabuse®** *see* Disulfiram *on page 94*
- **Antara™** *see* Fenofibrate *on page 107*
- **Antivert®** *see* Meclizine *on page 136*
- **Anturane** *see* Sulfinpyrazone *on page 188*
- **Anucort-HC®** *see* Hydrocortisone *on page 121*
- **Anusol-HC®** *see* Hydrocortisone *on page 121*
- **Anusol® HC-1 [OTC]** *see* Hydrocortisone *on page 121*
- **APAP and Tramadol** *see* Acetaminophen and Tramadol *on page 53*
- **Apidra™** *see* Insulin Preparations *on page 125*
- **Apo-Acebutolol® (Can)** *see* Acebutolol *on page 52*
- **Apo-Acyclovir® (Can)** *see* Acyclovir *on page 54*
- **Apo-Alendronate® (Can)** *see* Alendronate *on page 55*
- **Apo-Allopurinol® (Can)** *see* Allopurinol *on page 55*
- **Apo-Alpraz® (Can)** *see* Alprazolam *on page 56*
- **Apo-Amiloride® (Can)** *see* Amiloride *on page 57*
- **Apo-Amiodarone® (Can)** *see* Amiodarone *on page 57*
- **Apo-Amitriptyline® (Can)** *see* Amitriptyline *on page 57*
- **Apo-Amoxi® (Can)** *see* Amoxicillin *on page 59*
- **Apo-Amoxi-Clav® (Can)** *see* Amoxicillin and Clavulanate Potassium *on page 59*
- **Apo-Atenol® (Can)** *see* Atenolol *on page 66*
- **Apo-Azathioprine® (Can)** *see* Azathioprine *on page 67*
- **Apo-Bromazepam® (Can)** *see* Bromazepam *on page 72*
- **Apo-Bromocriptine® (Can)** *see* Bromocriptine *on page 72*
- **Apo-Buspirone® (Can)** *see* BusPIRone *on page 73*
- **Apo-Butorphanol® (Can)** *see* Butorphanol *on page 74*
- **Apo-Capto® (Can)** *see* Captopril *on page 75*
- **Apo-Carbamazepine® (Can)** *see* Carbamazepine *on page 75*
- **Apo-Carvedilol® (Can)** *see* Carvedilol *on page 76*
- **Apo-Cephalex® (Can)** *see* Cephalexin *on page 78*
- **Apo-Cetirizine® (Can)** *see* Cetirizine *on page 78*

- ♦ **Apo-Chlordiazepoxide® (Can)** *see* Chlordiazepoxide *on page 78*
- ♦ **Apo-Chlorpromazine® (Can)** *see* ChlorproMAZINE *on page 79*
- ♦ **Apo-Chlorthalidone® (Can)** *see* Chlorthalidone *on page 79*
- ♦ **Apo-Cimetidine® (Can)** *see* Cimetidine *on page 80*
- ♦ **Apo-Ciproflox® (Can)** *see* Ciprofloxacin *on page 81*
- ♦ **Apo-Citalopram® (Can)** *see* Citalopram *on page 81*
- ♦ **Apo-Clindamycin® (Can)** *see* Clindamycin *on page 82*
- ♦ **Apo-Clobazam® (Can)** *see* Clobazam *on page 83*
- ♦ **Apo-Clomipramine® (Can)** *see* ClomiPRAMINE *on page 83*
- ♦ **Apo-Clonazepam® (Can)** *see* Clonazepam *on page 83*
- ♦ **Apo-Clonidine® (Can)** *see* Clonidine *on page 83*
- ♦ **Apo-Clorazepate® (Can)** *see* Clorazepate *on page 84*
- ♦ **Apo-Clozapine® (Can)** *see* Clozapine *on page 84*
- ♦ **Apo-Cyclobenzaprine® (Can)** *see* Cyclobenzaprine *on page 87*
- ♦ **Apo-Cyclosporine® (Can)** *see* CycloSPORINE *on page 87*
- ♦ **Apo-Desipramine® (Can)** *see* Desipramine *on page 89*
- ♦ **Apo-Diazepam® (Can)** *see* Diazepam *on page 90*
- ♦ **Apo-Diclo® (Can)** *see* Diclofenac *on page 91*
- ♦ **Apo-Diclo Rapide® (Can)** *see* Diclofenac *on page 91*
- ♦ **Apo-Diclo SR® (Can)** *see* Diclofenac *on page 91*
- ♦ **Apo-Diflunisal® (Can)** *see* Diflunisal *on page 91*
- ♦ **Apo-Diltiaz® (Can)** *see* Diltiazem *on page 93*
- ♦ **Apo-Diltiaz CD® (Can)** *see* Diltiazem *on page 93*
- ♦ **Apo-Diltiaz SR® (Can)** *see* Diltiazem *on page 93*
- ♦ **Apo-Dipyridamole FC® (Can)** *see* Dipyridamole *on page 93*
- ♦ **Apo-Divalproex® (Can)** *see* Valproic Acid and Derivatives *on page 201*
- ♦ **Apo-Domperidone® (Can)** *see* Domperidone *on page 94*
- ♦ **Apo-Doxazosin® (Can)** *see* Doxazosin *on page 95*
- ♦ **Apo-Doxepin® (Can)** *see* Doxepin *on page 95*
- ♦ **Apo-Doxy® (Can)** *see* Doxycycline *on page 96*
- ♦ **Apo-Doxy Tabs® (Can)** *see* Doxycycline *on page 96*
- ♦ **Apo-Erythro Base® (Can)** *see* Erythromycin *on page 99*
- ♦ **Apo-Erythro E-C® (Can)** *see* Erythromycin *on page 99*
- ♦ **Apo-Erythro-ES® (Can)** *see* Erythromycin *on page 99*
- ♦ **Apo-Erythro-S® (Can)** *see* Erythromycin *on page 99*
- ♦ **Apo-Etodolac® (Can)** *see* Etodolac *on page 105*
- ♦ **Apo-Famotidine® (Can)** *see* Famotidine *on page 106*
- ♦ **Apo-Fenofibrate® (Can)** *see* Fenofibrate *on page 107*
- ♦ **Apo-Feno-Micro® (Can)** *see* Fenofibrate *on page 107*
- ♦ **Apo-Ferrous Sulfate® (Can)** *see* Ferrous Sulfate *on page 108*
- ♦ **Apo-Fluconazole® (Can)** *see* Fluconazole *on page 109*
- ♦ **Apo-Fluoxetine® (Can)** *see* Fluoxetine *on page 109*
- ♦ **Apo-Fluphenazine® (Can)** *see* Fluphenazine *on page 110*
- ♦ **Apo-Fluphenazine Decanoate® (Can)** *see* Fluphenazine *on page 110*

- **Apo-Napro-Na® (Can)** *see* Naproxen *on page 148*
- **Apo-Napro-Na DS® (Can)** *see* Naproxen *on page 148*
- **Apo-Naproxen® (Can)** *see* Naproxen *on page 148*
- **Apo-Naproxen SR® (Can)** *see* Naproxen *on page 148*
- **Apo-Nifed® (Can)** *see* NIFEdipine *on page 150*
- **Apo-Nifed PA® (Can)** *see* NIFEdipine *on page 150*
- **Apo-Nitrofurantoin® (Can)** *see* Nitrofurantoin *on page 151*
- **Apo-Nortriptyline® (Can)** *see* Nortriptyline *on page 152*
- **Apo-Oflox® (Can)** *see* Ofloxacin *on page 158*
- **Apo-Ofloxacin® (Can)** *see* Ofloxacin *on page 158*
- **Apo-Omeprazole® (Can)** *see* Omeprazole *on page 159*
- **Apo-Oxaprozin® (Can)** *see* Oxaprozin *on page 160*
- **Apo-Paroxetine® (Can)** *see* Paroxetine *on page 162*
- **Apo-Pen VK® (Can)** *see* Penicillin V Potassium *on page 163*
- **Apo-Perphenazine® (Can)** *see* Perphenazine *on page 164*
- **Apo-Pimozide® (Can)** *see* Pimozide *on page 166*
- **Apo-Piroxicam® (Can)** *see* Piroxicam *on page 166*
- **Apo-Pravastatin® (Can)** *see* Pravastatin *on page 169*
- **Apo-Prednisone® (Can)** *see* PredniSONE *on page 169*
- **Apo-Procainamide® (Can)** *see* Procainamide *on page 170*
- **Apo-Prochlorperazine® (Can)** *see* Prochlorperazine *on page 171*
- **Apo-Propafenone® (Can)** *see* Propafenone *on page 172*
- **Apo-Propranolol® (Can)** *see* Propranolol *on page 173*
- **Apo-Quin-G® (Can)** *see* Quinidine *on page 174*
- **Apo-Quinidine® (Can)** *see* Quinidine *on page 174*
- **Apo-Quinine® (Can)** *see* Quinine *on page 175*
- **Apo-Ranitidine® (Can)** *see* Ranitidine *on page 176*
- **Apo-Salvent® (Can)** *see* Albuterol *on page 54*
- **Apo-Selegiline® (Can)** *see* Selegiline *on page 183*
- **Apo-Sertraline® (Can)** *see* Sertraline *on page 183*
- **Apo-Simvastatin® (Can)** *see* Simvastatin *on page 184*
- **Apo-Sotalol® (Can)** *see* Sotalol *on page 185*
- **Apo-Sulfatrim® (Can)** *see* Sulfamethoxazole and Trimethoprim *on page 187*
- **Apo-Sulfinpyrazone® (Can)** *see* Sulfinpyrazone *on page 188*
- **Apo-Sulin® (Can)** *see* Sulindac *on page 188*
- **Apo-Tamox® (Can)** *see* Tamoxifen *on page 190*
- **Apo-Temazepam® (Can)** *see* Temazepam *on page 191*
- **Apo-Terazosin® (Can)** *see* Terazosin *on page 191*
- **Apo-Tetra® (Can)** *see* Tetracycline *on page 192*
- **Apo-Theo LA® (Can)** *see* Theophylline *on page 192*
- **Apo-Thioridazine® (Can)** *see* Thioridazine *on page 193*
- **Apo-Tiaprofenic® (Can)** *see* Tiaprofenic Acid *on page 194*
- **Apo-Ticlopidine® (Can)** *see* Ticlopidine *on page 194*
- **Apo-Timol® (Can)** *see* Timolol *on page 195*
- **Apo-Timop® (Can)** *see* Timolol *on page 195*

- **Apo-Tizanidine® (Can)** *see* Tizanidine *on page 195*
- **Apo-Tolbutamide® (Can)** *see* TOLBUTamide *on page 195*
- **Apo-Trazodone® (Can)** *see* Trazodone *on page 197*
- **Apo-Trazodone D® (Can)** *see* Trazodone *on page 197*
- **Apo-Triazo® (Can)** *see* Triazolam *on page 198*
- **Apo-Trifluoperazine® (Can)** *see* Trifluoperazine *on page 198*
- **Apo-Trimethoprim® (Can)** *see* Trimethoprim *on page 199*
- **Apo-Trimip® (Can)** *see* Trimipramine *on page 199*
- **Apo-Verap® (Can)** *see* Verapamil *on page 201*
- **Apo-Warfarin® (Can)** *see* Warfarin *on page 203*
- **Apo-Zopiclone® (Can)** *see* Zopiclone *on page 206*

Aprepitant (ap RE pi tant)

Genes of Interest

CYP3A4 *on page 260*

U.S. Brand Names Emend®

Synonyms L 754030; MK 869

Pharmacologic Class Antiemetic; Substance P/Neurokinin 1 Receptor Antagonist

- **Apresoline® (Can)** *see* HydrALAZINE *on page 119*
- **Apri®** *see* Ethinyl Estradiol and Desogestrel *on page 103*
- **Aquacort® (Can)** *see* Hydrocortisone *on page 121*
- **Aquanil™ HC [OTC]** *see* Hydrocortisone *on page 121*
- **Aquatensen® (Can)** *see* Methyclothiazide *on page 140*
- **Aralen®** *see* Chloroquine *on page 79*
- **Aranelle™** *see* Ethinyl Estradiol and Norethindrone *on page 104*
- **Aricept®** *see* Donepezil *on page 95*
- **Aricept® ODT** *see* Donepezil *on page 95*

Aripiprazole (ay ri PIP ray zole)

Genes of Interest

$Alpha_1$-Adrenergic Receptor *on page 210*
CYP3A4 *on page 260*
D_2 Receptor *on page 263*
D_3 Receptor *on page 266*
5-HT_{1A} Receptor *on page 291*
5-HT_{2A} Receptor *on page 291*
5-HT_{2C} Receptor *on page 294*

U.S. Brand Names Abilify®

Synonyms BMS 337039; OPC-14597

Pharmacologic Class Antipsychotic Agent, Atypical

- **Aristocort®** *see* Triamcinolone *on page 198*
- **Aristocort® A** *see* Triamcinolone *on page 198*
- **Aristospan®** *see* Triamcinolone *on page 198*

Arsenic Trioxide (AR se nik tri OKS id)

Genes of Interest

Cardiac Potassium Ion Channel *on page 241*

Cardiac Sodium Channel *on page 242*

U.S. Brand Names Trisenox™

Synonyms NSC-706363

Pharmacologic Class Antineoplastic Agent, Miscellaneous

- **Arthrotec®** *see* Diclofenac and Misoprostol *on page 91*
- **ASA** *see* Aspirin *on page 65*
- **Asaphen (Can)** *see* Aspirin *on page 65*
- **Asaphen E.C. (Can)** *see* Aspirin *on page 65*
- **Ascriptin® [OTC]** *see* Aspirin *on page 65*
- **Ascriptin® Extra Strength [OTC]** *see* Aspirin *on page 65*
- **Asendin [DSC]** *see* Amoxapine *on page 59*
- **Asmanex® Twisthaler®** *see* Mometasone Furoate *on page 145*
- **Aspart, Insulin** *see* Insulin Preparations *on page 125*
- **Aspercin [OTC]** *see* Aspirin *on page 65*
- **Aspercin Extra [OTC]** *see* Aspirin *on page 65*
- **Aspergum® [OTC]** *see* Aspirin *on page 65*

Aspirin (AS pir in)

Genes of Interest

Glycoprotein IIIa Receptor *on page 285*

Leukotriene C4 Synthase *on page 302*

U.S. Brand Names Ascriptin® Extra Strength [OTC]; Ascriptin® [OTC]; Aspercin Extra [OTC]; Aspercin [OTC]; Aspergum® [OTC]; Bayer® Aspirin Extra Strength [OTC]; Bayer® Aspirin Regimen Adult Low Strength [OTC]; Bayer® Aspirin Regimen Children's [OTC]; Bayer® Aspirin Regimen Regular Strength [OTC]; Bayer® Aspirin [OTC]; Bayer® Extra Strength Arthritis Pain Regimen [OTC]; Bayer® Plus Extra Strength [OTC]; Bayer® Women's Aspirin Plus Calcium [OTC]; Bufferin® Extra Strength [OTC]; Bufferin® [OTC]; Buffinol Extra [OTC]; Buffinol [OTC]; Easprin®; Ecotrin® Low Strength [OTC]; Ecotrin® Maximum Strength [OTC]; Ecotrin® [OTC]; Halfprin® [OTC]; St. Joseph® Adult Aspirin [OTC]; Sureprin 81™ [OTC]; ZORprin®

Canadian Brand Names Asaphen E.C.; Asaphen; Entrophen®; Novasen

Synonyms ASA; Acetylsalicylic Acid

Pharmacologic Class Salicylate

Aspirin and Codeine (AS pir in & KOE deen)

Genes of Interest

COMT *on page 244*

CYP2D6 *on page 254*

Glycoprotein IIIa Receptor *on page 285*

Leukotriene C4 Synthase *on page 302*

(Continued)

Aspirin and Codeine *(Continued)*

Canadian Brand Names Coryphen® Codeine

Synonyms Codeine and Aspirin

Pharmacologic Class Analgesic, Narcotic

Aspirin and Dipyridamole (AS pir in & dye peer ID a mole)

Genes of Interest

ATP-Binding Cassette, Sub-Family B, Member 1 *on page 224*
Glycoprotein IIIa Receptor *on page 285*
Leukotriene C4 Synthase *on page 302*

U.S. Brand Names Aggrenox®

Canadian Brand Names Aggrenox®

Synonyms Aspirin and Extended-Release Dipyridamole; Dipyridamole and Aspirin

Pharmacologic Class Antiplatelet Agent

- **Aspirin and Extended-Release Dipyridamole** *see* Aspirin and Dipyridamole *on page 66*
- **Aspirin and Hydrocodone** *see* Hydrocodone and Aspirin *on page 120*
- **Aspirin and Oxycodone** *see* Oxycodone and Aspirin *on page 161*
- **Astelin®** *see* Azelastine *on page 67*
- **Astramorph/PF™** *see* Morphine Sulfate *on page 146*
- **Atacand®** *see* Candesartan *on page 74*
- **Atarax®** *see* HydrOXYzine *on page 122*

Atenolol (a TEN oh lole)

Genes of Interest

Angiotensin-Converting Enzyme *on page 214*
Angiotensinogen *on page 219*
Beta$_1$-Adrenergic Receptor *on page 230*
Bradykinin B$_2$-Receptor *on page 237*
Gs Protein Alpha-Subunit *on page 288*

U.S. Brand Names Tenormin®

Canadian Brand Names Apo-Atenol®; Gen-Atenolol; Novo-Atenol; Nu-Atenol; PMS-Atenolol; Rhoxal-atenolol; Tenolin; Tenormin®

Pharmacologic Class Beta Blocker, Beta$_1$ Selective

- **Ativan®** *see* Lorazepam *on page 134*

Atomoxetine (AT oh mox e teen)

Genes of Interest

CYP2D6 *on page 254*

U.S. Brand Names Strattera®

Canadian Brand Names Strattera®

Synonyms Atomoxetine Hydrochloride; LY139603; Methylphenoxy-Benzene Propanamine; Tomoxetine

Pharmacologic Class Norepinephrine Reuptake Inhibitor, Selective

- **Atomoxetine Hydrochloride** *see* Atomoxetine *on page 66*

Atorvastatin (a TORE va sta tin)

Genes of Interest

Angiotensin-Converting Enzyme *on page 214*
Apolipoprotein E *on page 220*
ATP-Binding Cassette, Sub-Family B, Member 1 *on page 224*
Beta-Fibrinogen *on page 236*
Cholesteryl Ester Transfer Protein *on page 243*
CYP3A4 *on page 260*
Glycoprotein IIIa Receptor *on page 285*
Low-Density Lipoprotein Receptor *on page 304*
Stromelysin-1 *on page 316*

U.S. Brand Names Lipitor®

Canadian Brand Names Lipitor®

Pharmacologic Class Antilipemic Agent, HMG-CoA Reductase Inhibitor

- **A/T/S®** *see* Erythromycin *on page 99*
- **Augmentin®** *see* Amoxicillin and Clavulanate Potassium *on page 59*
- **Augmentin ES-600®** *see* Amoxicillin and Clavulanate Potassium *on page 59*
- **Augmentin XR™** *see* Amoxicillin and Clavulanate Potassium *on page 59*
- **Avandia®** *see* Rosiglitazone *on page 181*
- **Avapro®** *see* Irbesartan *on page 126*
- **Avelox®** *see* Moxifloxacin *on page 146*
- **Avelox® I.V.** *see* Moxifloxacin *on page 146*
- **Aventyl® (Can)** *see* Nortriptyline *on page 152*
- **Aviane™** *see* Ethinyl Estradiol and Levonorgestrel *on page 104*
- **Avinza™** *see* Morphine Sulfate *on page 146*
- **Aygestin®** *see* Norethindrone *on page 151*
- **Azasan®** *see* Azathioprine *on page 67*

Azathioprine (ay za THYE oh preen)

Genes of Interest

Thiopurine Methyltransferase *on page 317*

U.S. Brand Names Azasan®; Imuran®

Canadian Brand Names Alti-Azathioprine; Apo-Azathioprine®; Gen-Azathioprine; Imuran®; Novo-Azathioprine

Synonyms Azathioprine Sodium

Pharmacologic Class Immunosuppressant Agent

- **Azathioprine Sodium** *see* Azathioprine *on page 67*

Azelastine (a ZEL as teen)

Genes of Interest

ATP-Binding Cassette, Sub-Family B, Member 1 *on page 224*
CYP2D6 *on page 254*
(Continued)

Azelastine *(Continued)*

U.S. Brand Names Astelin®; Optivar®

Canadian Brand Names Astelin®

Synonyms Azelastine Hydrochloride

Pharmacologic Class Antihistamine

- ♦ **Azelastine Hydrochloride** *see* Azelastine *on page 67*

Azithromycin (az ith roe MYE sin)

Genes of Interest None known

U.S. Brand Names Zithromax®; Zmax™

Canadian Brand Names Zithromax®

Synonyms Azithromycin Dihydrate; Zithromax® TRI-PAK™; Zithromax® Z-PAK®

Pharmacologic Class Antibiotic, Macrolide

- ♦ **Azithromycin Dihydrate** *see* Azithromycin *on page 68*
- ♦ **Azmacort®** *see* Triamcinolone *on page 198*
- ♦ **Azulfidine®** *see* Sulfasalazine *on page 188*
- ♦ **Azulfidine® EN-tabs®** *see* Sulfasalazine *on page 188*
- ♦ **Bactrim™** *see* Sulfamethoxazole and Trimethoprim *on page 187*
- ♦ **Bactrim™ DS** *see* Sulfamethoxazole and Trimethoprim *on page 187*
- ♦ **Bactroban®** *see* Mupirocin *on page 147*
- ♦ **Bactroban® Nasal** *see* Mupirocin *on page 147*
- ♦ **BAL** *see* Dimercaprol *on page 93*
- ♦ **Balacet 325™** *see* Propoxyphene and Acetaminophen *on page 172*
- ♦ **BAL in Oil®** *see* Dimercaprol *on page 93*
- ♦ **Bancap HC®** *see* Hydrocodone and Acetaminophen *on page 120*
- ♦ **Band-Aid® Hurt-Free™ Antiseptic Wash [OTC]** *see* Lidocaine *on page 131*
- ♦ **Bayer® Aspirin [OTC]** *see* Aspirin *on page 65*
- ♦ **Bayer® Aspirin Extra Strength [OTC]** *see* Aspirin *on page 65*
- ♦ **Bayer® Aspirin Regimen Adult Low Strength [OTC]** *see* Aspirin *on page 65*
- ♦ **Bayer® Aspirin Regimen Children's [OTC]** *see* Aspirin *on page 65*
- ♦ **Bayer® Aspirin Regimen Regular Strength [OTC]** *see* Aspirin *on page 65*
- ♦ **Bayer® Extra Strength Arthritis Pain Regimen [OTC]** *see* Aspirin *on page 65*
- ♦ **Bayer® Plus Extra Strength [OTC]** *see* Aspirin *on page 65*
- ♦ **Bayer® Women's Aspirin Plus Calcium [OTC]** *see* Aspirin *on page 65*
- ♦ **BCNU** *see* Carmustine *on page 76*

Belladonna and Opium (bel a DON a & OH pee um)

Genes of Interest

COMT *on page 244*

U.S. Brand Names B&O Supprettes®
Synonyms Opium and Belladonna
Pharmacologic Class Analgesic Combination (Narcotic); Antispasmodic Agent, Urinary

Benazepril (ben AY ze pril)

Genes of Interest
Aldosterone Synthase *on page 208*
Angiotensin II Type 1 Receptor *on page 213*
Angiotensin-Converting Enzyme *on page 214*
Angiotensinogen *on page 219*
Bradykinin B_2-Receptor *on page 237*
U.S. Brand Names Lotensin®
Canadian Brand Names Lotensin®
Synonyms Benazepril Hydrochloride
Pharmacologic Class Angiotensin-Converting Enzyme (ACE) Inhibitor

- **Benazepril and Amlodipine** *see* Amlodipine and Benazepril *on page 59*
- **Benazepril Hydrochloride** *see* Benazepril *on page 69*

Bendroflumethiazide (ben droe floo meth EYE a zide)

Genes of Interest
Alpha-Adducin *on page 212*
G-Protein $Beta_3$ Subunit *on page 286*
U.S. Brand Names Naturetin® [DSC]
Pharmacologic Class Diuretic, Thiazide

- **Benemid [DSC]** *see* Probenecid *on page 170*
- **Benicar®** *see* Olmesartan *on page 159*
- **Benuryl™ (Can)** *see* Probenecid *on page 170*

Benzonatate (ben ZOE na tate)

Genes of Interest None known
U.S. Brand Names Tessalon®
Canadian Brand Names Tessalon®
Pharmacologic Class Antitussive

Benzphetamine (benz FET a meen)

Genes of Interest
CYP3A4 *on page 260*
U.S. Brand Names Didrex®
Canadian Brand Names Didrex®
Synonyms Benzphetamine Hydrochloride
Pharmacologic Class Anorexiant

- **Benzphetamine Hydrochloride** *see* Benzphetamine *on page 69*

Bepridil (BE pri dil)

Genes of Interest
Cardiac Potassium Ion Channel *on page 241*
(Continued)

Bepridil *(Continued)*

Cardiac Sodium Channel *on page 242*

U.S. Brand Names Vascor® [DSC]

Canadian Brand Names Vascor®

Synonyms Bepridil Hydrochloride

Pharmacologic Class Calcium Channel Blocker

- **Bepridil Hydrochloride** *see* Bepridil *on page 69*
- **Berotec® (Can)** *see* Fenoterol *on page 107*
- **Betacaine® (Can)** *see* Lidocaine *on page 131*
- **Beta-HC®** *see* Hydrocortisone *on page 121*
- **Betaloc® (Can)** *see* Metoprolol *on page 142*
- **Betaloc® Durules® (Can)** *see* Metoprolol *on page 142*
- **Betapace®** *see* Sotalol *on page 185*
- **Betapace AF®** *see* Sotalol *on page 185*

Betaxolol (be TAKS oh lol)

Genes of Interest

Angiotensinogen *on page 219*
Beta$_1$-Adrenergic Receptor *on page 230*
Bradykinin B$_2$-Receptor *on page 237*
CYP1A2 *on page 246*
CYP2D6 *on page 254*
Gs Protein Alpha-Subunit *on page 288*

U.S. Brand Names Betoptic® S; Kerlone®

Canadian Brand Names Betoptic® S

Synonyms Betaxolol Hydrochloride

Pharmacologic Class Beta Blocker, Beta$_1$ Selective

- **Betaxolol Hydrochloride** *see* Betaxolol *on page 70*
- **Betimol®** *see* Timolol *on page 195*
- **Betoptic® S** *see* Betaxolol *on page 70*
- **Bextra®** *see* Valdecoxib *on page 200*

Bezafibrate (be za FYE brate)

Genes of Interest

Angiotensin-Converting Enzyme *on page 214*
Cholesteryl Ester Transfer Protein *on page 243*

Canadian Brand Names Bezalip®; PMS-Bezafibrate

Pharmacologic Class Antilipemic Agent, Fibric Acid

- **Bezalip® (Can)** *see* Bezafibrate *on page 70*
- **Biaxin®** *see* Clarithromycin *on page 82*
- **Biaxin® XL** *see* Clarithromycin *on page 82*
- **BiCNu®** *see* Carmustine *on page 76*
- **Biocef®** *see* Cephalexin *on page 78*
- **BioQuin® Durules™ (Can)** *see* Quinidine *on page 174*
- **bis-chloronitrosourea** *see* Carmustine *on page 76*

Bisoprolol (bis OH proe lol)

Genes of Interest

Angiotensin-Converting Enzyme *on page 214*
Angiotensinogen *on page 219*
$Beta_1$-Adrenergic Receptor *on page 230*
Bradykinin B_2-Receptor *on page 237*
CYP3A4 *on page 260*
Gs Protein Alpha-Subunit *on page 288*

U.S. Brand Names Zebeta®

Canadian Brand Names Monocor®; Zebeta®

Synonyms Bisoprolol Fumarate

Pharmacologic Class Beta Blocker, $Beta_1$ Selective

- ♦ **Bisoprolol Fumarate** *see* Bisoprolol *on page 71*
- ♦ **Bleph®-10** *see* Sulfacetamide *on page 187*
- ♦ **Blocadren®** *see* Timolol *on page 195*
- ♦ **BMS 337039** *see* Aripiprazole *on page 64*
- ♦ **Bonamine™ (Can)** *see* Meclizine *on page 136*
- ♦ **Bonine® [OTC]** *see* Meclizine *on page 136*

Bosentan (boe SEN tan)

Genes of Interest

CYP2C8 *on page 248*
CYP2C9 *on page 248*
CYP3A4 *on page 260*

U.S. Brand Names Tracleer®

Canadian Brand Names Tracleer®

Pharmacologic Class Endothelin Antagonist

- ♦ **B&O Supprettes®** *see* Belladonna and Opium *on page 68*
- ♦ **Brethaire [DSC]** *see* Terbutaline *on page 191*
- ♦ **Brethine®** *see* Terbutaline *on page 191*

Bretylium (bre TIL ee um)

Genes of Interest

Cardiac Potassium Ion Channel *on page 241*
Cardiac Sodium Channel *on page 242*

Synonyms Bretylium Tosylate

Pharmacologic Class Antiarrhythmic Agent, Class III

- ♦ **Bretylium Tosylate** *see* Bretylium *on page 71*
- ♦ **Brevibloc®** *see* Esmolol *on page 100*
- ♦ **Brevicon®** *see* Ethinyl Estradiol and Norethindrone *on page 104*
- ♦ **Brevicon® 0.5/35 (Can)** *see* Ethinyl Estradiol and Norethindrone *on page 104*
- ♦ **Brevicon® 1/35 (Can)** *see* Ethinyl Estradiol and Norethindrone *on page 104*
- ♦ **Bricanyl® (Can)** *see* Terbutaline *on page 191*
- ♦ **British Anti-Lewisite** *see* Dimercaprol *on page 93*

Bromazepam (broe MA ze pam)

Genes of Interest

CYP3A4 *on page 260*

Canadian Brand Names Apo-Bromazepam®; Gen-Bromazepam; Lectopam®; Novo-Bromazepam; Nu-Bromazepam

Pharmacologic Class Benzodiazepine

Bromocriptine (broe moe KRIP teen)

Genes of Interest

CYP3A4 *on page 260*

U.S. Brand Names Parlodel®

Canadian Brand Names Apo-Bromocriptine®; PMS-Bromocriptine; Parlodel®

Synonyms Bromocriptine Mesylate

Pharmacologic Class Anti-Parkinson's Agent, Dopamine Agonist; Ergot Derivative

- ♦ **Bromocriptine Mesylate** *see* Bromocriptine *on page 72*

Budesonide (byoo DES oh nide)

Genes of Interest None known

U.S. Brand Names Entocort™ EC; Pulmicort Respules®; Pulmicort Turbuhaler®; Rhinocort® Aqua®

Canadian Brand Names Entocort®; Gen-Budesonide AQ; Pulmicort®; Rhinocort® Turbuhaler®

Pharmacologic Class Corticosteroid, Inhalant (Oral); Corticosteroid, Nasal; Corticosteroid, Systemic

- ♦ **Bufferin® [OTC]** *see* Aspirin *on page 65*
- ♦ **Bufferin® Extra Strength [OTC]** *see* Aspirin *on page 65*
- ♦ **Buffinol [OTC]** *see* Aspirin *on page 65*
- ♦ **Buffinol Extra [OTC]** *see* Aspirin *on page 65*
- ♦ **Buprenex®** *see* Buprenorphine *on page 72*

Buprenorphine (byoo pre NOR feen)

Genes of Interest

COMT *on page 244*

CYP3A4 *on page 260*

U.S. Brand Names Buprenex®; Subutex®

Canadian Brand Names Buprenex®; Subutex®

Synonyms Buprenorphine Hydrochloride

Pharmacologic Class Analgesic, Narcotic

Buprenorphine and Naloxone

(byoo pre NOR feen & nal OKS one)

Genes of Interest

COMT *on page 244*

CYP3A4 *on page 260*

U.S. Brand Names Suboxone®

Synonyms Buprenorphine Hydrochloride and Naloxone Hydrochloride Dihydrate; Naloxone Hydrochloride Dihydrate and Buprenorphine Hydrochloride; Naloxone and Buprenorphine

Pharmacologic Class Analgesic, Narcotic

- **Buprenorphine Hydrochloride** *see* Buprenorphine *on page 72*
- **Buprenorphine Hydrochloride and Naloxone Hydrochloride Dihydrate** *see* Buprenorphine and Naloxone *on page 72*

BuPROPion (byoo PROE pee on)

Genes of Interest

CYP2D6 *on page 254*

U.S. Brand Names Wellbutrin SR®; Wellbutrin XL™; Wellbutrin®; Zyban®

Canadian Brand Names Novo-Bupropion SR; Wellbutrin®; Zyban®

Pharmacologic Class Antidepressant, Dopamine-Reuptake Inhibitor; Smoking Cessation Aid

- **Burnamycin [OTC]** *see* Lidocaine *on page 131*
- **Burn Jel [OTC]** *see* Lidocaine *on page 131*
- **Burn-O-Jel [OTC]** *see* Lidocaine *on page 131*
- **BuSpar®** *see* BusPIRone *on page 73*
- **Buspirex (Can)** *see* BusPIRone *on page 73*

BusPIRone (byoo SPYE rone)

Genes of Interest

CYP3A4 *on page 260*

U.S. Brand Names BuSpar®

Canadian Brand Names Apo-Buspirone®; BuSpar®; Buspirex; Gen-Buspirone; Lin-Buspirone; Novo-Buspirone; Nu-Buspirone; PMS-Buspirone

Synonyms Buspirone Hydrochloride

Pharmacologic Class Antianxiety Agent, Miscellaneous

- **Buspirone Hydrochloride** *see* BusPIRone *on page 73*

Busulfan (byoo SUL fan)

Genes of Interest

CYP3A4 *on page 260*

U.S. Brand Names Busulfex®; Myleran®

Canadian Brand Names Busulfex®; Myleran®

Pharmacologic Class Antineoplastic Agent, Alkylating Agent

- **Busulfex®** *see* Busulfan *on page 73*

Butalbital, Acetaminophen, Caffeine, and Codeine

(byoo TAL bi tal, a seet a MIN oh fen, KAF een, & KOE deen)

Genes of Interest

COMT *on page 244*

CYP2D6 *on page 254*

(Continued)

Butalbital, Acetaminophen, Caffeine, and Codeine *(Continued)*

U.S. Brand Names Fioricet® with Codeine

Synonyms Acetaminophen, Caffeine, Codeine, and Butalbital; Caffeine, Acetaminophen, Butalbital, and Codeine; Codeine, Acetaminophen, Butalbital, and Caffeine

Pharmacologic Class Analgesic Combination (Narcotic); Barbiturate

Butalbital, Aspirin, Caffeine, and Codeine

(byoo TAL bi tal, AS pir in, KAF een, & KOE deen)

Genes of Interest

COMT *on page 244*

CYP2D6 *on page 254*

U.S. Brand Names Fiorinal® With Codeine; Phrenilin® With Caffeine and Codeine

Canadian Brand Names Fiorinal®-C 1/2; Fiorinal®-C 1/4; Tecnal C 1/2; Tecnal C 1/4

Synonyms Butalbital Compound and Codeine; Codeine and Butalbital Compound; Codeine, Butalbital, Aspirin, and Caffeine

Pharmacologic Class Analgesic Combination (Narcotic); Barbiturate

♦ **Butalbital Compound and Codeine** *see* Butalbital, Aspirin, Caffeine, and Codeine *on page 74*

Butorphanol (byoo TOR fa nole)

Genes of Interest

COMT *on page 244*

U.S. Brand Names Stadol® NS [DSC]; Stadol®

Canadian Brand Names Apo-Butorphanol®; PMS-Butorphanol

Synonyms Butorphanol Tartrate

Pharmacologic Class Analgesic, Narcotic

♦ **Butorphanol Tartrate** *see* Butorphanol *on page 74*

♦ **C7E3** *see* Abciximab *on page 52*

♦ **Caffeine, Acetaminophen, Butalbital, and Codeine** *see* Butalbital, Acetaminophen, Caffeine, and Codeine *on page 73*

♦ **Calan®** *see* Verapamil *on page 201*

♦ **Calan® SR** *see* Verapamil *on page 201*

♦ **Caldecort® [OTC]** *see* Hydrocortisone *on page 121*

♦ **Camila™** *see* Norethindrone *on page 151*

♦ **Camphorated Tincture of Opium (error-prone synonym)** *see* Paregoric *on page 162*

♦ **Camptosar®** *see* Irinotecan *on page 126*

♦ **Camptothecin-11** *see* Irinotecan *on page 126*

Candesartan (kan de SAR tan)

Genes of Interest

Adipocyte-Derived Leucine Aminopeptidase *on page 208*

Aldosterone Synthase *on page 208*

Angiotensin II Type 1 Receptor *on page 213*
Angiotensin-Converting Enzyme *on page 214*
Angiotensinogen *on page 219*
Bradykinin B_2-Receptor *on page 237*
CYP2C9 *on page 248*

U.S. Brand Names Atacand®

Canadian Brand Names Atacand®

Synonyms Candesartan Cilexetil

Pharmacologic Class Angiotensin II Receptor Blocker

♦ **Candesartan Cilexetil** *see* Candesartan *on page 74*

Capecitabine (ka pe SITE a been)

Genes of Interest

Dihydropyrimidine Dehydrogenase *on page 270*
Thymidylate Synthetase *on page 318*

U.S. Brand Names Xeloda®

Canadian Brand Names Xeloda®

Pharmacologic Class Antineoplastic Agent, Antimetabolite

♦ **Capital® and Codeine** *see* Acetaminophen and Codeine *on page 52*

♦ **Capoten®** *see* Captopril *on page 75*

Captopril (KAP toe pril)

Genes of Interest

Aldosterone Synthase *on page 208*
Angiotensin II Type 1 Receptor *on page 213*
Angiotensin-Converting Enzyme *on page 214*
Angiotensinogen *on page 219*
Bradykinin B_2-Receptor *on page 237*

U.S. Brand Names Capoten®

Canadian Brand Names Alti-Captopril; Apo-Capto®; Capoten™; Gen-Captopril; Novo-Captopril; Nu-Capto; PMS-Captopril

Synonyms ACE

Pharmacologic Class Angiotensin-Converting Enzyme (ACE) Inhibitor

♦ **Carac™** *see* Fluorouracil *on page 109*

♦ **Carapres® (Can)** *see* Clonidine *on page 83*

Carbamazepine (kar ba MAZ e peen)

Genes of Interest

CYP3A4 *on page 260*

U.S. Brand Names Carbatrol®; Epitol®; Equetro™; Tegretol®-XR; Tegretol®

Canadian Brand Names Apo-Carbamazepine®; Gen-Carbamazepine CR; Novo-Carbamaz; Nu-Carbamazepine; PMS-Carbamazepine; Taro-Carbamazepine Chewable; Tegretol®

Synonyms CBZ; SPD417

Pharmacologic Class Anticonvulsant, Miscellaneous

♦ **Carbatrol®** *see* Carbamazepine *on page 75*

- **Carbolith™ (Can)** *see* Lithium *on page 133*

Carboplatin (KAR boe pla tin)

Genes of Interest

Excision Repair Cross-Complementing Rodent Repair Deficiency, Complementation Group 2 *on page 277*

U.S. Brand Names Paraplatin®

Canadian Brand Names Paraplatin-AQ

Synonyms CBDCA

Pharmacologic Class Antineoplastic Agent, Alkylating Agent

- **Cardene®** *see* NiCARdipine *on page 149*
- **Cardene® I.V.** *see* NiCARdipine *on page 149*
- **Cardene® SR** *see* NiCARdipine *on page 149*
- **Cardizem®** *see* Diltiazem *on page 93*
- **Cardizem® CD** *see* Diltiazem *on page 93*
- **Cardizem® LA** *see* Diltiazem *on page 93*
- **Cardizem® SR [DSC]** *see* Diltiazem *on page 93*
- **Cardura®** *see* Doxazosin *on page 95*
- **Cardura-1™ (Can)** *see* Doxazosin *on page 95*
- **Cardura-2™ (Can)** *see* Doxazosin *on page 95*
- **Cardura-4™ (Can)** *see* Doxazosin *on page 95*
- **Carisoprodate** *see* Carisoprodol *on page 76*

Carisoprodol (kar eye soe PROE dole)

Genes of Interest

CYP2C19 *on page 251*

U.S. Brand Names Soma®

Canadian Brand Names Soma®

Synonyms Carisoprodate; Isobamate

Pharmacologic Class Skeletal Muscle Relaxant

- **Carmol® Scalp** *see* Sulfacetamide *on page 187*

Carmustine (kar MUS teen)

Genes of Interest

Methylguanine-DNA Methyltransferase *on page 305*

U.S. Brand Names BiCNu®; Gliadel®

Canadian Brand Names BiCNu®

Synonyms BCNU; Carmustinum; NSC-409962; WR-139021; bis-chloronitrosourea

Pharmacologic Class Antineoplastic Agent; Antineoplastic Agent, Alkylating Agent (Nitrosourea); Antineoplastic Agent, DNA Adduct-Forming Agent; Antineoplastic Agent, DNA Binding Agent

- **Carmustinum** *see* Carmustine *on page 76*
- **Cartia XT™** *see* Diltiazem *on page 93*

Carvedilol (KAR ve dil ole)

Genes of Interest

Angiotensin-Converting Enzyme *on page 214*

ATP-Binding Cassette, Sub-Family B, Member 1 *on page 224*
$Beta_1$-Adrenergic Receptor *on page 230*
$Beta_2$-Adrenergic Receptor *on page 233*
CYP2C8 *on page 248*
CYP2C9 *on page 248*
CYP2D6 *on page 254*
Gs Protein Alpha-Subunit *on page 288*

U.S. Brand Names Coreg®

Canadian Brand Names Apo-Carvedilol®; Coreg®; Novo-Carvedilol; PMS-Carvedilol; ratio-Carvedilol

Pharmacologic Class Beta Blocker With Alpha-Blocking Activity

- **Cataflam®** *see* Diclofenac *on page 91*
- **Catapres®** *see* Clonidine *on page 83*
- **Catapres-TTS®** *see* Clonidine *on page 83*
- **CBDCA** *see* Carboplatin *on page 76*
- **CBZ** *see* Carbamazepine *on page 75*
- **CDDP** *see* Cisplatin *on page 81*
- **Cedocard®-SR (Can)** *see* Isosorbide Dinitrate *on page 127*
- **CEE** *see* Estrogens (Conjugated/Equine) *on page 102*

Cefdinir (SEF di ner)

Genes of Interest None known

U.S. Brand Names Omnicef®

Canadian Brand Names Omnicef®

Synonyms CFDN

Pharmacologic Class Antibiotic, Cephalosporin (Third Generation)

Cefprozil (sef PROE zil)

Genes of Interest None known

U.S. Brand Names Cefzil®

Canadian Brand Names Cefzil®

Pharmacologic Class Antibiotic, Cephalosporin (Second Generation)

- **Cefzil®** *see* Cefprozil *on page 77*
- **Celebrex®** *see* Celecoxib *on page 77*

Celecoxib (se le KOKS ib)

Genes of Interest

Leukotriene C4 Synthase *on page 302*

U.S. Brand Names Celebrex®

Canadian Brand Names Celebrex®

Pharmacologic Class Nonsteroidal Anti-inflammatory Drug (NSAID), COX-2 Selective

- **Celexa™** *see* Citalopram *on page 81*
- **Celontin®** *see* Methsuximide *on page 140*
- **Cenestin (Can)** *see* Estrogens (Conjugated/Equine) *on page 102*
- **Centany™** *see* Mupirocin *on page 147*

Cephalexin (sef a LEKS in)

Genes of Interest None known

U.S. Brand Names Biocef®; Keflex®; Panixine DisperDose™

Canadian Brand Names Apo-Cephalex®; Keftab®; Novo-Lexin; Nu-Cephalex

Synonyms Cephalexin Monohydrate

Pharmacologic Class Antibiotic, Cephalosporin (First Generation)

- **Cephalexin Monohydrate** *see* Cephalexin *on page 78*
- **Cerebyx®** *see* Fosphenytoin *on page 113*
- **C.E.S.® (Can)** *see* Estrogens (Conjugated/Equine) *on page 102*
- **Cetacort®** *see* Hydrocortisone *on page 121*
- **Cetamide™ (Can)** *see* Sulfacetamide *on page 187*
- **Ceta-Plus®** *see* Hydrocodone and Acetaminophen *on page 120*

Cetirizine (se TI ra zeen)

Genes of Interest None known

U.S. Brand Names Zyrtec®

Canadian Brand Names Apo-Cetirizine®; Reactine™

Synonyms Cetirizine Hydrochloride; P-071; UCB-P071

Pharmacologic Class Antihistamine

- **Cetirizine Hydrochloride** *see* Cetirizine *on page 78*
- **CFDN** *see* Cefdinir *on page 77*
- **CGP 57148B** *see* Imatinib *on page 123*

Chloramphenicol (klor am FEN i kole)

Genes of Interest
Glucose-6-Phosphate Dehydrogenase *on page 281*

U.S. Brand Names Chloromycetin® Sodium Succinate

Canadian Brand Names Chloromycetin®; Diochloram®; Pentamycetin®

Pharmacologic Class Antibiotic, Miscellaneous

Chlordiazepoxide (klor dye az e POKS ide)

Genes of Interest
CYP3A4 *on page 260*

U.S. Brand Names Librium®

Canadian Brand Names Apo-Chlordiazepoxide®

Synonyms Methaminodiazepoxide Hydrochloride

Pharmacologic Class Benzodiazepine

- **Chlordiazepoxide and Amitriptyline** *see* Amitriptyline and Chlordiazepoxide *on page 58*
- **Chlormeprazine** *see* Prochlorperazine *on page 171*
- **Chloromycetin® (Can)** *see* Chloramphenicol *on page 78*
- **Chloromycetin® Sodium Succinate** *see* Chloramphenicol *on page 78*

Chloroquine (KLOR oh kwin)

Genes of Interest

Glucose-6-Phosphate Dehydrogenase *on page 281*

U.S. Brand Names Aralen®

Canadian Brand Names Aralen®; Novo-Chloroquine

Synonyms Chloroquine Phosphate

Pharmacologic Class Aminoquinoline (Antimalarial)

♦ **Chloroquine Phosphate** *see* Chloroquine *on page 79*

Chlorothiazide (klor oh THYE a zide)

Genes of Interest

Alpha-Adducin *on page 212*

G-Protein $Beta_3$ Subunit *on page 286*

U.S. Brand Names Diuril®

Canadian Brand Names Diuril®

Pharmacologic Class Diuretic, Thiazide

♦ **Chlorphen [OTC]** *see* Chlorpheniramine *on page 79*

Chlorpheniramine (klor fen IR a meen)

Genes of Interest

CYP2D6 *on page 254*

CYP3A4 *on page 260*

U.S. Brand Names Aller-Chlor® [OTC]; Chlor-Trimeton® [OTC]; Chlorphen [OTC]; Diabetic Tussin® Allergy Relief [OTC]; Teldrin® HBP [OTC]

Canadian Brand Names Chlor-Tripolon®; Novo-Pheniram

Synonyms CTM; Chlorpheniramine Maleate

Pharmacologic Class Antihistamine

♦ **Chlorpheniramine Maleate** *see* Chlorpheniramine *on page 79*

ChlorproMAZINE (klor PROE ma zeen)

Genes of Interest

$Alpha_1$-Adrenergic Receptor *on page 210*

ATP-Binding Cassette, Sub-Family B, Member 1 *on page 224*

Cardiac Potassium Ion Channel *on page 241*

Cardiac Sodium Channel *on page 242*

D_2 Receptor *on page 263*

U.S. Brand Names Thorazine® [DSC]

Canadian Brand Names Apo-Chlorpromazine®; Largactil®; Novo-Chlorpromazine

Synonyms CPZ; Chlorpromazine Hydrochloride

Pharmacologic Class Antipsychotic Agent, Typical, Phenothiazine

♦ **Chlorpromazine Hydrochloride** *see* ChlorproMAZINE *on page 79*

Chlorthalidone (klor THAL i done)

Genes of Interest

Alpha-Adducin *on page 212*

G-Protein $Beta_3$ Subunit *on page 286*

(Continued)

Chlorthalidone *(Continued)*

U.S. Brand Names Thalitone®

Canadian Brand Names Apo-Chlorthalidone®

Synonyms Hygroton

Pharmacologic Class Diuretic, Thiazide

♦ **Chlor-Trimeton® [OTC]** *see* Chlorpheniramine *on page 79*

♦ **Chlor-Tripolon® (Can)** *see* Chlorpheniramine *on page 79*

♦ **Chronovera® (Can)** *see* Verapamil *on page 201*

Cilazapril (sye LAY za pril)

Genes of Interest

Aldosterone Synthase *on page 208*

Angiotensin-Converting Enzyme *on page 214*

Angiotensin II Type 1 Receptor *on page 213*

Angiotensinogen *on page 219*

Bradykinin B_2-Receptor *on page 237*

Canadian Brand Names Inhibace®; Novo-Cilazapril

Synonyms Cilazapril Monohydrate

Pharmacologic Class Angiotensin-Converting Enzyme (ACE) Inhibitor

♦ **Cilazapril Monohydrate** *see* Cilazapril *on page 80*

Cilostazol (sil OH sta zol)

Genes of Interest

Glycoprotein IIIa Receptor *on page 285*

U.S. Brand Names Pletal®

Canadian Brand Names Pletal®

Synonyms OPC-13013

Pharmacologic Class Antiplatelet Agent; Phosphodiesterase Enzyme Inhibitor

♦ **Ciloxan®** *see* Ciprofloxacin *on page 81*

Cimetidine (sye MET i deen)

Genes of Interest

ATP-Binding Cassette, Sub-Family B, Member 1 *on page 224*

CYP2D6 *on page 254*

U.S. Brand Names Tagamet® HB 200 [OTC]; Tagamet®

Canadian Brand Names Apo-Cimetidine®; Gen-Cimetidine; Novo-Cimetidine; Nu-Cimet; PMS-Cimetidine; Tagamet® HB

Pharmacologic Class Histamine H_2 Antagonist

♦ **Cipralex® (Can)** *see* Escitalopram *on page 100*

♦ **Cipro®** *see* Ciprofloxacin *on page 81*

♦ **Cipro® XL (Can)** *see* Ciprofloxacin *on page 81*

Ciprofloxacin (sip roe FLOKS a sin)

Genes of Interest None known

U.S. Brand Names Ciloxan®; Cipro® XR; Cipro®; Proquin® XR

Canadian Brand Names Apo-Ciproflox®; CO Ciprofloxacin; Ciloxan®; Cipro® XL; Cipro®; Gen-Ciprofloxacin; Novo-Ciprofloxacin; PMS-Ciprofloxacin; Rhoxal-ciprofloxacin; ratio-Ciprofloxacin

Synonyms Ciprofloxacin Hydrochloride

Pharmacologic Class Antibiotic, Ophthalmic; Antibiotic, Quinolone

- **Ciprofloxacin Hydrochloride** *see* Ciprofloxacin *on page 81*
- **Cipro® XR** *see* Ciprofloxacin *on page 81*

Cisapride (SIS a pride)

Genes of Interest

Cardiac Potassium Ion Channel *on page 241*
Cardiac Sodium Channel *on page 242*
CYP3A4 *on page 260*

U.S. Brand Names Propulsid®

Pharmacologic Class Gastrointestinal Agent, Prokinetic

Cisplatin (SIS pla tin)

Genes of Interest

Excision Repair Cross-Complementing Rodent Repair Deficiency, Complementation Group 1 *on page 274*
Excision Repair Cross-Complementing Rodent Repair Deficiency, Complementation Group 2 *on page 277*
p53 *on page 311*
Xeroderma Pigmentosum, Complementation Group C *on page 330*
XRCC1 *on page 331*

U.S. Brand Names Platinol®-AQ [DSC]

Synonyms CDDP

Pharmacologic Class Antineoplastic Agent, Alkylating Agent

Citalopram (sye TAL oh pram)

Genes of Interest

CYP2C19 *on page 251*
CYP3A4 *on page 260*
G-Protein Beta$_3$ Subunit *on page 286*
Gs Protein Alpha-Subunit *on page 288*
5-HT$_{2A}$ Receptor *on page 291*
5-HT Transporter *on page 297*
Monoamine Oxidase A *on page 307*

U.S. Brand Names Celexa™

Canadian Brand Names Apo-Citalopram®; CO Citalopram; Celexa™; Gen-Citalopram; Novo-Citalopram; PMS-Citalopram; Rhoxal-citalopram; ratio-Citalopram

Synonyms Citalopram Hydrobromide; Nitalapram

Pharmacologic Class Antidepressant, Selective Serotonin Reuptake Inhibitor

- **Citalopram Hydrobromide** *see* Citalopram *on page 81*

- **Cl-719** *see* Gemfibrozil *on page 115*
- **Clarinex®** *see* Desloratadine *on page 89*

Clarithromycin (kla RITH roe mye sin)

Genes of Interest

ATP-Binding Cassette, Sub-Family B, Member 1 *on page 224*
Cardiac Potassium Ion Channel *on page 241*
Cardiac Sodium Channel *on page 242*
CYP3A4 *on page 260*

U.S. Brand Names Biaxin® XL; Biaxin®

Canadian Brand Names Biaxin® XL; Biaxin®; ratio-Clarithromycin

Pharmacologic Class Antibiotic, Macrolide

- **Claritin® [OTC]** *see* Loratadine *on page 133*
- **Claritin® Hives Relief [OTC]** *see* Loratadine *on page 133*
- **Claritin® Kids (Can)** *see* Loratadine *on page 133*
- **Clavulin® (Can)** *see* Amoxicillin and Clavulanate Potassium *on page 59*

Clemastine (KLEM as teen)

Genes of Interest

CYP2D6 *on page 254*

U.S. Brand Names Dayhist® Allergy [OTC]; Tavist® Allergy [OTC]

Synonyms Clemastine Fumarate

Pharmacologic Class Antihistamine

- **Clemastine Fumarate** *see* Clemastine *on page 82*
- **Cleocin®** *see* Clindamycin *on page 82*
- **Cleocin HCl®** *see* Clindamycin *on page 82*
- **Cleocin Pediatric®** *see* Clindamycin *on page 82*
- **Cleocin Phosphate®** *see* Clindamycin *on page 82*
- **Cleocin T®** *see* Clindamycin *on page 82*
- **Climara®** *see* Estradiol *on page 101*
- **Clindagel®** *see* Clindamycin *on page 82*
- **ClindaMax™** *see* Clindamycin *on page 82*

Clindamycin (klin da MYE sin)

Genes of Interest None known

U.S. Brand Names Cleocin HCl®; Cleocin Pediatric®; Cleocin Phosphate®; Cleocin T®; Cleocin®; ClindaMax™; Clindagel®; Clindesse™; Clindets®; Evoclin™

Canadian Brand Names Alti-Clindamycin; Apo-Clindamycin®; Clindoxyl®; Dalacin® C; Dalacin® T; Dalacin® Vaginal; Novo-Clindamycin

Synonyms Clindamycin Hydrochloride; Clindamycin Palmitate; Clindamycin Phosphate

Pharmacologic Class Antibiotic, Miscellaneous

- **Clindamycin Hydrochloride** *see* Clindamycin *on page 82*
- **Clindamycin Palmitate** *see* Clindamycin *on page 82*
- **Clindamycin Phosphate** *see* Clindamycin *on page 82*

♦ **Clindesse™** *see* Clindamycin *on page 82*
♦ **Clindets®** *see* Clindamycin *on page 82*
♦ **Clindoxyl® (Can)** *see* Clindamycin *on page 82*
♦ **Clinoril®** *see* Sulindac *on page 188*

Clobazam (KLOE ba zam)

Genes of Interest

CYP3A4 *on page 260*

Canadian Brand Names Alti-Clobazam; Apo-Clobazam®; Frisium®; Novo-Clobazam; PMS-Clobazam

Pharmacologic Class Benzodiazepine

Clofibrate

Genes of Interest

Angiotensin-Converting Enzyme *on page 214*
Cholesteryl Ester Transfer Protein *on page 243*

ClomiPRAMINE (kloe MI pra meen)

Genes of Interest

Alpha$_1$-Adrenergic Receptor *on page 210*
CYP1A2 *on page 246*
CYP2C19 *on page 251*
CYP2D6 *on page 254*
G-Protein Beta$_3$ Subunit *on page 286*
Gs Protein Alpha-Subunit *on page 288*

U.S. Brand Names Anafranil®

Canadian Brand Names Anafranil®; Apo-Clomipramine®; CO Clomipramine; Gen-Clomipramine

Synonyms Clomipramine Hydrochloride

Pharmacologic Class Antidepressant, Tricyclic (Tertiary Amine)

♦ **Clomipramine Hydrochloride** *see* ClomiPRAMINE *on page 83*
♦ **Clonapam (Can)** *see* Clonazepam *on page 83*

Clonazepam (kloe NA ze pam)

Genes of Interest

CYP3A4 *on page 260*

U.S. Brand Names Klonopin®

Canadian Brand Names Alti-Clonazepam; Apo-Clonazepam®; Clonapam; Gen-Clonazepam; Klonopin®; Novo-Clonazepam; Nu-Clonazepam; PMS-Clonazepam; Rho-Clonazepam; Rivotril®

Pharmacologic Class Benzodiazepine

Clonidine (KLON i deen)

Genes of Interest None known

U.S. Brand Names Catapres-TTS®; Catapres®; Duraclon™

Canadian Brand Names Apo-Clonidine®; Carapres®; Dixarit®; Novo-Clonidine; Nu-Clonidine

(Continued)

Clonidine *(Continued)*

Synonyms Clonidine Hydrochloride

Pharmacologic Class $Alpha_2$-Adrenergic Agonist

- **Clonidine Hydrochloride** *see* Clonidine *on page 83*

Clopidogrel (kloh PID oh grel)

Genes of Interest

Glycoprotein IIIa Receptor *on page 285*
P2RY12 *on page 310*

U.S. Brand Names Plavix®

Canadian Brand Names Plavix®

Synonyms Clopidogrel Bisulfate

Pharmacologic Class Antiplatelet Agent

- **Clopidogrel Bisulfate** *see* Clopidogrel *on page 84*
- **Clopixol® (Can)** *see* Zuclopenthixol *on page 206*
- **Clopixol-Acuphase® (Can)** *see* Zuclopenthixol *on page 206*
- **Clopixol® Depot (Can)** *see* Zuclopenthixol *on page 206*

Clorazepate (klor AZ e pate)

Genes of Interest

CYP3A4 *on page 260*

U.S. Brand Names T-Tab®; Tranxene® SD™-Half Strength; Tranxene® SD™; Tranxene®

Canadian Brand Names Apo-Clorazepate®; Novo-Clopate

Synonyms Clorazepate Dipotassium; Tranxene T-Tab®

Pharmacologic Class Benzodiazepine

- **Clorazepate Dipotassium** *see* Clorazepate *on page 84*

Clozapine (KLOE za peen)

Genes of Interest

$Alpha_1$-Adrenergic Receptor *on page 210*
$Beta_3$-Adrenergic Receptor *on page 236*
CYP1A2 *on page 246*
D_2 Receptor *on page 263*
D_3 Receptor *on page 266*
D_4 Receptor *on page 268*
G-Protein $Beta_3$ Subunit *on page 286*
Gs Protein Alpha-Subunit *on page 288*
Histamine 1 and 2 Receptors *on page 289*
HLA-A1 *on page 289*
5-HT_{1A} Receptor *on page 291*
5-HT_{2A} Receptor *on page 291*
5-HT_{2C} Receptor *on page 294*
5-HT_6 Receptor *on page 297*
5-HT Transporter *on page 297*
TNF-Alpha *on page 319*

U.S. Brand Names Clozaril®; FazaClo®

Canadian Brand Names Apo-Clozapine®; Clozaril®; Gen-Clozapine

Pharmacologic Class Antipsychotic Agent, Atypical

- **Clozaril®** *see* Clozapine *on page 84*

Cocaine (koe KANE)

Genes of Interest

CYP2D6 *on page 254*
CYP3A4 *on page 260*

Synonyms Cocaine Hydrochloride

Pharmacologic Class Local Anesthetic

- **Cocaine Hydrochloride** *see* Cocaine *on page 85*
- **CO Ciprofloxacin (Can)** *see* Ciprofloxacin *on page 81*
- **CO Citalopram (Can)** *see* Citalopram *on page 81*
- **CO Clomipramine (Can)** *see* ClomiPRAMINE *on page 83*

Codeine (KOE deen)

Genes of Interest

COMT *on page 244*
CYP2D6 *on page 254*

Canadian Brand Names Codeine Contin®

Synonyms Codeine Phosphate; Codeine Sulfate; Methylmorphine

Pharmacologic Class Analgesic, Narcotic; Antitussive

- **Codeine, Acetaminophen, Butalbital, and Caffeine** *see* Butalbital, Acetaminophen, Caffeine, and Codeine *on page 73*
- **Codeine and Acetaminophen** *see* Acetaminophen and Codeine *on page 52*
- **Codeine and Aspirin** *see* Aspirin and Codeine *on page 65*
- **Codeine and Butalbital Compound** *see* Butalbital, Aspirin, Caffeine, and Codeine *on page 74*
- **Codeine and Promethazine** *see* Promethazine and Codeine *on page 172*
- **Codeine, Butalbital, Aspirin, and Caffeine** *see* Butalbital, Aspirin, Caffeine, and Codeine *on page 74*
- **Codeine Contin® (Can)** *see* Codeine *on page 85*
- **Codeine Phosphate** *see* Codeine *on page 85*
- **Codeine Sulfate** *see* Codeine *on page 85*
- **CO Fluoxetine (Can)** *see* Fluoxetine *on page 109*
- **Co-Gesic®** *see* Hydrocodone and Acetaminophen *on page 120*
- **Cognex®** *see* Tacrine *on page 189*

Colchicine (KOL chi seen)

Genes of Interest

CYP3A4 *on page 260*

Pharmacologic Class Colchicine

- **Colocort®** *see* Hydrocortisone *on page 121*
- **CO Lovastatin (Can)** *see* Lovastatin *on page 135*
- **Combivent®** *see* Ipratropium and Albuterol *on page 125*

- **CO Meloxicam (Can)** *see* Meloxicam *on page 137*
- **Compazine® [DSC]** *see* Prochlorperazine *on page 171*
- **Compound F** *see* Hydrocortisone *on page 121*
- **Compro™** *see* Prochlorperazine *on page 171*
- **Concerta®** *see* Methylphenidate *on page 141*
- **CO Paroxetine (Can)** *see* Paroxetine *on page 162*
- **CO Pravastatin (Can)** *see* Pravastatin *on page 169*
- **CO Ranitidine (Can)** *see* Ranitidine *on page 176*
- **Cordarone®** *see* Amiodarone *on page 57*
- **Coreg®** *see* Carvedilol *on page 76*
- **Corgard®** *see* Nadolol *on page 147*
- **Coronex® (Can)** *see* Isosorbide Dinitrate *on page 127*
- **Cortaid® Intensive Therapy [OTC]** *see* Hydrocortisone *on page 121*
- **Cortaid® Maximum Strength [OTC]** *see* Hydrocortisone *on page 121*
- **Cortaid® Sensitive Skin [OTC]** *see* Hydrocortisone *on page 121*
- **Cortamed® (Can)** *see* Hydrocortisone *on page 121*
- **Cortef®** *see* Hydrocortisone *on page 121*
- **Cortenema® (Can)** *see* Hydrocortisone *on page 121*
- **Corticool® [OTC]** *see* Hydrocortisone *on page 121*
- **Cortifoam®** *see* Hydrocortisone *on page 121*
- **Cortisol** *see* Hydrocortisone *on page 121*
- **Cortizone®-10 Maximum Strength [OTC]** *see* Hydrocortisone *on page 121*
- **Cortizone®-10 Plus Maximum Strength [OTC]** *see* Hydrocortisone *on page 121*
- **Cortizone®-10 Quick Shot [OTC]** *see* Hydrocortisone *on page 121*
- **Corvert®** *see* Ibutilide *on page 123*
- **Coryphen® Codeine (Can)** *see* Aspirin and Codeine *on page 65*
- **CO Simvastatin (Can)** *see* Simvastatin *on page 184*
- **CO Temazepam (Can)** *see* Temazepam *on page 191*
- **Co-Trimoxazole** *see* Sulfamethoxazole and Trimethoprim *on page 187*
- **Coumadin®** *see* Warfarin *on page 203*
- **Covera® (Can)** *see* Verapamil *on page 201*
- **Covera-HS®** *see* Verapamil *on page 201*
- **Coversyl® (Can)** *see* Perindopril Erbumine *on page 164*
- **Cozaar®** *see* Losartan *on page 134*
- **CPM** *see* Cyclophosphamide *on page 87*
- **CPT-11** *see* Irinotecan *on page 126*
- **CPZ** *see* ChlorproMAZINE *on page 79*
- **Crestor®** *see* Rosuvastatin *on page 181*
- **Crinone®** *see* Progesterone *on page 171*
- **Cryselle™** *see* Ethinyl Estradiol and Norgestrel *on page 105*
- **Crystodigin** *see* Digitoxin *on page 91*
- **CsA** *see* CycloSPORINE *on page 87*

- **CTM** *see* Chlorpheniramine *on page 79*
- **CTX** *see* Cyclophosphamide *on page 87*
- **Cutivate®** *see* Fluticasone *on page 111*
- **CyA** *see* CycloSPORINE *on page 87*
- **Cyclen® (Can)** *see* Ethinyl Estradiol and Norgestimate *on page 105*
- **Cyclessa®** *see* Ethinyl Estradiol and Desogestrel *on page 103*

Cyclobenzaprine (sye kloe BEN za preen)

Genes of Interest

CYP1A2 *on page 246*

U.S. Brand Names Flexeril®

Canadian Brand Names Apo-Cyclobenzaprine®; Flexeril®; Flexitec; Gen-Cyclobenzaprine; Novo-Cycloprine; Nu-Cyclobenzaprine

Synonyms Cyclobenzaprine Hydrochloride

Pharmacologic Class Skeletal Muscle Relaxant

- **Cyclobenzaprine Hydrochloride** *see* Cyclobenzaprine *on page 87*

Cyclophosphamide (sye kloe FOS fa mide)

Genes of Interest

CYP2C19 *on page 251*
CYP3A4 *on page 260*
Glutathione-S-Transferase Alpha 1 *on page 282*
Glutathione-S-Transferase Pi *on page 283*

U.S. Brand Names Cytoxan®

Canadian Brand Names Cytoxan®; Procytox®

Synonyms CPM; CTX; CYT; NSC-26271

Pharmacologic Class Antineoplastic Agent, Alkylating Agent

- **Cyclosporin A** *see* CycloSPORINE *on page 87*

CycloSPORINE (SYE kloe spor een)

Genes of Interest

ATP-Binding Cassette, Sub-Family B, Member 1 *on page 224*
CYP3A4 *on page 260*

U.S. Brand Names Gengraf®; Neoral®; Restasis™; Sandimmune®

Canadian Brand Names Apo-Cyclosporine®; Neoral®; Rhoxal-cyclosporine; Sandimmune® I.V.

Synonyms CsA; CyA; Cyclosporin A

Pharmacologic Class Immunosuppressant Agent

- **CYT** *see* Cyclophosphamide *on page 87*
- **Cytoxan®** *see* Cyclophosphamide *on page 87*

Dacarbazine (da KAR ba zeen)

Genes of Interest

CYP1A2 *on page 246*

(Continued)

Dacarbazine *(Continued)*

U.S. Brand Names DTIC-Dome®

Canadian Brand Names DTIC®

Synonyms DIC; DTIC; Dimethyl Triazeno Imidazole Carboxamide; Imidazole Carboxamide Dimethyltriazene; Imidazole Carboxamide; WR-139007

Pharmacologic Class Antineoplastic Agent, Alkylating Agent (Triazene)

- **Dalacin® C (Can)** *see* Clindamycin *on page 82*
- **Dalacin® T (Can)** *see* Clindamycin *on page 82*
- **Dalacin® Vaginal (Can)** *see* Clindamycin *on page 82*
- **Dalmane®** *see* Flurazepam *on page 110*
- **Damason-P®** *see* Hydrocodone and Aspirin *on page 120*
- **Dantrium®** *see* Dantrolene *on page 88*

Dantrolene (DAN troe leen)

Genes of Interest

CYP3A4 *on page 260*

U.S. Brand Names Dantrium®

Canadian Brand Names Dantrium®

Synonyms Dantrolene Sodium

Pharmacologic Class Skeletal Muscle Relaxant

- **Dantrolene Sodium** *see* Dantrolene *on page 88*

Dapsone (DAP sone)

Genes of Interest

CYP3A4 *on page 260*

Glucose-6-Phosphate Dehydrogenase *on page 281*

U.S. Brand Names Aczone™

Synonyms Diaminodiphenylsulfone

Pharmacologic Class Antibiotic, Miscellaneous

- **Darvocet A500™** *see* Propoxyphene and Acetaminophen *on page 172*
- **Darvocet-N® 50** *see* Propoxyphene and Acetaminophen *on page 172*
- **Darvocet-N® 100** *see* Propoxyphene and Acetaminophen *on page 172*
- **Darvon®** *see* Propoxyphene *on page 172*
- **Darvon-N®** *see* Propoxyphene *on page 172*
- **Dayhist® Allergy [OTC]** *see* Clemastine *on page 82*
- **Daypro®** *see* Oxaprozin *on page 160*
- **Dehydrobenzperidol** *see* Droperidol *on page 96*
- **Delatestryl®** *see* Testosterone *on page 192*
- **Delestrogen®** *see* Estradiol *on page 101*
- **Deltacortisone** *see* PredniSONE *on page 169*
- **Deltadehydrocortisone** *see* PredniSONE *on page 169*
- **Demadex®** *see* Torsemide *on page 196*

- **Demerol®** *see* Meperidine *on page 138*
- **Demulen®** *see* Ethinyl Estradiol and Ethynodiol Diacetate *on page 103*
- **Demulen® 30 (Can)** *see* Ethinyl Estradiol and Ethynodiol Diacetate *on page 103*
- **Depacon®** *see* Valproic Acid and Derivatives *on page 201*
- **Depakene®** *see* Valproic Acid and Derivatives *on page 201*
- **Depakote® Delayed Release** *see* Valproic Acid and Derivatives *on page 201*
- **Depakote® ER** *see* Valproic Acid and Derivatives *on page 201*
- **Depakote® Sprinkle®** *see* Valproic Acid and Derivatives *on page 201*
- **DepoDur™** *see* Morphine Sulfate *on page 146*
- **Depo®-Estradiol** *see* Estradiol *on page 101*
- **Depo-Medrol®** *see* MethylPREDNISolone *on page 141*
- **Depo-Prevera® (Can)** *see* MedroxyPROGESTERone *on page 137*
- **Depo-Provera®** *see* MedroxyPROGESTERone *on page 137*
- **Depo-Provera® Contraceptive** *see* MedroxyPROGESTERone *on page 137*
- **depo-subQ provera 104™** *see* MedroxyPROGESTERone *on page 137*
- **Depotest® 100 (Can)** *see* Testosterone *on page 192*
- **Depo®-Testosterone** *see* Testosterone *on page 192*
- **Deprenyl** *see* Selegiline *on page 183*
- **Dermarest Dricort® [OTC]** *see* Hydrocortisone *on page 121*
- **Dermtex® HC [OTC]** *see* Hydrocortisone *on page 121*

Desipramine (des IP ra meen)

Genes of Interest

Alpha$_1$-Adrenergic Receptor *on page 210*
ATP-Binding Cassette, Sub-Family B, Member 1 *on page 224*
G-Protein Beta$_3$ Subunit *on page 286*
Gs Protein Alpha-Subunit *on page 288*

U.S. Brand Names Norpramin®

Canadian Brand Names Alti-Desipramine; Apo-Desipramine®; Norpramin®; Nu-Desipramine; PMS-Desipramine

Synonyms Desipramine Hydrochloride; Desmethylimipramine Hydrochloride

Pharmacologic Class Antidepressant, Tricyclic (Secondary Amine)

- **Desipramine Hydrochloride** *see* Desipramine *on page 89*

Desloratadine (des lor AT a deen)

Genes of Interest None known

U.S. Brand Names Clarinex®

Canadian Brand Names Aerius®

Pharmacologic Class Antihistamine, Nonsedating

- **Desmethylimipramine Hydrochloride** *see* Desipramine *on page 89*
- **Desogen®** *see* Ethinyl Estradiol and Desogestrel *on page 103*

- **Desogestrel and Ethinyl Estradiol** *see* Ethinyl Estradiol and Desogestrel *on page 103*
- **Desyrel®** *see* Trazodone *on page 197*
- **Detrol®** *see* Tolterodine *on page 196*
- **Detrol® LA** *see* Tolterodine *on page 196*

Dexmedetomidine (deks MED e toe mi deen)

Genes of Interest

CYP2D6 *on page 254*

U.S. Brand Names Precedex™

Canadian Brand Names Precedex™

Synonyms Dexmedetomidine Hydrochloride

Pharmacologic Class $Alpha_2$-Adrenergic Agonist; Sedative

- **Dexmedetomidine Hydrochloride** *see* Dexmedetomidine *on page 90*

Dexrazoxane (deks ray ZOKS ane)

Genes of Interest

ATP-Binding Cassette, Sub-Family B, Member 1 *on page 224*

U.S. Brand Names Zinecard®

Canadian Brand Names Zinecard®

Synonyms ICRF-187

Pharmacologic Class Cardioprotectant

Dextroamphetamine and Amphetamine

(deks troe am FET a meen & am FET a meen)

Genes of Interest None known

U.S. Brand Names Adderall XR®; Adderall®

Canadian Brand Names Adderall XR®

Synonyms Amphetamine and Dextroamphetamine

Pharmacologic Class Stimulant

- **Dextropropoxyphene** *see* Propoxyphene *on page 172*
- **DHE** *see* Dihydroergotamine *on page 92*
- **D.H.E. 45®** *see* Dihydroergotamine *on page 92*
- **Diabeta** *see* GlyBURIDE *on page 117*
- **Diabetic Tussin® Allergy Relief [OTC]** *see* Chlorpheniramine *on page 79*
- **Diaβeta®** *see* GlyBURIDE *on page 117*
- **Diaminocyclohexane Oxalatoplatinum** *see* Oxaliplatin *on page 160*
- **Diaminodiphenylsulfone** *see* Dapsone *on page 88*
- **Diastat®** *see* Diazepam *on page 90*
- **Diazemuls® (Can)** *see* Diazepam *on page 90*

Diazepam (dye AZ e pam)

Genes of Interest

CYP2C19 *on page 251*

CYP3A4 *on page 260*

U.S. Brand Names Diastat®; Diazepam Intensol®; Valium®

Canadian Brand Names Apo-Diazepam®; Diastat®; Diazemuls®; Novo-Dipam; Valium®

Pharmacologic Class Benzodiazepine

- **Diazepam Intensol®** *see* Diazepam *on page 90*
- **DIC** *see* Dacarbazine *on page 87*

Diclofenac (dye KLOE fen ak)

Genes of Interest

Leukotriene C4 Synthase *on page 302*

U.S. Brand Names Cataflam®; Solaraze™; Voltaren Ophthalmic®; Voltaren®-XR; Voltaren®

Canadian Brand Names Apo-Diclo Rapide®; Apo-Diclo SR®; Apo-Diclo®; Cataflam®; Novo-Difenac K; Novo-Difenac-SR; Novo-Difenac; Nu-Diclo-SR; Nu-Diclo; PMS-Diclofenac SR; PMS-Diclofenac; Pennsaid®; Riva-Diclofenac-K; Riva-Diclofenac; Voltaren Ophtha®; Voltaren Rapide®; Voltaren®

Synonyms Diclofenac Potassium; Diclofenac Sodium

Pharmacologic Class Nonsteroidal Anti-inflammatory Drug (NSAID); Nonsteroidal Anti-inflammatory Drug (NSAID), Ophthalmic; Nonsteroidal Anti-inflammatory Drug (NSAID), Oral

Diclofenac and Misoprostol

(dye KLOE fen ak & mye soe PROST ole)

Genes of Interest

Leukotriene C4 Synthase *on page 302*

U.S. Brand Names Arthrotec®

Canadian Brand Names Arthrotec®

Synonyms Misoprostol and Diclofenac

Pharmacologic Class Nonsteroidal Anti-inflammatory Drug (NSAID), Oral; Prostaglandin

- **Diclofenac Potassium** *see* Diclofenac *on page 91*
- **Diclofenac Sodium** *see* Diclofenac *on page 91*
- **Didrex®** *see* Benzphetamine *on page 69*
- **Diflucan®** *see* Fluconazole *on page 109*

Diflunisal (dye FLOO ni sal)

Genes of Interest

Leukotriene C4 Synthase *on page 302*

U.S. Brand Names Dolobid®

Canadian Brand Names Apo-Diflunisal®; Novo-Diflunisal; Nu-Diflunisal

Pharmacologic Class Nonsteroidal Anti-inflammatory Drug (NSAID), Oral

- **Digitek®** *see* Digoxin *on page 92*

Digitoxin (di ji TOKS in)

Genes of Interest

CYP3A4 *on page 260*

(Continued)

Digitoxin *(Continued)*

Synonyms Crystodigin

Pharmacologic Class Antiarrhythmic Agent, Class IV

Digoxin (di JOKS in)

Genes of Interest

ATP-Binding Cassette, Sub-Family B, Member 1 *on page 224*

U.S. Brand Names Digitek®; Lanoxicaps®; Lanoxin®

Canadian Brand Names Digoxin CSD; Lanoxicaps®; Lanoxin®; Novo-Digoxin

Pharmacologic Class Antiarrhythmic Agent, Class IV; Cardiac Glycoside

- ♦ **Digoxin CSD (Can)** *see* Digoxin *on page 92*

Dihydrocodeine, Aspirin, and Caffeine

(dye hye droe KOE deen, AS pir in, & KAF een)

Genes of Interest

COMT *on page 244*

CYP2D6 *on page 254*

U.S. Brand Names Synalgos®-DC

Synonyms Dihydrocodeine Compound

Pharmacologic Class Analgesic, Narcotic

- ♦ **Dihydrocodeine Compound** *see* Dihydrocodeine, Aspirin, and Caffeine *on page 92*

Dihydroergotamine (dye hye droe er GOT a meen)

Genes of Interest

CYP3A4 *on page 260*

U.S. Brand Names D.H.E. 45®; Migranal®

Canadian Brand Names Migranal®

Synonyms DHE; Dihydroergotamine Mesylate

Pharmacologic Class Ergot Derivative

- ♦ **Dihydroergotamine Mesylate** *see* Dihydroergotamine *on page 92*
- ♦ **Dihydroergotoxine** *see* Ergoloid Mesylates *on page 98*
- ♦ **Dihydrogenated Ergot Alkaloids** *see* Ergoloid Mesylates *on page 98*
- ♦ **Dihydrohydroxycodeinone** *see* Oxycodone *on page 161*
- ♦ **Dihydromorphinone** *see* Hydromorphone *on page 122*
- ♦ **Dihydroxydeoxynorvinkaleukoblastine** *see* Vinorelbine *on page 203*
- ♦ **Dilacor® XR** *see* Diltiazem *on page 93*
- ♦ **Dilantin®** *see* Phenytoin *on page 165*
- ♦ **Dilatrate®-SR** *see* Isosorbide Dinitrate *on page 127*
- ♦ **Dilaudid®** *see* Hydromorphone *on page 122*
- ♦ **Dilaudid-HP®** *see* Hydromorphone *on page 122*
- ♦ **Dilaudid-HP-Plus® (Can)** *see* Hydromorphone *on page 122*
- ♦ **Dilaudid® Sterile Powder (Can)** *see* Hydromorphone *on page 122*
- ♦ **Dilaudid-XP® (Can)** *see* Hydromorphone *on page 122*

- **Diltia XT®** *see* Diltiazem *on page 93*

Diltiazem (dil TYE a zem)

Genes of Interest

ATP-Binding Cassette, Sub-Family B, Member 1 *on page 224*
CYP3A4 *on page 260*

U.S. Brand Names Cardizem® CD; Cardizem® LA; Cardizem® SR [DSC]; Cardizem®; Cartia XT™; Dilacor® XR; Diltia XT®; Taztia XT™; Tiazac®

Canadian Brand Names Alti-Diltiazem CD; Apo-Diltiaz CD®; Apo-Diltiaz SR®; Apo-Diltiaz®; Cardizem® CD; Cardizem® SR; Cardizem®; Gen-Diltiazem CD; Gen-Diltiazem; Med-Diltiazem; Novo-Diltazem-CD; Novo-Diltazem; Nu-Diltiaz-CD; Nu-Diltiaz; Rhoxal-diltiazem CD; Rhoxal-diltiazem SR; Syn-Diltiazem®; Tiazac® ; Tiazac® XC; ratio-Diltiazem CD

Synonyms Diltiazem Hydrochloride

Pharmacologic Class Calcium Channel Blocker

- **Diltiazem Hydrochloride** *see* Diltiazem *on page 93*

Dimercaprol (dye mer KAP role)

Genes of Interest

Glucose-6-Phosphate Dehydrogenase *on page 281*

U.S. Brand Names BAL in Oil®

Synonyms BAL; British Anti-Lewisite; Dithioglycerol

Pharmacologic Class Antidote

- **Dimetapp® Children's ND [OTC]** *see* Loratadine *on page 133*
- **Dimethyl Triazeno Imidazole Carboxamide** *see* Dacarbazine *on page 87*
- **Diochloram® (Can)** *see* Chloramphenicol *on page 78*
- **Diomycin® (Can)** *see* Erythromycin *on page 99*
- **Diosulf™ (Can)** *see* Sulfacetamide *on page 187*
- **Diovan®** *see* Valsartan *on page 201*
- **Diphenylhydantoin** *see* Phenytoin *on page 165*
- **Diprivan®** *see* Propofol *on page 172*
- **Dipropylacetic Acid** *see* Valproic Acid and Derivatives *on page 201*

Dipyridamole (dye peer ID a mole)

Genes of Interest

ATP-Binding Cassette, Sub-Family B, Member 1 *on page 224*
Glycoprotein IIIa Receptor *on page 285*

U.S. Brand Names Persantine®

Canadian Brand Names Apo-Dipyridamole FC®; Persantine®

Pharmacologic Class Antiplatelet Agent; Vasodilator

- **Dipyridamole and Aspirin** *see* Aspirin and Dipyridamole *on page 66*

Disopyramide (dye soe PEER a mide)

Genes of Interest

Cardiac Potassium Ion Channel *on page 241*

(Continued)

Disopyramide *(Continued)*

Cardiac Sodium Channel *on page 242*
CYP3A4 *on page 260*

U.S. Brand Names Norpace® CR; Norpace®
Canadian Brand Names Norpace®; Rythmodan®-LA; Rythmodan®
Synonyms Disopyramide Phosphate
Pharmacologic Class Antiarrhythmic Agent, Class Ia

- ♦ **Disopyramide Phosphate** *see* Disopyramide *on page 93*
- ♦ **DisperMox™** *see* Amoxicillin *on page 59*

Disulfiram (dye SUL fi ram)

Genes of Interest
ATP-Binding Cassette, Sub-Family B, Member 1 *on page 224*

U.S. Brand Names Antabuse®
Pharmacologic Class Aldehyde Dehydrogenase Inhibitor

- ♦ **Dithioglycerol** *see* Dimercaprol *on page 93*
- ♦ **Diucardin® [DSC]** *see* Hydroflumethiazide *on page 121*
- ♦ **Diuril®** *see* Chlorothiazide *on page 79*
- ♦ **Divalproex Sodium** *see* Valproic Acid and Derivatives *on page 201*
- ♦ **Dixarit® (Can)** *see* Clonidine *on page 83*

Docetaxel (doe se TAKS el)

Genes of Interest
CYP3A4 *on page 260*

U.S. Brand Names Taxotere®
Canadian Brand Names Taxotere®
Synonyms NSC-628503; RP-6976
Pharmacologic Class Antineoplastic Agent, Natural Source (Plant) Derivative

Dofetilide (doe FET il ide)

Genes of Interest
Cardiac Potassium Ion Channel *on page 241*
Cardiac Sodium Channel *on page 242*

U.S. Brand Names Tikosyn™
Canadian Brand Names Tikosyn™
Pharmacologic Class Antiarrhythmic Agent, Class III

- ♦ **Dolobid®** *see* Diflunisal *on page 91*
- ♦ **Dolophine®** *see* Methadone *on page 140*
- ♦ **Dom-Domperidone (Can)** *see* Domperidone *on page 94*

Domperidone (dom PE ri done)

Genes of Interest
Cardiac Potassium Ion Channel *on page 241*
Cardiac Sodium Channel *on page 242*

Canadian Brand Names Alti-Domperidone; Apo-Domperidone®; Dom-Domperidone; FTP-Domperidone Maleate; Motilium®; Novo-Domperidone; Nu-Domperidone; ratio-Domperidone

Synonyms Domperidone Maleate
Pharmacologic Class Dopamine Antagonist, Peripheral; Gastrointestinal Agent, Prokinetic

- ♦ **Domperidone Maleate** *see* Domperidone *on page 94*
- ♦ **Dom-Tiaprofenic® (Can)** *see* Tiaprofenic Acid *on page 194*

Donepezil (doh NEP e zil)

Genes of Interest
Apolipoprotein E *on page 220*
U.S. Brand Names Aricept® ODT; Aricept®
Canadian Brand Names Aricept®
Synonyms E2020
Pharmacologic Class Acetylcholinesterase Inhibitor (Central)

- ♦ **Doryx®** *see* Doxycycline *on page 96*

Doxazosin (doks AY zoe sin)

Genes of Interest None known
U.S. Brand Names Cardura®
Canadian Brand Names Alti-Doxazosin; Apo-Doxazosin®; Cardura-1™; Cardura-2™; Cardura-4™; Gen-Doxazosin; Novo-Doxazosin
Synonyms Doxazosin Mesylate
Pharmacologic Class $Alpha_1$ Blocker

- ♦ **Doxazosin Mesylate** *see* Doxazosin *on page 95*

Doxepin (DOKS e pin)

Genes of Interest
$Alpha_1$-Adrenergic Receptor *on page 210*
ATP-Binding Cassette, Sub-Family B, Member 1 *on page 224*
CYP1A2 *on page 246*
CYP3A4 *on page 260*
G-Protein $Beta_3$ Subunit *on page 286*
Gs Protein Alpha-Subunit *on page 288*
U.S. Brand Names Prudoxin™; Sinequan®; Zonalon®
Canadian Brand Names Apo-Doxepin®; Novo-Doxepin; Sinequan®; Zonalon®
Synonyms Doxepin Hydrochloride
Pharmacologic Class Antidepressant, Tricyclic (Tertiary Amine); Topical Skin Product

- ♦ **Doxepin Hydrochloride** *see* Doxepin *on page 95*

DOXOrubicin (doks oh ROO bi sin)

Genes of Interest CYP3A4 *on page 260*
U.S. Brand Names Adriamycin PFS®; Adriamycin RDF®; Rubex®
Canadian Brand Names Adriamycin®
Synonyms ADR (error-prone abbreviation); Adria; Doxorubicin Hydrochloride; Hydroxydaunomycin Hydrochloride; Hydroxyldaunorubicin Hydrochloride; NSC-123127
Pharmacologic Class Antineoplastic Agent, Anthracycline

- **Doxorubicin Hydrochloride** *see* DOXOrubicin *on page 95*
- **Doxy-100®** *see* Doxycycline *on page 96*
- **Doxycin (Can)** *see* Doxycycline *on page 96*

Doxycycline (doks i SYE kleen)

Genes of Interest None known

U.S. Brand Names Adoxa™; Doryx®; Doxy-100®; Monodox®; Periostat®; Vibra-Tabs®; Vibramycin®

Canadian Brand Names Apo-Doxy Tabs®; Apo-Doxy®; Doxycin; Doxytec; Novo-Doxylin; Nu-Doxycycline; Periostat®; Vibra-Tabs®

Synonyms Doxycycline Calcium; Doxycycline Hyclate; Doxycycline Monohydrate

Pharmacologic Class Antibiotic, Tetracycline Derivative

- **Doxycycline Calcium** *see* Doxycycline *on page 96*
- **Doxycycline Hyclate** *see* Doxycycline *on page 96*
- **Doxycycline Monohydrate** *see* Doxycycline *on page 96*
- **Doxytec (Can)** *see* Doxycycline *on page 96*
- **DPA** *see* Valproic Acid and Derivatives *on page 201*
- **DPH** *see* Phenytoin *on page 165*
- **Dramamine® Less Drowsy Formula [OTC]** *see* Meclizine *on page 136*

Droperidol (droe PER i dole)

Genes of Interest

Alpha$_1$-Adrenergic Receptor *on page 210*
Cardiac Potassium Ion Channel *on page 241*
Cardiac Sodium Channel *on page 242*
D_2 Receptor *on page 263*

U.S. Brand Names Inapsine®

Synonyms Dehydrobenzperidol

Pharmacologic Class Antiemetic; Antipsychotic Agent, Typical

- **Drospirenone and Ethinyl Estradiol** *see* Ethinyl Estradiol and Drospirenone *on page 103*
- **DTIC® (Can)** *see* Dacarbazine *on page 87*
- **DTIC-Dome®** *see* Dacarbazine *on page 87*
- **DTO (error-prone abbreviation)** *see* Opium Tincture *on page 159*
- **DuoNeb™** *see* Ipratropium and Albuterol *on page 125*
- **DuP 753** *see* Losartan *on page 134*
- **Duraclon™** *see* Clonidine *on page 83*
- **Duragesic®** *see* Fentanyl *on page 107*
- **Duralith® (Can)** *see* Lithium *on page 133*
- **Duramorph®** *see* Morphine Sulfate *on page 146*
- **Dynacin®** *see* Minocycline *on page 144*
- **DynaCirc®** *see* Isradipine *on page 127*
- **DynaCirc® CR** *see* Isradipine *on page 127*

- ♦ **7E3** *see* Abciximab *on page 52*
- ♦ **E2020** *see* Donepezil *on page 95*
- ♦ **EarSol® HC** *see* Hydrocortisone *on page 121*
- ♦ **Easprin®** *see* Aspirin *on page 65*
- ♦ **EC-Naprosyn®** *see* Naproxen *on page 148*
- ♦ **Ecotrin® [OTC]** *see* Aspirin *on page 65*
- ♦ **Ecotrin® Low Strength [OTC]** *see* Aspirin *on page 65*
- ♦ **Ecotrin® Maximum Strength [OTC]** *see* Aspirin *on page 65*
- ♦ **E.E.S.®** *see* Erythromycin *on page 99*
- ♦ **Effexor®** *see* Venlafaxine *on page 201*
- ♦ **Effexor® XR** *see* Venlafaxine *on page 201*
- ♦ **Efudex®** *see* Fluorouracil *on page 109*
- ♦ **Elavil® [DSC]** *see* Amitriptyline *on page 57*
- ♦ **Eldepryl®** *see* Selegiline *on page 183*

Eletriptan (el e TRIP tan)

Genes of Interest

CYP3A4 *on page 260*

U.S. Brand Names Relpax®

Canadian Brand Names Relpax®

Synonyms Eletriptan Hydrobromide

Pharmacologic Class Serotonin $5\text{-}HT_{1B,\ 1D}$ Receptor Agonist

- ♦ **Eletriptan Hydrobromide** *see* Eletriptan *on page 97*
- ♦ **Elitek™** *see* Rasburicase *on page 176*
- ♦ **Elixophyllin®** *see* Theophylline *on page 192*
- ♦ **ElixSure™ IB [OTC]** *see* Ibuprofen *on page 123*
- ♦ **Elocom® (Can)** *see* Mometasone Furoate *on page 145*
- ♦ **Elocon®** *see* Mometasone Furoate *on page 145*
- ♦ **Eloxatin™** *see* Oxaliplatin *on page 160*
- ♦ **Eltroxin® (Can)** *see* Levothyroxine *on page 131*
- ♦ **Emend®** *see* Aprepitant *on page 64*
- ♦ **EMLA®** *see* Lidocaine and Prilocaine *on page 131*
- ♦ **Emo-Cort® (Can)** *see* Hydrocortisone *on page 121*
- ♦ **ENA 713** *see* Rivastigmine *on page 180*

Enalapril (e NAL a pril)

Genes of Interest

Aldosterone Synthase *on page 208*
Angiotensin II Type 1 Receptor *on page 213*
Angiotensin-Converting Enzyme *on page 214*
Angiotensinogen *on page 219*
Bradykinin B_2-Receptor *on page 237*

U.S. Brand Names Vasotec®

Canadian Brand Names Vasotec®

Synonyms Enalapril Maleate; Enalaprilat

Pharmacologic Class Angiotensin-Converting Enzyme (ACE) Inhibitor

♦ **Enalaprilat** *see* Enalapril *on page 97*
♦ **Enalapril Maleate** *see* Enalapril *on page 97*
♦ **Endocet®** *see* Oxycodone and Acetaminophen *on page 161*
♦ **Endodan®** *see* Oxycodone and Aspirin *on page 161*
♦ **Enduron® [DSC]** *see* Methyclothiazide *on page 140*
♦ **Enpresse™** *see* Ethinyl Estradiol and Levonorgestrel *on page 104*
♦ **Entocort® (Can)** *see* Budesonide *on page 72*
♦ **Entocort™ EC** *see* Budesonide *on page 72*
♦ **Entrophen® (Can)** *see* Aspirin *on page 65*
♦ **Epipodophyllotoxin** *see* Etoposide *on page 106*
♦ **Epitol®** *see* Carbamazepine *on page 75*
♦ **Epival® I.V. (Can)** *see* Valproic Acid and Derivatives *on page 201*

Eplerenone (e PLER en one)

Genes of Interest

CYP3A4 *on page 260*

U.S. Brand Names Inspra™

Pharmacologic Class Antihypertensive; Selective Aldosterone Blocker

Eprosartan (ep roe SAR tan)

Genes of Interest

Adipocyte-Derived Leucine Aminopeptidase *on page 208*
Aldosterone Synthase *on page 208*
Angiotensin II Type 1 Receptor *on page 213*
Angiotensin-Converting Enzyme *on page 214*
Angiotensinogen *on page 219*
Bradykinin B_2-Receptor *on page 237*
CYP2C9 *on page 248*

U.S. Brand Names Teveten®

Canadian Brand Names Teveten®

Pharmacologic Class Angiotensin II Receptor Blocker

♦ **EPT** *see* Teniposide *on page 191*

Eptifibatide (ep TIF i ba tide)

Genes of Interest

Glycoprotein IIIa Receptor *on page 285*

U.S. Brand Names Integrilin®

Canadian Brand Names Integrilin®

Synonyms Intrifiban

Pharmacologic Class Antiplatelet Agent, Glycoprotein IIb/IIIa Inhibitor

♦ **Equetro™** *see* Carbamazepine *on page 75*

Ergoloid Mesylates (ER goe loid MES i lates)

Genes of Interest

CYP3A4 *on page 260*

Canadian Brand Names Hydergine®

Synonyms Dihydroergotoxine; Dihydrogenated Ergot Alkaloids; Hydergine [DSC]

Pharmacologic Class Ergot Derivative

- **Ergomar®** *see* Ergotamine *on page 99*
- **Ergometrine Maleate** *see* Ergonovine *on page 99*

Ergonovine (er goe NOE veen)

Genes of Interest

CYP3A4 *on page 260*

Synonyms Ergometrine Maleate; Ergonovine Maleate

Pharmacologic Class Ergot Derivative

- **Ergonovine Maleate** *see* Ergonovine *on page 99*

Ergotamine (er GOT a meen)

Genes of Interest

CYP3A4 *on page 260*

U.S. Brand Names Ergomar®

Synonyms Ergotamine Tartrate

Pharmacologic Class Ergot Derivative

- **Ergotamine Tartrate** *see* Ergotamine *on page 99*
- **Errin™** *see* Norethindrone *on page 151*
- **Erybid™ (Can)** *see* Erythromycin *on page 99*
- **Eryc®** *see* Erythromycin *on page 99*
- **Eryderm®** *see* Erythromycin *on page 99*
- **Erygel®** *see* Erythromycin *on page 99*
- **EryPed®** *see* Erythromycin *on page 99*
- **Ery-Tab®** *see* Erythromycin *on page 99*
- **Erythrocin®** *see* Erythromycin *on page 99*

Erythromycin (er ith roe MYE sin)

Genes of Interest

ATP-Binding Cassette, Sub-Family B, Member 1 *on page 224*
Cardiac Potassium Ion Channel *on page 241*
Cardiac Sodium Channel *on page 242*
CYP3A4 *on page 260*

U.S. Brand Names A/T/S®; Akne-Mycin®; E.E.S.®; Ery-Tab®; EryPed®; Eryc®; Eryderm®; Erygel®; Erythrocin®; PCE®; Romycin®; Staticin® [DSC]; T-Stat® [DSC]; Theramycin Z®

Canadian Brand Names Apo-Erythro Base®; Apo-Erythro E-C®; Apo-Erythro-ES®; Apo-Erythro-S®; Diomycin®; EES®; Erybid™; Eryc®; Novo-Rythro Estolate; Novo-Rythro Ethylsuccinate; Nu-Erythromycin-S; PCE®; PMS-Erythromycin; Sans Acne®

Synonyms Erythromycin Base; Erythromycin Estolate; Erythromycin Ethylsuccinate; Erythromycin Gluceptate; Erythromycin Lactobionate; Erythromycin Stearate

Pharmacologic Class Antibiotic, Macrolide; Antibiotic, Ophthalmic; Antibiotic, Topical; Topical Skin Product; Topical Skin Product, Acne

Erythromycin and Sulfisoxazole

(er ith roe MYE sin & sul fi SOKS a zole)

Genes of Interest

ATP-Binding Cassette, Sub-Family B, Member 1 *on page 224*
Cardiac Potassium Ion Channel *on page 241*
Cardiac Sodium Channel *on page 242*
CYP2C9 *on page 248*
CYP3A4 *on page 260*
Glucose-6-Phosphate Dehydrogenase *on page 281*
N-Acetyltransferase 2 Enzyme *on page 308*

U.S. Brand Names Pediazole®

Canadian Brand Names Pediazole®

Synonyms Sulfisoxazole and Erythromycin

Pharmacologic Class Antibiotic, Macrolide; Antibiotic, Macrolide Combination; Antibiotic, Sulfonamide Derivative

- ♦ **Erythromycin Base** *see* Erythromycin *on page 99*
- ♦ **Erythromycin Estolate** *see* Erythromycin *on page 99*
- ♦ **Erythromycin Ethylsuccinate** *see* Erythromycin *on page 99*
- ♦ **Erythromycin Gluceptate** *see* Erythromycin *on page 99*
- ♦ **Erythromycin Lactobionate** *see* Erythromycin *on page 99*
- ♦ **Erythromycin Stearate** *see* Erythromycin *on page 99*

Escitalopram (es sye TAL oh pram)

Genes of Interest

CYP2C19 *on page 251*
CYP3A4 *on page 260*
G-Protein $Beta_3$ Subunit *on page 286*
Gs Protein Alpha-Subunit *on page 288*
5-HT_{2A} Receptor *on page 291*
5-HT Transporter *on page 297*
Monoamine Oxidase A *on page 307*

U.S. Brand Names Lexapro™

Canadian Brand Names Cipralex®

Synonyms Escitalopram Oxalate; Lu-26-054; S-Citalopram

Pharmacologic Class Antidepressant, Selective Serotonin Reuptake Inhibitor

- ♦ **Escitalopram Oxalate** *see* Escitalopram *on page 100*
- ♦ **Esclim®** *see* Estradiol *on page 101*
- ♦ **Eskalith®** *see* Lithium *on page 133*
- ♦ **Eskalith CR®** *see* Lithium *on page 133*

Esmolol (ES moe lol)

Genes of Interest

Angiotensinogen *on page 219*
$Beta_1$-Adrenergic Receptor *on page 230*
Bradykinin B_2-Receptor *on page 237*
Gs Protein Alpha-Subunit *on page 288*

U.S. Brand Names Brevibloc®

Canadian Brand Names Brevibloc®

Synonyms Esmolol Hydrochloride

Pharmacologic Class Antiarrhythmic Agent, Class II; Beta Blocker, $Beta_1$ Selective

♦ **Esmolol Hydrochloride** *see* Esmolol *on page 100*

Esomeprazole (es oh ME pray zol)

Genes of Interest None known

U.S. Brand Names Nexium®

Canadian Brand Names Nexium®

Synonyms Esomeprazole Magnesium

Pharmacologic Class Proton Pump Inhibitor; Substituted Benzimidazole

♦ **Esomeprazole Magnesium** *see* Esomeprazole *on page 101*

♦ **Esterified Estrogens** *see* Estrogens (Esterified) *on page 102*

♦ **Estrace®** *see* Estradiol *on page 101*

♦ **Estraderm®** *see* Estradiol *on page 101*

Estradiol (es tra DYE ole)

Genes of Interest

CYP1A2 *on page 246*

Factor V *on page 279*

Prothrombin *on page 315*

U.S. Brand Names Alora®; Climara®; Delestrogen®; Depo®-Estradiol; Esclim®; Estrace®; Estraderm®; Estrasorb™; Estring®; EstroGel®; Femring™; Femtrace®; Gynodiol®; Menostar™; Vagifem®; Vivelle-Dot®; Vivelle®

Canadian Brand Names Climara®; Depo®-Estradiol; Estrace®; Estraderm®; Estradot®; Estring®; EstroGel®; Oesclim®; Vagifem®

Synonyms Estradiol Acetate; Estradiol Cypionate; Estradiol Hemihydrate; Estradiol Transdermal; Estradiol Valerate

Pharmacologic Class Estrogen Derivative

♦ **Estradiol Acetate** *see* Estradiol *on page 101*

♦ **Estradiol Cypionate** *see* Estradiol *on page 101*

♦ **Estradiol Hemihydrate** *see* Estradiol *on page 101*

♦ **Estradiol Transdermal** *see* Estradiol *on page 101*

♦ **Estradiol Valerate** *see* Estradiol *on page 101*

♦ **Estradot® (Can)** *see* Estradiol *on page 101*

♦ **Estrasorb™** *see* Estradiol *on page 101*

♦ **Estratab® (Can)** *see* Estrogens (Esterified) *on page 102*

♦ **Estring®** *see* Estradiol *on page 101*

♦ **EstroGel®** *see* Estradiol *on page 101*

♦ **Estrogenic Substances, Conjugated** *see* Estrogens (Conjugated/Equine) *on page 102*

Estrogens (Conjugated A/Synthetic)

(ES troe jenz, KON joo gate ed, aye, sin THET ik)

Genes of Interest

CYP1A2 *on page 246*
Factor V *on page 279*
Prothrombin *on page 315*

U.S. Brand Names Cenestin®

Pharmacologic Class Estrogen Derivative

Estrogens (Conjugated/Equine)

(ES troe jenz KON joo gate ed, EE kwine)

Genes of Interest

CYP1A2 *on page 246*
Factor V *on page 279*
Prothrombin *on page 315*

U.S. Brand Names Premarin®

Canadian Brand Names C.E.S.®; Cenestin; Premarin®

Synonyms C.E.S.; CEE; Estrogenic Substances, Conjugated

Pharmacologic Class Estrogen Derivative

Estrogens (Conjugated/Equine) and Medroxyprogesterone

(ES troe jenz KON joo gate ed/EE kwine & me DROKS ee proe JES te rone)

Genes of Interest

Factor V *on page 279*
Prothrombin *on page 315*

U.S. Brand Names Premphase®; Prempro™

Canadian Brand Names Premphase®; Premplus®; Prempro™

Synonyms MPA and Estrogens (Conjugated); Medroxyprogesterone and Estrogens (Conjugated)

Pharmacologic Class Estrogen and Progestin Combination

Estrogens (Esterified) (ES troe jenz, es TER i fied)

Genes of Interest

CYP1A2 *on page 246*
Factor V *on page 279*
Prothrombin *on page 315*

U.S. Brand Names Menest®

Canadian Brand Names Estratab®; Menest®

Synonyms Esterified Estrogens

Pharmacologic Class Estrogen Derivative

Estropipate (ES troe pih pate)

Genes of Interest

CYP1A2 *on page 246*
Factor V *on page 279*
Prothrombin *on page 315*

U.S. Brand Names Ogen®; Ortho-Est®
Canadian Brand Names Ogen®
Synonyms Ortho Est; Piperazine Estrone Sulfate
Pharmacologic Class Estrogen Derivative

♦ **Estrostep® Fe** *see* Ethinyl Estradiol and Norethindrone *on page 104*

Ethinyl Estradiol and Desogestrel

(ETH in il es tra DYE ole & des oh JES trel)

Genes of Interest

BRCA Genes *on page 240*
Factor V *on page 279*
Prothrombin *on page 315*

U.S. Brand Names Apri®; Cyclessa®; Desogen®; Kariva™; Mircette®; Ortho-Cept®; Solia™; Velivet™
Canadian Brand Names Marvelon®; Ortho-Cept®
Synonyms Desogestrel and Ethinyl Estradiol; Ortho Cept
Pharmacologic Class Contraceptive; Estrogen and Progestin Combination

Ethinyl Estradiol and Drospirenone

(ETH in il es tra DYE ole & droh SPYE re none)

Genes of Interest

BRCA Genes *on page 240*
Factor V *on page 279*
Prothrombin *on page 315*

U.S. Brand Names Yasmin®
Canadian Brand Names Yasmin®
Synonyms Drospirenone and Ethinyl Estradiol
Pharmacologic Class Contraceptive; Estrogen and Progestin Combination

Ethinyl Estradiol and Ethynodiol Diacetate

(ETH in il es tra DYE ole & e thye noe DYE ole dye AS e tate)

Genes of Interest

BRCA Genes *on page 240*
Factor V *on page 279*
Prothrombin *on page 315*

U.S. Brand Names Demulen®; Zovia™
Canadian Brand Names Demulen® 30
Synonyms Ethynodiol Diacetate and Ethinyl Estradiol
Pharmacologic Class Contraceptive; Estrogen and Progestin Combination

Ethinyl Estradiol and Etonogestrel

(ETH in il es tra DYE ole & et oh noe JES trel)

Genes of Interest

BRCA Genes *on page 240*
Factor V *on page 279*
Prothrombin *on page 315*
(Continued)

Ethinyl Estradiol and Etonogestrel *(Continued)*

U.S. Brand Names NuvaRing®
Canadian Brand Names NuvaRing®
Synonyms Etonogestrel and Ethinyl Estradiol
Pharmacologic Class Contraceptive; Estrogen and Progestin Combination

Ethinyl Estradiol and Levonorgestrel

(ETH in il es tra DYE ole & LEE voe nor jes trel)

Genes of Interest

BRCA Genes *on page 240*
Factor V *on page 279*
Prothrombin *on page 315*

U.S. Brand Names Alesse®; Aviane™; Enpresse™; Lessina™; Levlen®; Levlite™; Levora®; Lutera™; Nordette®; PREVEN®; Portia™; Seasonale®; Tri-Levlen®; Triphasil®; Trivora®
Canadian Brand Names Alesse®; Min-Ovral®; Triphasil®; Triquilar®
Synonyms Levonorgestrel and Ethinyl Estradiol
Pharmacologic Class Contraceptive; Estrogen and Progestin Combination

♦ **Ethinyl Estradiol and NGM** *see* Ethinyl Estradiol and Norgestimate *on page 105*

Ethinyl Estradiol and Norelgestromin

(ETH in il es tra DYE ole & nor el JES troe min)

Genes of Interest

BRCA Genes *on page 240*
Factor V *on page 279*
Prothrombin *on page 315*

U.S. Brand Names Ortho Evra™
Canadian Brand Names Evra™
Synonyms Norelgestromin and Ethinyl Estradiol; Ortho-Evra
Pharmacologic Class Contraceptive; Estrogen and Progestin Combination

Ethinyl Estradiol and Norethindrone

(ETH in il es tra DYE ole & nor eth IN drone)

Genes of Interest

BRCA Genes *on page 240*
Factor V *on page 279*
Prothrombin *on page 315*

U.S. Brand Names Aranelle™; Brevicon®; Estrostep® Fe; Junel™ Fe; Junel™; Loestrin® Fe; Loestrin®; Microgestin™ Fe; Microgestin™; Modicon®; Necon® 0.5/35; Necon® 1/35; Necon® 10/11; Necon® 7/7/7; Norinyl® 1+35; Nortrel™ 7/7/7; Nortrel™; Ortho-Novum®; Ovcon®; Tri-Norinyl®; femhrt®
Canadian Brand Names Brevicon® 0.5/35; Brevicon® 1/35; FemHRT®; Loestrin™ 1.5.30; Minestrin™ 1/20; Ortho® 0.5/35; Ortho® 1/35; Ortho® 7/7/7; Select™ 1/35; Synphasic®

Synonyms Norethindrone Acetate and Ethinyl Estradiol; Ortho Novum

Pharmacologic Class Contraceptive; Estrogen and Progestin Combination

Ethinyl Estradiol and Norgestimate

(ETH in il es tra DYE ole & nor JES ti mate)

Genes of Interest

BRCA Genes *on page 240*

Factor V *on page 279*

Prothrombin *on page 315*

U.S. Brand Names MonoNessa™; Ortho Tri-Cyclen® Lo; Ortho Tri-Cyclen®; Ortho-Cyclen®; Previfem™; Sprintec™; Tri-Previfem™; Tri-Sprintec™; TriNessa™

Canadian Brand Names Cyclen®; Tri-Cyclen® ; Tri-Cyclen® Lo

Synonyms Ethinyl Estradiol and NGM; Norgestimate and Ethinyl Estradiol; Ortho Cyclen; Ortho Tri Cyclen

Pharmacologic Class Contraceptive; Estrogen and Progestin Combination

Ethinyl Estradiol and Norgestrel

(ETH in il es tra DYE ole & nor JES trel)

Genes of Interest

BRCA Genes *on page 240*

Factor V *on page 279*

Prothrombin *on page 315*

U.S. Brand Names Cryselle™; Lo/Ovral®; Low-Ogestrel®; Ogestrel®; Ovral® [DSC]

Canadian Brand Names Ovral®

Synonyms Morning After Pill; Norgestrel and Ethinyl Estradiol

Pharmacologic Class Contraceptive; Estrogen and Progestin Combination

♦ **Ethmozine®** *see* Moricizine *on page 146*

Ethosuximide (eth oh SUKS i mide)

Genes of Interest

CYP3A4 *on page 260*

U.S. Brand Names Zarontin®

Canadian Brand Names Zarontin®

Pharmacologic Class Anticonvulsant, Succinimide

♦ **Ethynodiol Diacetate and Ethinyl Estradiol** *see* Ethinyl Estradiol and Ethynodiol Diacetate *on page 103*

Etodolac (ee toe DOE lak)

Genes of Interest

Leukotriene C4 Synthase *on page 302*

U.S. Brand Names Lodine® XL [DSC]; Lodine®

Canadian Brand Names Apo-Etodolac®; Lodine®; Utradol™

Synonyms Etodolic Acid

Pharmacologic Class Nonsteroidal Anti-inflammatory Drug (NSAID), Oral

- **Etodolic Acid** *see* Etodolac *on page 105*
- **Etonogestrel and Ethinyl Estradiol** *see* Ethinyl Estradiol and Etonogestrel *on page 103*

Etoposide (e toe POE side)

Genes of Interest

CYP3A4 *on page 260*

U.S. Brand Names Toposar®; VePesid®

Canadian Brand Names VePesid®

Synonyms Epipodophyllotoxin; VP-16-213; VP-16

Pharmacologic Class Antineoplastic Agent, Podophyllotoxin Derivative

- **Etrafon® (Can)** *see* Amitriptyline and Perphenazine *on page 58*
- **Euflex® (Can)** *see* Flutamide *on page 111*
- **Euglucon® (Can)** *see* GlyBURIDE *on page 117*
- **Eulexin®** *see* Flutamide *on page 111*
- **Everone® 200 (Can)** *see* Testosterone *on page 192*
- **Evista®** *see* Raloxifene *on page 175*
- **Evoclin™** *see* Clindamycin *on page 82*
- **Evra™ (Can)** *see* Ethinyl Estradiol and Norelgestromin *on page 104*
- **Exelon®** *see* Rivastigmine *on page 180*

Famotidine (fa MOE ti deen)

Genes of Interest None known

U.S. Brand Names Fluxid™; Pepcid® AC [OTC]; Pepcid®

Canadian Brand Names Apo-Famotidine®; Famotidine Omega; Gen-Famotidine; Novo-Famotidine; Nu-Famotidine; Pepcid® AC; Pepcid® I.V.; Pepcid®; Riva-Famotidine; ratio-Famotidine

Pharmacologic Class Histamine H_2 Antagonist

- **Famotidine Omega (Can)** *see* Famotidine *on page 106*
- **Fansidar®** *see* Sulfadoxine and Pyrimethamine *on page 187*
- **Fasturtec® (Can)** *see* Rasburicase *on page 176*
- **FazaClo®** *see* Clozapine *on page 84*

Felbamate (FEL ba mate)

Genes of Interest

CYP3A4 *on page 260*

U.S. Brand Names Felbatol®

Pharmacologic Class Anticonvulsant, Miscellaneous

- **Felbatol®** *see* Felbamate *on page 106*
- **Feldene®** *see* Piroxicam *on page 166*

Felodipine (fe LOE di peen)

Genes of Interest

ATP-Binding Cassette, Sub-Family B, Member 1 *on page 224*

CYP3A4 *on page 260*

U.S. Brand Names Plendil®
Canadian Brand Names Plendil®; Renedil®
Pharmacologic Class Calcium Channel Blocker

- ♦ **femhrt®** *see* Ethinyl Estradiol and Norethindrone *on page 104*
- ♦ **Femring™** *see* Estradiol *on page 101*
- ♦ **Femtrace®** *see* Estradiol *on page 101*

Fenofibrate (fen oh FYE brate)

Genes of Interest
Angiotensin-Converting Enzyme *on page 214*
Cholesteryl Ester Transfer Protein *on page 243*
U.S. Brand Names Antara™; Lofibra™; TriCor®; Triglide™
Canadian Brand Names Apo-Feno-Micro®; Apo-Fenofibrate®; Gen-Fenofibrate Micro; Lipidil EZ®; Lipidil Micro®; Lipidil Supra®; Novo-Fenofibrate; Nu-Fenofibrate; PMS-Fenofibrate Micro; TriCor®; ratio-Fenofibrate MC
Synonyms Procetofene; Proctofene
Pharmacologic Class Antilipemic Agent, Fibric Acid

Fenoprofen (fen oh PROE fen)

Genes of Interest
Leukotriene C4 Synthase *on page 302*
U.S. Brand Names Nalfon®
Canadian Brand Names Nalfon®
Synonyms Fenoprofen Calcium
Pharmacologic Class Nonsteroidal Anti-inflammatory Drug (NSAID), Oral

- ♦ **Fenoprofen Calcium** *see* Fenoprofen *on page 107*

Fenoterol (fen oh TER ole)

Genes of Interest
Beta$_2$-Adrenergic Receptor *on page 233*
Canadian Brand Names Berotec®
Synonyms Fenoterol Hydrobromide
Pharmacologic Class Beta$_2$-Adrenergic Agonist

- ♦ **Fenoterol Hydrobromide** *see* Fenoterol *on page 107*

Fentanyl (FEN ta nil)

Genes of Interest
COMT *on page 244*
CYP3A4 *on page 260*
U.S. Brand Names Actiq®; Duragesic®; Sublimaze®
Canadian Brand Names Actiq®; Duragesic®
Synonyms Fentanyl Citrate
Pharmacologic Class Analgesic, Narcotic; General Anesthetic

- ♦ **Fentanyl Citrate** *see* Fentanyl *on page 107*
- ♦ **Feosol® [OTC]** *see* Ferrous Sulfate *on page 108*
- ♦ **Feratab® [OTC]** *see* Ferrous Sulfate *on page 108*

- **Fer-Gen-Sol [OTC]** *see* Ferrous Sulfate *on page 108*
- **Fer-In-Sol® [OTC]** *see* Ferrous Sulfate *on page 108*
- **Fer-Iron® [OTC]** *see* Ferrous Sulfate *on page 108*
- **Ferodan™ (Can)** *see* Ferrous Sulfate *on page 108*

Ferrous Sulfate (FER us SUL fate)

Genes of Interest None known

U.S. Brand Names Feosol® [OTC]; Fer-Gen-Sol [OTC]; Fer-In-Sol® [OTC]; Fer-Iron® [OTC]; Feratab® [OTC]; Slow FE® [OTC]

Canadian Brand Names Apo-Ferrous Sulfate®; Fer-In-Sol®; Ferodan™

Synonyms $FeSO_4$; Iron Sulfate

Pharmacologic Class Iron Salt

- **$FeSO_4$** *see* Ferrous Sulfate *on page 108*

Fexofenadine (feks oh FEN a deen)

Genes of Interest

ATP-Binding Cassette, Sub-Family B, Member 1 *on page 224*

U.S. Brand Names Allegra®

Canadian Brand Names Allegra®

Synonyms Fexofenadine Hydrochloride

Pharmacologic Class Antihistamine, Nonsedating

- **Fexofenadine Hydrochloride** *see* Fexofenadine *on page 108*
- **Fioricet® with Codeine** *see* Butalbital, Acetaminophen, Caffeine, and Codeine *on page 73*
- **Fiorinal®-C 1/2 (Can)** *see* Butalbital, Aspirin, Caffeine, and Codeine *on page 74*
- **Fiorinal®-C 1/4 (Can)** *see* Butalbital, Aspirin, Caffeine, and Codeine *on page 74*
- **Fiorinal® With Codeine** *see* Butalbital, Aspirin, Caffeine, and Codeine *on page 74*
- **First® Testosterone** *see* Testosterone *on page 192*
- **First® Testosterone MC** *see* Testosterone *on page 192*
- **FK506** *see* Tacrolimus *on page 189*
- **Flagyl®** *see* Metronidazole *on page 142*
- **Flagyl ER®** *see* Metronidazole *on page 142*
- **Flagyl® I.V. RTU™** *see* Metronidazole *on page 142*
- **Flamazine® (Can)** *see* Silver Sulfadiazine *on page 184*

Flecainide (fle KAY nide)

Genes of Interest

Cardiac Potassium Ion Channel *on page 241*

Cardiac Sodium Channel *on page 242*

CYP2D6 *on page 254*

U.S. Brand Names Tambocor™
Canadian Brand Names Tambocor™
Synonyms Flecainide Acetate
Pharmacologic Class Antiarrhythmic Agent, Class Ic

♦ **Flecainide Acetate** *see* Flecainide *on page 108*
♦ **Flexeril®** *see* Cyclobenzaprine *on page 87*
♦ **Flexitec (Can)** *see* Cyclobenzaprine *on page 87*
♦ **Flomax®** *see* Tamsulosin *on page 190*
♦ **Flonase®** *see* Fluticasone *on page 111*
♦ **Florazole® ER (Can)** *see* Metronidazole *on page 142*
♦ **Flovent® [DSC]** *see* Fluticasone *on page 111*
♦ **Flovent® Diskus® (Can)** *see* Fluticasone *on page 111*
♦ **Flovent® HFA** *see* Fluticasone *on page 111*
♦ **Floxin®** *see* Ofloxacin *on page 158*
♦ **Floxin Otic Singles** *see* Ofloxacin *on page 158*
♦ **Fluanxol® (Can)** *see* Flupenthixol *on page 110*

Fluconazole (floo KOE na zole)

Genes of Interest None known
U.S. Brand Names Diflucan®
Canadian Brand Names Apo-Fluconazole®; Diflucan®; Fluconazole Omega; Gen-Fluconazole; Novo-Fluconazole
Pharmacologic Class Antifungal Agent, Oral; Antifungal Agent, Parenteral

♦ **Fluconazole Omega (Can)** *see* Fluconazole *on page 109*
♦ **Fluoroplex®** *see* Fluorouracil *on page 109*

Fluorouracil (flure oh YOOR a sil)

Genes of Interest
Dihydropyrimidine Dehydrogenase *on page 270*
Excision Repair Cross-Complementing Rodent Repair Deficiency, Complementation Group 1 *on page 274*
5,10-Methylenetetrahydrofolate Reductase *on page 304*
Thymidylate Synthetase *on page 318*
XRCC1 *on page 331*
U.S. Brand Names Adrucil®; Carac™; Efudex®; Fluoroplex®
Canadian Brand Names Efudex®
Synonyms 5-Fluorouracil; FU; 5-FU
Pharmacologic Class Antineoplastic Agent, Antimetabolite

♦ **5-Fluorouracil** *see* Fluorouracil *on page 109*

Fluoxetine (floo OKS e teen)

Genes of Interest
Cardiac Potassium Ion Channel *on page 241*
Cardiac Sodium Channel *on page 242*
CYP2C8 *on page 248*
CYP2C9 *on page 248*
CYP2D6 *on page 254*
(Continued)

Fluoxetine *(Continued)*

G-Protein $Beta_3$ Subunit *on page 286*
Gs Protein Alpha-Subunit *on page 288*
5-HT_{2A} Receptor *on page 291*
5-HT Transporter *on page 297*
Monoamine Oxidase A *on page 307*

U.S. Brand Names Prozac® Weekly™; Prozac®; Sarafem™

Canadian Brand Names Alti-Fluoxetine; Apo-Fluoxetine®; CO Fluoxetine; FXT; Gen-Fluoxetine; Novo-Fluoxetine; Nu-Fluoxetine; PMS-Fluoxetine; Prozac®; Rhoxal-fluoxetine

Synonyms Fluoxetine Hydrochloride

Pharmacologic Class Antidepressant, Selective Serotonin Reuptake Inhibitor

♦ **Fluoxetine Hydrochloride** *see* Fluoxetine *on page 109*

Flupenthixol (floo pen THIKS ol)

Genes of Interest

$Alpha_1$-Adrenergic Receptor *on page 210*
Cardiac Potassium Ion Channel *on page 241*
Cardiac Sodium Channel *on page 242*
D_2 Receptor *on page 263*

Canadian Brand Names Fluanxol®

Synonyms Flupenthixol Decanoate; Flupenthixol Dihydrochloride

Pharmacologic Class Antipsychotic Agent, Typical

♦ **Flupenthixol Decanoate** *see* Flupenthixol *on page 110*

♦ **Flupenthixol Dihydrochloride** *see* Flupenthixol *on page 110*

Fluphenazine (floo FEN a zeen)

Genes of Interest

$Alpha_1$-Adrenergic Receptor *on page 210*
ATP-Binding Cassette, Sub-Family B, Member 1 *on page 224*
D_2 Receptor *on page 263*

U.S. Brand Names Prolixin Decanoate®; Prolixin® [DSC]

Canadian Brand Names Apo-Fluphenazine Decanoate®; Apo-Fluphenazine®; Modecate®; PMS-Fluphenazine Decanoate

Synonyms Fluphenazine Decanoate

Pharmacologic Class Antipsychotic Agent, Typical, Phenothiazine

♦ **Fluphenazine Decanoate** *see* Fluphenazine *on page 110*

Flurazepam (flure AZ e pam)

Genes of Interest

CYP3A4 *on page 260*

U.S. Brand Names Dalmane®

Canadian Brand Names Apo-Flurazepam®

Synonyms Flurazepam Hydrochloride

Pharmacologic Class Benzodiazepine

♦ **Flurazepam Hydrochloride** *see* Flurazepam *on page 110*

Flurbiprofen (flure BI proe fen)

Genes of Interest

Leukotriene C4 Synthase *on page 302*

U.S. Brand Names Ansaid®; Ocufen®

Canadian Brand Names Alti-Flurbiprofen; Ansaid®; Apo-Flurbiprofen®; Froben-SR®; Froben®; Novo-Flurprofen; Nu-Flurprofen; Ocufen®

Synonyms Flurbiprofen Sodium

Pharmacologic Class Nonsteroidal Anti-inflammatory Drug (NSAID), Ophthalmic; Nonsteroidal Anti-inflammatory Drug (NSAID), Oral

♦ **Flurbiprofen Sodium** *see* Flurbiprofen *on page 111*

Flutamide (FLOO ta mide)

Genes of Interest

CYP1A2 *on page 246*

CYP3A4 *on page 260*

U.S. Brand Names Eulexin®

Canadian Brand Names Apo-Flutamide®; Euflex®; Eulexin®; Novo-Flutamide

Synonyms 4′-Nitro-3′-Trifluoromethylisobutyrantide; NSC-147834; Niftolid; SCH 13521

Pharmacologic Class Antineoplastic Agent, Antiandrogen

Fluticasone (floo TIK a sone)

Genes of Interest None known

U.S. Brand Names Cutivate®; Flonase®; Flovent® HFA; Flovent® [DSC]

Canadian Brand Names Cutivate™; Flonase®; Flovent® Diskus®; Flovent® HFA

Synonyms Fluticasone Propionate

Pharmacologic Class Corticosteroid, Inhalant (Oral); Corticosteroid, Nasal; Corticosteroid, Topical; Corticosteroid, Topical (Medium Potency)

Fluticasone and Salmeterol

(floo TIK a sone & sal ME te role)

Genes of Interest

Beta$_2$-Adrenergic Receptor *on page 233*

U.S. Brand Names Advair Diskus®

Canadian Brand Names Advair Diskus®

Synonyms Salmeterol and Fluticasone

Pharmacologic Class Beta$_2$-Adrenergic Agonist; Corticosteroid, Inhalant (Oral)

♦ **Fluticasone Propionate** *see* Fluticasone *on page 111*

Fluvastatin (FLOO va sta tin)

Genes of Interest

Angiotensin-Converting Enzyme *on page 214*

Apolipoprotein E *on page 220*

(Continued)

Fluvastatin *(Continued)*

Beta-Fibrinogen *on page 236*
Cholesteryl Ester Transfer Protein *on page 243*
Glycoprotein IIIa Receptor *on page 285*
Low-Density Lipoprotein Receptor *on page 304*
Stromelysin-1 *on page 316*

U.S. Brand Names Lescol® XL; Lescol®

Canadian Brand Names Lescol®

Pharmacologic Class Antilipemic Agent, HMG-CoA Reductase Inhibitor

Fluvoxamine (floo VOKS a meen)

Genes of Interest

CYP1A2 *on page 246*
D_2 Receptor *on page 263*
D_4 Receptor *on page 268*
G-Protein $Beta_3$ Subunit *on page 286*
Gs Protein Alpha-Subunit *on page 288*
5-HT_{2A} Receptor *on page 291*
5-HT Transporter *on page 297*
Monoamine Oxidase A *on page 307*
Tryptophan Hydroxylase *on page 321*

Canadian Brand Names Alti-Fluvoxamine; Apo-Fluvoxamine®; Luvox®; Novo-Fluvoxamine; Nu-Fluvoxamine; PMS-Fluvoxamine; Rhoxal-fluvoxamine

Synonyms Luvox

Pharmacologic Class Antidepressant, Selective Serotonin Reuptake Inhibitor

- **Fluxid™** *see* Famotidine *on page 106*
- **Foradil® (Can)** *see* Formoterol *on page 112*
- **Foradil® Aerolizer™** *see* Formoterol *on page 112*

Formoterol (for MOH te rol)

Genes of Interest

$Beta_2$-Adrenergic Receptor *on page 233*

U.S. Brand Names Foradil® Aerolizer™

Canadian Brand Names Foradil®; Oxeze® Turbuhaler®

Synonyms Formoterol Fumarate

Pharmacologic Class $Beta_2$-Adrenergic Agonist

- **Formoterol Fumarate** *see* Formoterol *on page 112*
- **Fortamet™** *see* Metformin *on page 139*
- **Fortovase® [DSC]** *see* Saquinavir *on page 182*
- **Fosamax®** *see* Alendronate *on page 55*

Foscarnet (fos KAR net)

Genes of Interest

Cardiac Potassium Ion Channel *on page 241*
Cardiac Sodium Channel *on page 242*

U.S. Brand Names Foscavir®

Canadian Brand Names Foscavir®

Synonyms PFA; Phosphonoformate; Phosphonoformic Acid

Pharmacologic Class Antiviral Agent

- **Foscavir®** *see* Foscarnet *on page 112*

Fosinopril (foe SIN oh pril)

Genes of Interest

Aldosterone Synthase *on page 208*
Angiotensin II Type 1 Receptor *on page 213*
Angiotensin-Converting Enzyme *on page 214*
Angiotensinogen *on page 219*
Bradykinin B_2-Receptor *on page 237*

U.S. Brand Names Monopril®

Canadian Brand Names Monopril®; Novo-Fosinopril

Synonyms Fosinopril Sodium

Pharmacologic Class Angiotensin-Converting Enzyme (ACE) Inhibitor

- **Fosinopril Sodium** *see* Fosinopril *on page 113*

Fosphenytoin (FOS fen i toyn)

Genes of Interest

CYP2C8 *on page 248*
CYP2C9 *on page 248*
CYP2C19 *on page 251*

U.S. Brand Names Cerebyx®

Canadian Brand Names Cerebyx®

Synonyms Fosphenytoin Sodium

Pharmacologic Class Anticonvulsant, Hydantoin

- **Fosphenytoin Sodium** *see* Fosphenytoin *on page 113*
- **Frisium® (Can)** *see* Clobazam *on page 83*
- **Froben® (Can)** *see* Flurbiprofen *on page 111*
- **Froben-SR® (Can)** *see* Flurbiprofen *on page 111*
- **Frusemide** *see* Furosemide *on page 114*
- **FTP-Domperidone Maleate (Can)** *see* Domperidone *on page 94*
- **FU** *see* Fluorouracil *on page 109*
- **5-FU** *see* Fluorouracil *on page 109*
- **Furadantin®** *see* Nitrofurantoin *on page 151*

Furazolidone (fyoor a ZOE li done)

Genes of Interest

Glucose-6-Phosphate Dehydrogenase *on page 281*

(Continued)

Furazolidone *(Continued)*

Canadian Brand Names Furoxone®

Synonyms Furoxone

Pharmacologic Class Antiprotozoal

Furosemide (fyoor OH se mide)

Genes of Interest

Alpha-Adducin *on page 212*

U.S. Brand Names Lasix®

Canadian Brand Names Apo-Furosemide®; Lasix® Special; Lasix®; Novo-Semide

Synonyms Frusemide

Pharmacologic Class Diuretic, Loop

- **Furoxone® (Can)** *see* Furazolidone *on page 113*
- **FXT (Can)** *see* Fluoxetine *on page 109*

Gabapentin (GA ba pen tin)

Genes of Interest None known

U.S. Brand Names Neurontin®

Canadian Brand Names Apo-Gabapentin®; Gen-Gabapentin; Neurontin®; Novo-Gabapentin; Nu-Gabapentin; PMS-Gabapentin

Pharmacologic Class Anticonvulsant, Miscellaneous

- **Gabitril®** *see* Tiagabine *on page 194*

Galantamine (ga LAN ta meen)

Genes of Interest

Apolipoprotein E *on page 220*

U.S. Brand Names Razadyne™ ER; Razadyne™; Reminyl®

Canadian Brand Names Reminyl®

Synonyms Galantamine Hydrobromide

Pharmacologic Class Acetylcholinesterase Inhibitor (Central)

- **Galantamine Hydrobromide** *see* Galantamine *on page 114*
- **Gantrisin®** *see* SulfiSOXAZOLE *on page 188*

Gatifloxacin (gat i FLOKS a sin)

Genes of Interest

Cardiac Potassium Ion Channel *on page 241*

Cardiac Sodium Channel *on page 242*

U.S. Brand Names Tequin®; Zymar™

Canadian Brand Names Tequin®; Zymar™

Pharmacologic Class Antibiotic, Ophthalmic; Antibiotic, Quinolone

Gefitinib (ge FI tye nib)

Genes of Interest

Epidermal Growth Factor Receptor *on page 271*

U.S. Brand Names IRESSA®
Synonyms NSC-715055; ZD1839
Pharmacologic Class Antineoplastic Agent, Tyrosine Kinase Inhibitor

Gemcitabine (jem SITE a been)

Genes of Interest
Excision Repair Cross-Complementing Rodent Repair Deficiency, Complementation Group 1 *on page 274*
U.S. Brand Names Gemzar®
Canadian Brand Names Gemzar®
Synonyms Gemcitabine Hydrochloride
Pharmacologic Class Antineoplastic Agent, Antimetabolite (Pyrimidine Antagonist)

- **Gemcitabine Hydrochloride** *see* Gemcitabine *on page 115*

Gemfibrozil (jem FI broe zil)

Genes of Interest
Angiotensin-Converting Enzyme *on page 214*
Cholesteryl Ester Transfer Protein *on page 243*
U.S. Brand Names Lopid®
Canadian Brand Names Apo-Gemfibrozil®; Gen-Gemfibrozil; Lopid®; Novo-Gemfibrozil; Nu-Gemfibrozil; PMS-Gemfibrozil
Synonyms CI-719
Pharmacologic Class Antilipemic Agent, Fibric Acid

- **Gemzar®** *see* Gemcitabine *on page 115*
- **Gen-Acebutolol (Can)** *see* Acebutolol *on page 52*
- **Gen-Acyclovir (Can)** *see* Acyclovir *on page 54*
- **Gen-Alprazolam (Can)** *see* Alprazolam *on page 56*
- **Gen-Amiodarone (Can)** *see* Amiodarone *on page 57*
- **Gen-Amoxicillin (Can)** *see* Amoxicillin *on page 59*
- **Gen-Atenolol (Can)** *see* Atenolol *on page 66*
- **Gen-Azathioprine (Can)** *see* Azathioprine *on page 67*
- **Gen-Bromazepam (Can)** *see* Bromazepam *on page 72*
- **Gen-Budesonide AQ (Can)** *see* Budesonide *on page 72*
- **Gen-Buspirone (Can)** *see* BusPIRone *on page 73*
- **Gen-Captopril (Can)** *see* Captopril *on page 75*
- **Gen-Carbamazepine CR (Can)** *see* Carbamazepine *on page 75*
- **Gen-Cimetidine (Can)** *see* Cimetidine *on page 80*
- **Gen-Ciprofloxacin (Can)** *see* Ciprofloxacin *on page 81*
- **Gen-Citalopram (Can)** *see* Citalopram *on page 81*
- **Gen-Clomipramine (Can)** *see* ClomiPRAMINE *on page 83*
- **Gen-Clonazepam (Can)** *see* Clonazepam *on page 83*
- **Gen-Clozapine (Can)** *see* Clozapine *on page 84*
- **Gen-Cyclobenzaprine (Can)** *see* Cyclobenzaprine *on page 87*
- **Gen-Diltiazem (Can)** *see* Diltiazem *on page 93*
- **Gen-Diltiazem CD (Can)** *see* Diltiazem *on page 93*

- **Gen-Divalproex (Can)** *see* Valproic Acid and Derivatives *on page 201*
- **Gen-Doxazosin (Can)** *see* Doxazosin *on page 95*
- **Genesec® [OTC]** *see* Acetaminophen and Phenyltoloxamine *on page 53*
- **Gen-Famotidine (Can)** *see* Famotidine *on page 106*
- **Gen-Fenofibrate Micro (Can)** *see* Fenofibrate *on page 107*
- **Gen-Fluconazole (Can)** *see* Fluconazole *on page 109*
- **Gen-Fluoxetine (Can)** *see* Fluoxetine *on page 109*
- **Gen-Gabapentin (Can)** *see* Gabapentin *on page 114*
- **Gen-Gemfibrozil (Can)** *see* Gemfibrozil *on page 115*
- **Gen-Glybe (Can)** *see* GlyBURIDE *on page 117*
- **Gengraf®** *see* CycloSPORINE *on page 87*
- **Gen-Hydroxychloroquine (Can)** *see* Hydroxychloroquine *on page 122*
- **Gen-Indapamide (Can)** *see* Indapamide *on page 124*
- **Gen-Lovastatin (Can)** *see* Lovastatin *on page 135*
- **Gen-Medroxy (Can)** *see* MedroxyPROGESTERone *on page 137*
- **Gen-Meloxicam (Can)** *see* Meloxicam *on page 137*
- **Gen-Metformin (Can)** *see* Metformin *on page 139*
- **Gen-Minocycline (Can)** *see* Minocycline *on page 144*
- **Gen-Mirtazapine (Can)** *see* Mirtazapine *on page 144*
- **Gen-Nabumetone (Can)** *see* Nabumetone *on page 147*
- **Gen-Naproxen EC (Can)** *see* Naproxen *on page 148*
- **Gen-Nitro (Can)** *see* Nitroglycerin *on page 151*
- **Gen-Nortriptyline (Can)** *see* Nortriptyline *on page 152*
- **Gen-Paroxetine (Can)** *see* Paroxetine *on page 162*
- **Gen-Piroxicam (Can)** *see* Piroxicam *on page 166*
- **Genpril® [OTC]** *see* Ibuprofen *on page 123*
- **Gen-Ranidine (Can)** *see* Ranitidine *on page 176*
- **Gen-Salbutamol (Can)** *see* Albuterol *on page 54*
- **Gen-Selegiline (Can)** *see* Selegiline *on page 183*
- **Gen-Sertraline (Can)** *see* Sertraline *on page 183*
- **Gen-Simvastatin (Can)** *see* Simvastatin *on page 184*
- **Gen-Sotalol (Can)** *see* Sotalol *on page 185*
- **Gen-Tamoxifen (Can)** *see* Tamoxifen *on page 190*
- **Gen-Temazepam (Can)** *see* Temazepam *on page 191*
- **Gen-Ticlopidine (Can)** *see* Ticlopidine *on page 194*
- **Gen-Timolol (Can)** *see* Timolol *on page 195*
- **Gen-Trazodone (Can)** *see* Trazodone *on page 197*
- **Gen-Triazolam (Can)** *see* Triazolam *on page 198*
- **Gen-Verapamil (Can)** *see* Verapamil *on page 201*
- **Gen-Verapamil SR (Can)** *see* Verapamil *on page 201*
- **Gen-Warfarin (Can)** *see* Warfarin *on page 203*
- **Gen-Zopiclone (Can)** *see* Zopiclone *on page 206*
- **Geodon®** *see* Ziprasidone *on page 205*

- **GI87084B** *see* Remifentanil *on page 177*
- **Glargine, Insulin** *see* Insulin Preparations *on page 125*
- **Gleevec®** *see* Imatinib *on page 123*
- **Gliadel®** *see* Carmustine *on page 76*
- **Glibenclamide** *see* GlyBURIDE *on page 117*

Glimepiride (GLYE me pye ride)

Genes of Interest
CYP2C8 *on page 248*
CYP2C9 *on page 248*
U.S. Brand Names Amaryl®
Canadian Brand Names Amaryl®
Pharmacologic Class Antidiabetic Agent, Sulfonylurea

GlipiZIDE (GLIP i zide)

Genes of Interest
CYP2C8 *on page 248*
CYP2C9 *on page 248*
U.S. Brand Names Glucotrol® XL; Glucotrol®
Synonyms Glydiazinamide
Pharmacologic Class Antidiabetic Agent, Sulfonylurea

- **Glivec** *see* Imatinib *on page 123*
- **GlucoNorm® (Can)** *see* Repaglinide *on page 177*
- **Glucophage®** *see* Metformin *on page 139*
- **Glucophage® XR** *see* Metformin *on page 139*
- **Glucotrol®** *see* GlipiZIDE *on page 117*
- **Glucotrol® XL** *see* GlipiZIDE *on page 117*
- **Glucovance®** *see* Glyburide and Metformin *on page 117*
- **Glulisine, Insulin** *see* Insulin Preparations *on page 125*
- **Glybenclamide** *see* GlyBURIDE *on page 117*
- **Glybenzcyclamide** *see* GlyBURIDE *on page 117*

GlyBURIDE (GLYE byoor ide)

Genes of Interest None known
U.S. Brand Names Diaβeta®; Glynase® PresTab®; Micronase®
Canadian Brand Names Albert® Glyburide; Apo-Glyburide®; Diaβeta®; Euglucon®; Gen-Glybe; Novo-Glyburide; Nu-Glyburide; PMS-Glyburide; ratio-Glyburide
Synonyms Diabeta; Glibenclamide; Glybenclamide; Glybenzcyclamide
Pharmacologic Class Antidiabetic Agent, Sulfonylurea

Glyburide and Metformin (GLYE byoor ide & met FOR min)

Genes of Interest None known
U.S. Brand Names Glucovance®
Synonyms Glyburide and Metformin Hydrochloride; Metformin and Glyburide
Pharmacologic Class Antidiabetic Agent, Biguanide; Antidiabetic Agent, Sulfonylurea

- **Glyburide and Metformin Hydrochloride** *see* Glyburide and Metformin *on page 117*
- **Glyceryl Trinitrate** *see* Nitroglycerin *on page 151*
- **Glycon (Can)** *see* Metformin *on page 139*
- **Glydiazinamide** *see* GlipiZIDE *on page 117*
- **Glynase® PresTab®** *see* GlyBURIDE *on page 117*

Guanabenz (GWAHN a benz)

Genes of Interest

CYP1A2 *on page 246*

Canadian Brand Names Wytensin®

Synonyms Guanabenz Acetate

Pharmacologic Class Alpha$_2$-Adrenergic Agonist

- **Guanabenz Acetate** *see* Guanabenz *on page 118*
- **Gynodiol®** *see* Estradiol *on page 101*
- **Halcion®** *see* Triazolam *on page 198*
- **Haldol®** *see* Haloperidol *on page 118*
- **Haldol® Decanoate** *see* Haloperidol *on page 118*
- **Halfprin® [OTC]** *see* Aspirin *on page 65*

Halofantrine (ha loe FAN trin)

Genes of Interest

Cardiac Potassium Ion Channel *on page 241*
Cardiac Sodium Channel *on page 242*
CYP3A4 *on page 260*

Synonyms Halofantrine Hydrochloride

Pharmacologic Class Antimalarial Agent

- **Halofantrine Hydrochloride** *see* Halofantrine *on page 118*

Haloperidol (ha loe PER i dole)

Genes of Interest

Alpha$_1$-Adrenergic Receptor *on page 210*
ATP-Binding Cassette, Sub-Family B, Member 1 *on page 224*
Cardiac Potassium Ion Channel *on page 241*
Cardiac Sodium Channel *on page 242*
CYP2D6 *on page 254*
CYP3A4 *on page 260*
D_2 Receptor *on page 263*
D_3 Receptor *on page 266*
D_4 Receptor *on page 268*

U.S. Brand Names Haldol® Decanoate; Haldol®

Canadian Brand Names Apo-Haloperidol LA®; Apo-Haloperidol®; Haloperidol Long Acting; Haloperidol-LA Omega; Novo-Peridol; PMS-Haloperidol LA; Peridol

Synonyms Haloperidol Decanoate; Haloperidol Lactate

Pharmacologic Class Antipsychotic Agent, Typical

- **Haloperidol Decanoate** *see* Haloperidol *on page 118*
- **Haloperidol Lactate** *see* Haloperidol *on page 118*

- **Haloperidol-LA Omega (Can)** *see* Haloperidol *on page 118*
- **Haloperidol Long Acting (Can)** *see* Haloperidol *on page 118*
- **HCTZ (error-prone abbreviation)** *see* Hydrochlorothiazide *on page 120*
- **Hemorrhoidal HC** *see* Hydrocortisone *on page 121*
- **Hemril®-30** *see* Hydrocortisone *on page 121*
- **Hepalean® (Can)** *see* Heparin *on page 119*
- **Hepalean® Leo (Can)** *see* Heparin *on page 119*
- **Hepalean®-LOK (Can)** *see* Heparin *on page 119*

Heparin (HEP a rin)

Genes of Interest

Platelet Fc Gamma Receptor *on page 312*

U.S. Brand Names Hep-Lock®; HepFlush®-10

Canadian Brand Names Hepalean® Leo; Hepalean®-LOK; Hepalean®

Synonyms Heparin Calcium; Heparin Lock Flush; Heparin Sodium

Pharmacologic Class Anticoagulant

- **Heparin Calcium** *see* Heparin *on page 119*
- **Heparin Lock Flush** *see* Heparin *on page 119*
- **Heparin Sodium** *see* Heparin *on page 119*
- **HepFlush®-10** *see* Heparin *on page 119*
- **Hep-Lock®** *see* Heparin *on page 119*
- **Humalog®** *see* Insulin Preparations *on page 125*
- **Humalog® Mix 25™ (Can)** *see* Insulin Preparations *on page 125*
- **Humalog® Mix 75/25™** *see* Insulin Preparations *on page 125*
- **Humulin® (Can)** *see* Insulin Preparations *on page 125*
- **Humulin® L [DSC]** *see* Insulin Preparations *on page 125*
- **Humulin® 50/50** *see* Insulin Preparations *on page 125*
- **Humulin® 70/30** *see* Insulin Preparations *on page 125*
- **Humulin® N** *see* Insulin Preparations *on page 125*
- **Humulin® R** *see* Insulin Preparations *on page 125*
- **Humulin® R (Concentrated) U-500** *see* Insulin Preparations *on page 125*
- **Humulin® U [DSC]** *see* Insulin Preparations *on page 125*
- **hycet™** *see* Hydrocodone and Acetaminophen *on page 120*
- **Hycort™ (Can)** *see* Hydrocortisone *on page 121*
- **Hydergine® (Can)** *see* Ergoloid Mesylates *on page 98*
- **Hyderm (Can)** *see* Hydrocortisone *on page 121*

HydrALAZINE (hye DRAL a zeen)

Genes of Interest

N-Acetyltransferase 2 Enzyme *on page 308*

Canadian Brand Names Apo-Hydralazine®; Apresoline®; Novo-Hylazin; Nu-Hydral

(Continued)

HydrALAZINE *(Continued)*

Synonyms Apresoline [DSC]; Hydralazine Hydrochloride

Pharmacologic Class Vasodilator

♦ **Hydralazine Hydrochloride** *see* HydrALAZINE *on page 119*

Hydrochlorothiazide (hye droe klor oh THYE a zide)

Genes of Interest

Alpha-Adducin *on page 212*

G-Protein $Beta_3$ Subunit *on page 286*

U.S. Brand Names Microzide™

Canadian Brand Names Apo-Hydro®; Novo-Hydrazide; pms-Hydrochlorothiazide

Synonyms HCTZ (error-prone abbreviation)

Pharmacologic Class Diuretic, Thiazide

♦ **Hydrochlorothiazide and Lisinopril** *see* Lisinopril and Hydrochlorothiazide *on page 132*

♦ **Hydrochlorothiazide and Losartan** *see* Losartan and Hydrochlorothiazide *on page 134*

Hydrocodone and Acetaminophen

(hye droe KOE done & a seet a MIN oh fen)

Genes of Interest

COMT *on page 244*

U.S. Brand Names Anexsia®; Bancap HC®; Ceta-Plus®; Co-Gesic®; Lorcet® 10/650; Lorcet® Plus; Lorcet®-HD [DSC]; Lortab®; Margesic® H; Maxidone™; Norco®; Stagesic®; Vicodin® ES; Vicodin® HP; Vicodin®; Zydone®; hycet™

Synonyms Acetaminophen and Hydrocodone

Pharmacologic Class Analgesic Combination (Narcotic)

Hydrocodone and Aspirin

(hye droe KOE done & AS pir in)

Genes of Interest

COMT *on page 244*

Glycoprotein IIIa Receptor *on page 285*

Leukotriene C4 Synthase *on page 302*

U.S. Brand Names Damason-P®

Synonyms Aspirin and Hydrocodone

Pharmacologic Class Analgesic Combination (Narcotic)

Hydrocodone and Ibuprofen

(hye droe KOE done & eye byoo PROE fen)

Genes of Interest

COMT *on page 244*

Leukotriene C4 Synthase *on page 302*

U.S. Brand Names Reprexain™; Vicoprofen®

Canadian Brand Names Vicoprofen®

Synonyms Ibuprofen and Hydrocodone

Pharmacologic Class Analgesic, Narcotic; Nonsteroidal Anti-inflammatory Drug (NSAID), Oral

Hydrocortisone (hye droe KOR ti sone)

Genes of Interest

ATP-Binding Cassette, Sub-Family B, Member 1 *on page 224*

U.S. Brand Names Anucort-HC®; Anusol-HC®; Anusol® HC-1 [OTC]; Aquanil™ HC [OTC]; Beta-HC®; Caldecort® [OTC]; Cetacort®; Colocort®; Cortaid® Intensive Therapy [OTC]; Cortaid® Maximum Strength [OTC]; Cortaid® Sensitive Skin [OTC]; Cortef®; Corticool® [OTC]; Cortifoam®; Cortizone® 10 Quick Shot [OTC]; Cortizone®-10 Maximum Strength [OTC]; Cortizone®-10 Plus Maximum Strength [OTC]; Dermarest Dricort® [OTC]; Dermtex® HC [OTC]; EarSol® HC; Hemril®-30; HydroZone Plus [OTC]; Hytone®; IvySoothe® [OTC]; Locoid Lipocream®; Locoid®; Nupercainal® Hydrocortisone Cream [OTC]; Nutracort®; Pandel®; Post Peel Healing Balm [OTC]; Preparation H® Hydrocortisone [OTC]; Procto-Kit™; Procto-Pak™; ProctoCream® HC; Proctocort®; Proctosert; Proctosol-HC®; Proctozone-HC™; Sarnol®-HC [OTC]; Solu-Cortef®; Summer's Eve® SpecialCare™ Medicated Anti-Itch Cream [OTC]; Texacort®; Tucks® Anti-Itch [OTC]; Westcort®

Canadian Brand Names Aquacort®; Cortamed®; Cortef®; Cortenema®; Cortifoam™; Emo-Cort®; Hycort™; Hyderm; HydroVal®; Locoid®; Prevex® HC; Sarna® HC; Solu-Cortef®; Westcort®

Synonyms A-hydroCort; Compound F; Cortisol; Hemorrhoidal HC; Hydrocortisone Acetate; Hydrocortisone Butyrate; Hydrocortisone Probutate; Hydrocortisone Sodium Succinate; Hydrocortisone Valerate

Pharmacologic Class Corticosteroid, Rectal; Corticosteroid, Systemic; Corticosteroid, Topical

- **Hydrocortisone Acetate** *see* Hydrocortisone *on page 121*
- **Hydrocortisone Butyrate** *see* Hydrocortisone *on page 121*
- **Hydrocortisone Probutate** *see* Hydrocortisone *on page 121*
- **Hydrocortisone Sodium Succinate** *see* Hydrocortisone *on page 121*
- **Hydrocortisone Valerate** *see* Hydrocortisone *on page 121*

Hydroflumethiazide (hye droe floo meth EYE a zide)

Genes of Interest

Alpha-Adducin *on page 212*

G-Protein Beta$_3$ Subunit *on page 286*

U.S. Brand Names Diucardin® [DSC]; Saluron® [DSC]

Canadian Brand Names Diucardin®; Saluron®

Pharmacologic Class Diuretic, Thiazide

- **Hydromorph Contin® (Can)** *see* Hydromorphone *on page 122*
- **Hydromorph-IR® (Can)** *see* Hydromorphone *on page 122*

Hydromorphone (hye droe MOR fone)

Genes of Interest

COMT *on page 244*

U.S. Brand Names Dilaudid-HP®; Dilaudid®; Palladone™

Canadian Brand Names Dilaudid-HP-Plus®; Dilaudid-HP®; Dilaudid-XP®; Dilaudid® Sterile Powder; Dilaudid®; Hydromorph Contin®; Hydromorph-IR®; Hydromorphone HP; PMS-Hydromorphone

Synonyms Dihydromorphinone; Hydromorphone Hydrochloride

Pharmacologic Class Analgesic, Narcotic

- **Hydromorphone HP (Can)** *see* Hydromorphone *on page 122*
- **Hydromorphone Hydrochloride** *see* Hydromorphone *on page 122*
- **HydroVal® (Can)** *see* Hydrocortisone *on page 121*

Hydroxychloroquine (hye droks ee KLOR oh kwin)

Genes of Interest

Glucose-6-Phosphate Dehydrogenase *on page 281*

U.S. Brand Names Plaquenil®

Canadian Brand Names Apo-Hydroxyquine®; Gen-Hydroxychloroquine; Plaquenil®

Synonyms Hydroxychloroquine Sulfate

Pharmacologic Class Aminoquinoline (Antimalarial)

- **Hydroxychloroquine Sulfate** *see* Hydroxychloroquine *on page 122*
- **Hydroxydaunomycin Hydrochloride** *see* DOXOrubicin *on page 95*
- **Hydroxyldaunorubicin Hydrochloride** *see* DOXOrubicin *on page 95*

HydrOXYzine (hye DROKS i zeen)

Genes of Interest

ATP-Binding Cassette, Sub-Family B, Member 1 *on page 224*

U.S. Brand Names Atarax®; Vistaril®

Canadian Brand Names Apo-Hydroxyzine®; Atarax®; Novo-Hydroxyzin; PMS-Hydroxyzine; Vistaril®

Synonyms Hydroxyzine Hydrochloride; Hydroxyzine Pamoate

Pharmacologic Class Antiemetic; Antihistamine

- **Hydroxyzine Hydrochloride** *see* HydrOXYzine *on page 122*
- **Hydroxyzine Pamoate** *see* HydrOXYzine *on page 122*
- **HydroZone Plus [OTC]** *see* Hydrocortisone *on page 121*
- **Hygroton** *see* Chlorthalidone *on page 79*
- **Hytone®** *see* Hydrocortisone *on page 121*
- **Hytrin®** *see* Terazosin *on page 191*
- **Hyzaar®** *see* Losartan and Hydrochlorothiazide *on page 134*
- **Hyzaar® DS (Can)** *see* Losartan and Hydrochlorothiazide *on page 134*
- **Ibu-200 [OTC]** *see* Ibuprofen *on page 123*

Ibuprofen (eye byoo PROE fen)

Genes of Interest

Leukotriene C4 Synthase *on page 302*

U.S. Brand Names Advil® Children's [OTC]; Advil® Infants' [OTC]; Advil® Junior [OTC]; Advil® Migraine [OTC]; Advil® [OTC]; ElixSure™ IB [OTC] ; Genpril® [OTC]; I-Prin [OTC]; Ibu-200 [OTC]; Menadol® [OTC] [DSC]; Midol® Cramp and Body Aches [OTC]; Motrin® Children's [OTC]; Motrin® IB [OTC]; Motrin® Infants' [OTC]; Motrin® Junior Strength [OTC]; Motrin®; Proprinal [OTC]; Ultraprin [OTC]

Canadian Brand Names Advil®; Apo-Ibuprofen®; Motrin® (Children's); Motrin® IB; Novo-Profen; Nu-Ibuprofen

Synonyms *p*-Isobutylhydratropic Acid

Pharmacologic Class Nonsteroidal Anti-inflammatory Drug (NSAID), Oral

- **Ibuprofen and Hydrocodone** *see* Hydrocodone and Ibuprofen *on page 120*

Ibutilide (i BYOO ti lide)

Genes of Interest

Cardiac Potassium Ion Channel *on page 241*
Cardiac Sodium Channel *on page 242*

U.S. Brand Names Corvert®

Synonyms Ibutilide Fumarate

Pharmacologic Class Antiarrhythmic Agent, Class III

- **Ibutilide Fumarate** *see* Ibutilide *on page 123*
- **ICI-204,219** *see* Zafirlukast *on page 204*
- **ICI-46474** *see* Tamoxifen *on page 190*
- **ICI-D1694** *see* Raltitrexed *on page 175*
- **ICRF-187** *see* Dexrazoxane *on page 90*
- **Ifex®** *see* Ifosfamide *on page 123*

Ifosfamide (eye FOSS fa mide)

Genes of Interest

CYP2C8 *on page 248*
CYP2C9 *on page 248*
CYP2C19 *on page 251*
CYP3A4 *on page 260*

U.S. Brand Names Ifex®

Canadian Brand Names Ifex®

Synonyms Isophosphamide; NSC-109724; Z4942

Pharmacologic Class Antineoplastic Agent, Alkylating Agent; Antineoplastic Agent, Alkylating Agent (Nitrogen Mustard)

- **Iletin® II Pork (Can)** *see* Insulin Preparations *on page 125*

Imatinib (eye MAT eh nib)

Genes of Interest

CYP3A4 *on page 260*

(Continued)

Imatinib *(Continued)*

U.S. Brand Names Gleevec®

Canadian Brand Names Gleevec®

Synonyms CGP 57148B; Glivec; Imatinib Mesylate; STI571

Pharmacologic Class Antineoplastic Agent, Tyrosine Kinase Inhibitor

- **Imatinib Mesylate** *see* Imatinib *on page 123*
- **Imidazole Carboxamide** *see* Dacarbazine *on page 87*
- **Imidazole Carboxamide Dimethyltriazene** *see* Dacarbazine *on page 87*

Imipramine (im IP ra meen)

Genes of Interest

Alpha$_1$-Adrenergic Receptor *on page 210*
ATP-Binding Cassette, Sub-Family B, Member 1 *on page 224*
Cardiac Potassium Ion Channel *on page 241*
Cardiac Sodium Channel *on page 242*
CYP2C19 *on page 251*
G-Protein Beta$_3$ Subunit *on page 286*
Gs Protein Alpha-Subunit *on page 288*

U.S. Brand Names Tofranil-PM®; Tofranil®

Canadian Brand Names Apo-Imipramine®; Novo-Pramine; Tofranil®

Synonyms Imipramine Hydrochloride; Imipramine Pamoate

Pharmacologic Class Antidepressant, Tricyclic (Tertiary Amine)

- **Imipramine Hydrochloride** *see* Imipramine *on page 124*
- **Imipramine Pamoate** *see* Imipramine *on page 124*
- **Imitrex®** *see* Sumatriptan *on page 189*
- **Imitrex® DF (Can)** *see* Sumatriptan *on page 189*
- **Imovane® (Can)** *see* Zopiclone *on page 206*
- **Imuran®** *see* Azathioprine *on page 67*
- **Inapsine®** *see* Droperidol *on page 96*

Indapamide (in DAP a mide)

Genes of Interest

Alpha-Adducin *on page 212*
Cardiac Potassium Ion Channel *on page 241*
Cardiac Sodium Channel *on page 242*
G-Protein Beta$_3$ Subunit *on page 286*

U.S. Brand Names Lozol®

Canadian Brand Names Apo-Indapamide®; Gen-Indapamide; Lozide®; Lozol®; Novo-Indapamide; Nu-Indapamide; PMS-Indapamide

Pharmacologic Class Diuretic, Thiazide-Related

- **Inderal®** *see* Propranolol *on page 173*
- **Inderal® LA** *see* Propranolol *on page 173*
- **Indocid® P.D.A. (Can)** *see* Indomethacin *on page 125*
- **Indocin®** *see* Indomethacin *on page 125*
- **Indocin® I.V.** *see* Indomethacin *on page 125*

♦ **Indocin® SR** *see* Indomethacin *on page 125*
♦ **Indo-Lemmon (Can)** *see* Indomethacin *on page 125*
♦ **Indometacin** *see* Indomethacin *on page 125*

Indomethacin (in doe METH a sin)

Genes of Interest

Leukotriene C4 Synthase *on page 302*

U.S. Brand Names Indocin® I.V.; Indocin® SR; Indocin®

Canadian Brand Names Apo-Indomethacin®; Indo-Lemmon; Indocid® P.D.A.; Indocin®; Indotec; Novo-Methacin; Nu-Indo; Rhodacine®

Synonyms Indometacin; Indomethacin Sodium Trihydrate

Pharmacologic Class Nonsteroidal Anti-inflammatory Drug (NSAID), Oral; Nonsteroidal Anti-inflammatory Drug (NSAID), Parenteral

♦ **Indomethacin Sodium Trihydrate** *see* Indomethacin *on page 125*
♦ **Indotec (Can)** *see* Indomethacin *on page 125*
♦ **Infumorph®** *see* Morphine Sulfate *on page 146*
♦ **INH** *see* Isoniazid *on page 126*
♦ **Inhibace® (Can)** *see* Cilazapril *on page 80*
♦ **InnoPran XL™** *see* Propranolol *on page 173*
♦ **Inspra™** *see* Eplerenone *on page 98*

Insulin Preparations (IN su lin prep a RAY shuns)

Genes of Interest None known

U.S. Brand Names Apidra™; Humalog® Mix 75/25™; Humalog®; Humulin® 50/50; Humulin® 70/30; Humulin® L [DSC]; Humulin® N; Humulin® R (Concentrated) U-500; Humulin® R; Humulin® U [DSC]; Lantus®; NPH Iletin® II [DSC]; NovoLog® Mix 70/30; NovoLog®; Novolin® 70/30; Novolin® N; Novolin® R; Regular Iletin® II [DSC]

Canadian Brand Names Humalog® Mix 25™; Humalog®; Humulin®; Iletin® II Pork; Lantus®; NovoRapid; Novolin® ge

Synonyms Aspart, Insulin; Glargine, Insulin; Glulisine, Insulin; Lente, Insulin; Lispro, Insulin; NPH, Insulin; Regular, Insulin

Pharmacologic Class Antidiabetic Agent, Insulin; Antidote

♦ **Integrilin®** *see* Eptifibatide *on page 98*
♦ **Intrifiban** *see* Eptifibatide *on page 98*
♦ **Invirase®** *see* Saquinavir *on page 182*

Ipratropium and Albuterol
(i pra TROE pee um & al BYOO ter ole)

Genes of Interest

$Beta_2$-Adrenergic Receptor *on page 233*

Glycoprotein IIIa Receptor *on page 285*

Leukotriene C4 Synthase *on page 302*

(Continued)

Ipratropium and Albuterol *(Continued)*

U.S. Brand Names Combivent®; DuoNeb™
Canadian Brand Names Combivent®
Synonyms Albuterol and Ipratropium
Pharmacologic Class Bronchodilator

- **I-Prin [OTC]** *see* Ibuprofen *on page 123*
- **Iproveratril Hydrochloride** *see* Verapamil *on page 201*
- **Iquix®** *see* Levofloxacin *on page 130*

Irbesartan (ir be SAR tan)

Genes of Interest

Adipocyte-Derived Leucine Aminopeptidase *on page 208*
Aldosterone Synthase *on page 208*
Angiotensin II Type 1 Receptor *on page 213*
Angiotensin-Converting Enzyme *on page 214*
Angiotensinogen *on page 219*
Bradykinin B_2-Receptor *on page 237*
CYP2C9 *on page 248*

U.S. Brand Names Avapro®
Canadian Brand Names Avapro®
Pharmacologic Class Angiotensin II Receptor Blocker

- **IRESSA®** *see* Gefitinib *on page 114*

Irinotecan (eye rye no TEE kan)

Genes of Interest

CYP3A4 *on page 260*
UDP-Glucuronosyltransferase 1 Family, Polypeptide A1 *on page 322*

U.S. Brand Names Camptosar®
Canadian Brand Names Camptosar®
Synonyms CPT-11; Camptothecin-11; NSC-616348
Pharmacologic Class Antineoplastic Agent, Natural Source (Plant) Derivative

- **Iron Sulfate** *see* Ferrous Sulfate *on page 108*
- **ISD** *see* Isosorbide Dinitrate *on page 127*
- **ISDN** *see* Isosorbide Dinitrate *on page 127*
- **Isobamate** *see* Carisoprodol *on page 76*
- **Isochron™** *see* Isosorbide Dinitrate *on page 127*

Isoniazid (eye soe NYE a zid)

Genes of Interest

N-Acetyltransferase 2 Enzyme *on page 308*

U.S. Brand Names Nydrazid® [DSC]
Canadian Brand Names Isotamine®; PMS-Isoniazid
Synonyms INH; Isonicotinic Acid Hydrazide
Pharmacologic Class Antitubercular Agent

- **Isonicotinic Acid Hydrazide** *see* Isoniazid *on page 126*
- **Isonipecaine Hydrochloride** *see* Meperidine *on page 138*

♦ **Isophosphamide** *see* Ifosfamide *on page 123*

Isoproterenol (eye soe proe TER e nole)

Genes of Interest

Beta$_2$-Adrenergic Receptor *on page 233*

U.S. Brand Names Isuprel®

Synonyms Isoproterenol Hydrochloride

Pharmacologic Class Beta$_1$- & Beta$_2$-Adrenergic Agonist Agent

♦ **Isoproterenol Hydrochloride** *see* Isoproterenol *on page 127*

♦ **Isoptin® SR** *see* Verapamil *on page 201*

♦ **Isordil®** *see* Isosorbide Dinitrate *on page 127*

Isosorbide Dinitrate (eye soe SOR bide dye NYE trate)

Genes of Interest

CYP3A4 *on page 260*

U.S. Brand Names Dilatrate®-SR; Isochron™; Isordil®

Canadian Brand Names Apo-ISDN®; Cedocard®-SR; Coronex®; Novo-Sorbide; PMS-Isosorbide

Synonyms ISD; ISDN

Pharmacologic Class Vasodilator

♦ **Isotamine® (Can)** *see* Isoniazid *on page 126*

Isradipine (iz RA di peen)

Genes of Interest

Cardiac Potassium Ion Channel *on page 241*

Cardiac Sodium Channel *on page 242*

CYP3A4 *on page 260*

U.S. Brand Names DynaCirc® CR; DynaCirc®

Canadian Brand Names DynaCirc®

Pharmacologic Class Calcium Channel Blocker

♦ **Istalol™** *see* Timolol *on page 195*

♦ **Isuprel®** *see* Isoproterenol *on page 127*

Itraconazole (i tra KOE na zole)

Genes of Interest

ATP-Binding Cassette, Sub-Family B, Member 1 *on page 224*

U.S. Brand Names Sporanox®

Canadian Brand Names Sporanox®

Pharmacologic Class Antifungal Agent, Oral

Ivermectin (eye ver MEK tin)

Genes of Interest

ATP-Binding Cassette, Sub-Family B, Member 1 *on page 224*

U.S. Brand Names Stromectol®

Pharmacologic Class Anthelmintic

♦ **IvySoothe® [OTC]** *see* Hydrocortisone *on page 121*

♦ **Jantoven™** *see* Warfarin *on page 203*

♦ **Jolivette™** *see* Norethindrone *on page 151*

♦ **Junel™** *see* Ethinyl Estradiol and Norethindrone *on page 104*
♦ **Junel™ Fe** *see* Ethinyl Estradiol and Norethindrone *on page 104*
♦ **K-10® (Can)** *see* Potassium Chloride *on page 169*
♦ **Kadian®** *see* Morphine Sulfate *on page 146*
♦ **Kaon-Cl-10®** *see* Potassium Chloride *on page 169*
♦ **Kaon-Cl® 20** *see* Potassium Chloride *on page 169*
♦ **Kariva™** *see* Ethinyl Estradiol and Desogestrel *on page 103*
♦ **Kay Ciel®** *see* Potassium Chloride *on page 169*
♦ **KCl** *see* Potassium Chloride *on page 169*
♦ **K-Dur® (Can)** *see* Potassium Chloride *on page 169*
♦ **K-Dur® 10** *see* Potassium Chloride *on page 169*
♦ **K-Dur® 20** *see* Potassium Chloride *on page 169*
♦ **Keflex®** *see* Cephalexin *on page 78*
♦ **Keftab® (Can)** *see* Cephalexin *on page 78*
♦ **Kenalog®** *see* Triamcinolone *on page 198*
♦ **Kenalog-10®** *see* Triamcinolone *on page 198*
♦ **Kenalog-40®** *see* Triamcinolone *on page 198*
♦ **Kenalog® in Orabase (Can)** *see* Triamcinolone *on page 198*
♦ **Keoxifene Hydrochloride** *see* Raloxifene *on page 175*
♦ **Kerlone®** *see* Betaxolol *on page 70*
♦ **Ketalar®** *see* Ketamine *on page 128*

Ketamine (KEET a meen)

Genes of Interest

CYP2C8 *on page 248*
CYP2C9 *on page 248*
CYP3A4 *on page 260*

U.S. Brand Names Ketalar®

Canadian Brand Names Ketalar®

Synonyms Ketamine Hydrochloride

Pharmacologic Class General Anesthetic

♦ **Ketamine Hydrochloride** *see* Ketamine *on page 128*

Ketoconazole (kee toe KOE na zole)

Genes of Interest

ATP-Binding Cassette, Sub-Family B, Member 1 *on page 224*

U.S. Brand Names Nizoral® A-D [OTC]; Nizoral®

Canadian Brand Names Apo-Ketoconazole®; Ketoderm®; Novo-Ketoconazole

Pharmacologic Class Antifungal Agent, Oral; Antifungal Agent, Topical

♦ **Ketoderm® (Can)** *see* Ketoconazole *on page 128*

Ketoprofen (kee toe PROE fen)

Genes of Interest

Leukotriene C4 Synthase *on page 302*

U.S. Brand Names Orudis® KT [OTC] [DSC]

Canadian Brand Names Apo-Keto SR®; Apo-Keto-E®; Apo-Keto®; Novo-Keto-EC; Novo-Keto; Nu-Ketoprofen-E; Nu-Ketoprofen; Oruvail®; Rhodis SR™; Rhodis-EC™; Rhodis™

Pharmacologic Class Nonsteroidal Anti-inflammatory Drug (NSAID), Oral

Ketorolac (KEE toe role ak)

Genes of Interest

Leukotriene C4 Synthase *on page 302*

U.S. Brand Names Acular LS™; Acular® PF; Acular®; Toradol®

Canadian Brand Names Acular LS™; Acular®; Apo-Ketorolac Injectable®; Apo-Ketorolac®; Novo-Ketorolac; Toradol® IM; Toradol®; ratio-Ketorolac

Synonyms Ketorolac Tromethamine

Pharmacologic Class Nonsteroidal Anti-inflammatory Drug (NSAID), Ophthalmic; Nonsteroidal Anti-inflammatory Drug (NSAID), Oral; Nonsteroidal Anti-inflammatory Drug (NSAID), Parenteral

- **Ketorolac Tromethamine** *see* Ketorolac *on page 129*
- **Klaron®** *see* Sulfacetamide *on page 187*
- **Klonopin®** *see* Clonazepam *on page 83*
- **K-Lor®** *see* Potassium Chloride *on page 169*
- **Klor-Con®** *see* Potassium Chloride *on page 169*
- **Klor-Con® 8** *see* Potassium Chloride *on page 169*
- **Klor-Con® 10** *see* Potassium Chloride *on page 169*
- **Klor-Con®/25** *see* Potassium Chloride *on page 169*
- **Klor-Con® M** *see* Potassium Chloride *on page 169*
- **K-Lyte®/Cl (Can)** *see* Potassium Chloride *on page 169*
- **K+ Potassium** *see* Potassium Chloride *on page 169*
- **K-Tab®** *see* Potassium Chloride *on page 169*
- **L-M-X™ 4 [OTC]** *see* Lidocaine *on page 131*
- **L-M-X™ 5 [OTC]** *see* Lidocaine *on page 131*
- **L 754030** *see* Aprepitant *on page 64*
- **Lanoxicaps®** *see* Digoxin *on page 92*
- **Lanoxin®** *see* Digoxin *on page 92*

Lansoprazole (lan SOE pra zole)

Genes of Interest

CYP2C19 *on page 251*

U.S. Brand Names Prevacid® SoluTab™; Prevacid®

Canadian Brand Names Prevacid®

Pharmacologic Class Proton Pump Inhibitor; Substituted Benzimidazole

- **Lantus®** *see* Insulin Preparations *on page 125*
- **Lanvis® (Can)** *see* Thioguanine *on page 193*
- **Largactil® (Can)** *see* ChlorproMAZINE *on page 79*
- **Lariam®** *see* Mefloquine *on page 137*
- **Lasix®** *see* Furosemide *on page 114*

♦ **Lasix® Special (Can)** *see* Furosemide *on page 114*

Latanoprost (la TA noe prost)

Genes of Interest None known

U.S. Brand Names Xalatan®

Canadian Brand Names Xalatan®

Pharmacologic Class Ophthalmic Agent, Antiglaucoma; Prostaglandin, Ophthalmic

♦ **LCR** *see* VinCRIStine *on page 202*
♦ **L-Deprenyl** *see* Selegiline *on page 183*
♦ **Lectopam® (Can)** *see* Bromazepam *on page 72*
♦ **Lente, Insulin** *see* Insulin Preparations *on page 125*
♦ **Lescol®** *see* Fluvastatin *on page 111*
♦ **Lescol® XL** *see* Fluvastatin *on page 111*
♦ **Lessina™** *see* Ethinyl Estradiol and Levonorgestrel *on page 104*
♦ **Leurocristine Sulfate** *see* VinCRIStine *on page 202*

Levalbuterol (leve al BYOO ter ole)

Genes of Interest

Beta$_2$-Adrenergic Receptor *on page 233*

U.S. Brand Names Xopenex HFA™; Xopenex®

Canadian Brand Names Xopenex®

Synonyms Levalbuterol Hydrochloride; Levalbuterol Tartrate; R-albuterol

Pharmacologic Class Beta$_2$-Adrenergic Agonist

♦ **Levalbuterol Hydrochloride** *see* Levalbuterol *on page 130*
♦ **Levalbuterol Tartrate** *see* Levalbuterol *on page 130*
♦ **Levaquin®** *see* Levofloxacin *on page 130*
♦ **Levate® (Can)** *see* Amitriptyline *on page 57*
♦ **Levlen®** *see* Ethinyl Estradiol and Levonorgestrel *on page 104*
♦ **Levlite™** *see* Ethinyl Estradiol and Levonorgestrel *on page 104*
♦ **Levo-Dromoran®** *see* Levorphanol *on page 131*

Levofloxacin (lee voe FLOKS a sin)

Genes of Interest

Cardiac Potassium Ion Channel *on page 241*
Cardiac Sodium Channel *on page 242*

U.S. Brand Names Iquix®; Levaquin®; Quixin™

Canadian Brand Names Levaquin®; Novo-Levofloxacin

Pharmacologic Class Antibiotic, Quinolone

♦ **Levomepromazine** *see* Methotrimeprazine *on page 140*

Levonorgestrel (LEE voe nor jes trel)

Genes of Interest

BRCA Genes *on page 240*
Prothrombin *on page 315*

U.S. Brand Names Mirena®; Plan B®

Canadian Brand Names Mirena®; Norplant® Implant; Plan B™

Synonyms LNg 20

Pharmacologic Class Contraceptive; Progestin

- **Levonorgestrel and Ethinyl Estradiol** *see* Ethinyl Estradiol and Levonorgestrel *on page 104*
- **Levora®** *see* Ethinyl Estradiol and Levonorgestrel *on page 104*

Levorphanol (lee VOR fa nole)

Genes of Interest

COMT *on page 244*

U.S. Brand Names Levo-Dromoran®

Synonyms Levorphan Tartrate; Levorphanol Tartrate

Pharmacologic Class Analgesic, Narcotic

- **Levorphanol Tartrate** *see* Levorphanol *on page 131*
- **Levorphan Tartrate** *see* Levorphanol *on page 131*
- **Levothroid®** *see* Levothyroxine *on page 131*

Levothyroxine (lee voe thye ROKS een)

Genes of Interest None known

U.S. Brand Names Levothroid®; Levoxyl®; Synthroid®; Unithroid®

Canadian Brand Names Eltroxin®; Synthroid®

Synonyms *L*-Thyroxine Sodium; Levothyroxine Sodium; T_4

Pharmacologic Class Thyroid Product

- **Levothyroxine Sodium** *see* Levothyroxine *on page 131*
- **Levoxyl®** *see* Levothyroxine *on page 131*
- **Lexapro™** *see* Escitalopram *on page 100*
- **Librium®** *see* Chlordiazepoxide *on page 78*
- **LidaMantle®** *see* Lidocaine *on page 131*

Lidocaine (LYE doe kane)

Genes of Interest

ATP-Binding Cassette, Sub-Family B, Member 1 *on page 224*
CYP3A4 *on page 260*

U.S. Brand Names Anestacon®; Band-Aid® Hurt-Free™ Antiseptic Wash [OTC]; Burn Jel [OTC]; Burn-O-Jel [OTC]; Burnamycin [OTC]; L-M-X™ 4 [OTC]; L-M-X™ 5 [OTC]; LTA® 360; LidaMantle®; Lidoderm®; Premjact® [OTC]; Solarcaine® Aloe Extra Burn Relief [OTC]; Topicaine® [OTC]; Xylocaine® MPF; Xylocaine® Viscous; Xylocaine®; Zilactin-L® [OTC]

Canadian Brand Names Betacaine®; Lidodan™; Lidoderm®; Xylocaine®; Xylocard®; Zilactin®

Synonyms Lidocaine Hydrochloride; Lignocaine Hydrochloride

Pharmacologic Class Analgesic, Topical; Antiarrhythmic Agent, Class Ib; Local Anesthetic

Lidocaine and Prilocaine (LYE doe kane & PRIL oh kane)

Genes of Interest

ATP-Binding Cassette, Sub-Family B, Member 1 *on page 224*

(Continued)

Lidocaine and Prilocaine *(Continued)*

CYP3A4 *on page 260*
Glucose-6-Phosphate Dehydrogenase *on page 281*

U.S. Brand Names EMLA®
Canadian Brand Names EMLA®
Synonyms Prilocaine and Lidocaine
Pharmacologic Class Local Anesthetic

- ♦ **Lidocaine Hydrochloride** *see* Lidocaine *on page 131*
- ♦ **Lidodan™ (Can)** *see* Lidocaine *on page 131*
- ♦ **Lidoderm®** *see* Lidocaine *on page 131*
- ♦ **Lignocaine Hydrochloride** *see* Lidocaine *on page 131*
- ♦ **Limbitrol®** *see* Amitriptyline and Chlordiazepoxide *on page 58*
- ♦ **Limbitrol® DS** *see* Amitriptyline and Chlordiazepoxide *on page 58*
- ♦ **Lin-Amox (Can)** *see* Amoxicillin *on page 59*
- ♦ **Lin-Buspirone (Can)** *see* BusPIRone *on page 73*
- ♦ **Lin-Sotalol (Can)** *see* Sotalol *on page 185*
- ♦ **Lipidil EZ® (Can)** *see* Fenofibrate *on page 107*
- ♦ **Lipidil Micro® (Can)** *see* Fenofibrate *on page 107*
- ♦ **Lipidil Supra® (Can)** *see* Fenofibrate *on page 107*
- ♦ **Lipitor®** *see* Atorvastatin *on page 67*

Lisinopril (lyse IN oh pril)

Genes of Interest

Aldosterone Synthase *on page 208*
Angiotensin II Type 1 Receptor *on page 213*
Angiotensin-Converting Enzyme *on page 214*
Angiotensinogen *on page 219*
Bradykinin B_2-Receptor *on page 237*

U.S. Brand Names Prinivil®; Zestril®
Canadian Brand Names Apo-Lisinopril®; Prinivil®; Zestril®
Pharmacologic Class Angiotensin-Converting Enzyme (ACE) Inhibitor

Lisinopril and Hydrochlorothiazide

(lyse IN oh pril & hye droe klor oh THYE a zide)

Genes of Interest

Aldosterone Synthase *on page 208*
Alpha-Adducin *on page 212*
Angiotensin II Type 1 Receptor *on page 213*
Angiotensin-Converting Enzyme *on page 214*
Angiotensinogen *on page 219*
Bradykinin B_2-Receptor *on page 237*
G-Protein $Beta_3$ Subunit *on page 286*

U.S. Brand Names Prinzide®; Zestoretic®
Canadian Brand Names Prinzide®; Zestoretic®
Synonyms Hydrochlorothiazide and Lisinopril
Pharmacologic Class Antihypertensive Agent, Combination

- ♦ **Lispro, Insulin** *see* Insulin Preparations *on page 125*

♦ **Lithane™ (Can)** *see* Lithium *on page 133*

Lithium (LITH ee um)

Genes of Interest

COMT *on page 244*

D_2 Receptor *on page 263*

D_3 Receptor *on page 266*

D_4 Receptor *on page 268*

Gamma-Aminobutyric Acid (GABA) Type A Receptor $Alpha_1$ Subunit *on page 280*

G-Protein $Beta_3$ Subunit *on page 286*

$5\text{-}HT_{2A}$ Receptor *on page 291*

$5\text{-}HT_{2C}$ Receptor *on page 294*

5-HT Transporter *on page 297*

Inositol Polyphosphate 1-Phosphatase *on page 301*

Monoamine Oxidase A *on page 307*

Tryptophan Hydroxylase *on page 321*

U.S. Brand Names Eskalith CR®; Eskalith®; Lithobid®

Canadian Brand Names Apo-Lithium®; Carbolith™; Duralith®; Lithane™; PMS-Lithium Carbonate; PMS-Lithium Citrate

Synonyms Lithium Carbonate; Lithium Citrate

Pharmacologic Class Lithium

♦ **Lithium Carbonate** *see* Lithium *on page 133*

♦ **Lithium Citrate** *see* Lithium *on page 133*

♦ **Lithobid®** *see* Lithium *on page 133*

♦ **LNg 20** *see* Levonorgestrel *on page 130*

♦ **Locoid®** *see* Hydrocortisone *on page 121*

♦ **Locoid Lipocream®** *see* Hydrocortisone *on page 121*

♦ **Lodine®** *see* Etodolac *on page 105*

♦ **Lodine® XL [DSC]** *see* Etodolac *on page 105*

♦ **Loestrin®** *see* Ethinyl Estradiol and Norethindrone *on page 104*

♦ **Loestrin™ 1.5.30 (Can)** *see* Ethinyl Estradiol and Norethindrone *on page 104*

♦ **Loestrin® Fe** *see* Ethinyl Estradiol and Norethindrone *on page 104*

♦ **Lofibra™** *see* Fenofibrate *on page 107*

♦ **L-OHP** *see* Oxaliplatin *on page 160*

♦ **Lo/Ovral®** *see* Ethinyl Estradiol and Norgestrel *on page 105*

♦ **Lopid®** *see* Gemfibrozil *on page 115*

♦ **Lopressor®** *see* Metoprolol *on page 142*

Loratadine (lor AT a deen)

Genes of Interest None known

U.S. Brand Names Alavert™ [OTC]; Claritin® Hives Relief [OTC]; Claritin® [OTC]; Dimetapp® Children's ND [OTC]; Tavist® ND [OTC]

(Continued)

Loratadine *(Continued)*

Canadian Brand Names Apo-Loratadine®; Claritin® Kids; Claritin®
Pharmacologic Class Antihistamine, Nonsedating

Lorazepam (lor A ze pam)

Genes of Interest None known
U.S. Brand Names Ativan®; Lorazepam Intensol®
Canadian Brand Names Apo-Lorazepam®; Ativan®; Novo-Lorazepam; Nu-Loraz; PMS-Lorazepam; Riva-Lorazepam
Pharmacologic Class Benzodiazepine

♦ **Lorazepam Intensol®** *see* Lorazepam *on page 134*

♦ **Lorcet® 10/650** *see* Hydrocodone and Acetaminophen *on page 120*

♦ **Lorcet®-HD [DSC]** *see* Hydrocodone and Acetaminophen *on page 120*

♦ **Lorcet® Plus** *see* Hydrocodone and Acetaminophen *on page 120*

♦ **Lortab®** *see* Hydrocodone and Acetaminophen *on page 120*

Losartan (loe SAR tan)

Genes of Interest
Adipocyte-Derived Leucine Aminopeptidase *on page 208*
Aldosterone Synthase *on page 208*
Angiotensin II Type 1 Receptor *on page 213*
Angiotensin-Converting Enzyme *on page 214*
Angiotensinogen *on page 219*
Bradykinin B_2-Receptor *on page 237*
CYP2C9 *on page 248*
U.S. Brand Names Cozaar®
Canadian Brand Names Cozaar®
Synonyms DuP 753; Losartan Potassium; MK594
Pharmacologic Class Angiotensin II Receptor Blocker

Losartan and Hydrochlorothiazide

(loe SAR tan & hye droe klor oh THYE a zide)
Genes of Interest
Adipocyte-Derived Leucine Aminopeptidase *on page 208*
Aldosterone Synthase *on page 208*
Alpha-Adducin *on page 212*
Angiotensin II Type 1 Receptor *on page 213*
Angiotensin-Converting Enzyme *on page 214*
Angiotensinogen *on page 219*
Bradykinin B_2-Receptor *on page 237*
CYP2C9 *on page 248*
G-Protein $Beta_3$ Subunit *on page 286*
U.S. Brand Names Hyzaar®
Canadian Brand Names Hyzaar® DS; Hyzaar®
Synonyms Hydrochlorothiazide and Losartan
Pharmacologic Class Angiotensin II Receptor Blocker Combination; Antihypertensive Agent, Combination; Diuretic, Thiazide

♦ **Losartan Potassium** *see* Losartan *on page 134*

- **Losec® (Can)** *see* Omeprazole *on page 159*
- **Losec MUPS® (Can)** *see* Omeprazole *on page 159*
- **Lotensin®** *see* Benazepril *on page 69*
- **Lotrel®** *see* Amlodipine and Benazepril *on page 59*
- **Lotronex®** *see* Alosetron *on page 56*

Lovastatin (LOE va sta tin)

Genes of Interest

Angiotensin-Converting Enzyme *on page 214*
Apolipoprotein E *on page 220*
ATP-Binding Cassette, Sub-Family B, Member 1 *on page 224*
Beta-Fibrinogen *on page 236*
Cholesteryl Ester Transfer Protein *on page 243*
CYP3A4 *on page 260*
Glycoprotein IIIa Receptor *on page 285*
Low-Density Lipoprotein Receptor *on page 304*
Stromelysin-1 *on page 316*

U.S. Brand Names Altoprev™; Mevacor®

Canadian Brand Names Apo-Lovastatin®; CO Lovastatin; Gen-Lovastatin; Mevacor®; Novo-Lovastatin; Nu-Lovastatin; PMS-Lovastatin; ratio-Lovastatin

Synonyms Mevinolin; Monacolin K

Pharmacologic Class Antilipemic Agent, HMG-CoA Reductase Inhibitor

- **Low-Ogestrel®** *see* Ethinyl Estradiol and Norgestrel *on page 105*

Loxapine (LOKS a peen)

Genes of Interest

$Alpha_1$-Adrenergic Receptor *on page 210*
Cardiac Potassium Ion Channel *on page 241*
Cardiac Sodium Channel *on page 242*
D_2 Receptor *on page 263*

U.S. Brand Names Loxitane®

Canadian Brand Names Apo-Loxapine®; Nu-Loxapine; PMS-Loxapine

Synonyms Loxapine Succinate; Oxilapine Succinate

Pharmacologic Class Antipsychotic Agent, Typical

- **Loxapine Succinate** *see* Loxapine *on page 135*
- **Loxitane®** *see* Loxapine *on page 135*
- **Lozide® (Can)** *see* Indapamide *on page 124*
- **Lozol®** *see* Indapamide *on page 124*
- **LTA® 360** *see* Lidocaine *on page 131*
- ***L*-Thyroxine Sodium** *see* Levothyroxine *on page 131*
- **Lu-26-054** *see* Escitalopram *on page 100*
- **Ludiomil** *see* Maprotiline *on page 136*
- **Luminal® Sodium** *see* Phenobarbital *on page 165*
- **Lutera™** *see* Ethinyl Estradiol and Levonorgestrel *on page 104*
- **Luvox® (Can)** *see* Fluvoxamine *on page 112*
- **LY139603** *see* Atomoxetine *on page 66*

- **LY170053** *see* Olanzapine *on page 158*
- **Macrobid®** *see* Nitrofurantoin *on page 151*
- **Macrodantin®** *see* Nitrofurantoin *on page 151*

Mafenide (MA fe nide)

Genes of Interest
Glucose-6-Phosphate Dehydrogenase *on page 281*
U.S. Brand Names Sulfamylon®
Synonyms Mafenide Acetate
Pharmacologic Class Antibiotic, Topical

- **Mafenide Acetate** *see* Mafenide *on page 136*
- **Manerix® (Can)** *see* Moclobemide *on page 144*

Maprotiline (ma PROE ti leen)

Genes of Interest
ATP-Binding Cassette, Sub-Family B, Member 1 *on page 224*
Canadian Brand Names Novo-Maprotiline
Synonyms Ludiomil; Maprotiline Hydrochloride
Pharmacologic Class Antidepressant, Tetracyclic

- **Maprotiline Hydrochloride** *see* Maprotiline *on page 136*
- **Margesic® H** *see* Hydrocodone and Acetaminophen *on page 120*
- **Marvelon® (Can)** *see* Ethinyl Estradiol and Desogestrel *on page 103*
- **Mavik®** *see* Trandolapril *on page 197*
- **Maxair™ Autohaler™** *see* Pirbuterol *on page 166*
- **Maxidone™** *see* Hydrocodone and Acetaminophen *on page 120*
- **Mebaral®** *see* Mephobarbital *on page 138*

Meclizine (MEK li zeen)

Genes of Interest None known
U.S. Brand Names Antivert®; Bonine® [OTC]; Dramamine® Less Drowsy Formula [OTC]
Canadian Brand Names Bonamine™; Bonine®
Synonyms Meclizine Hydrochloride; Meclozine Hydrochloride
Pharmacologic Class Antiemetic; Antihistamine

- **Meclizine Hydrochloride** *see* Meclizine *on page 136*

Meclofenamate (me kloe fen AM ate)

Genes of Interest
Leukotriene C4 Synthase *on page 302*
Canadian Brand Names Meclomen®
Synonyms Meclofenamate Sodium
Pharmacologic Class Nonsteroidal Anti-inflammatory Drug (NSAID), Oral

- **Meclofenamate Sodium** *see* Meclofenamate *on page 136*
- **Meclomen® (Can)** *see* Meclofenamate *on page 136*
- **Meclozine Hydrochloride** *see* Meclizine *on page 136*
- **Med-Diltiazem (Can)** *see* Diltiazem *on page 93*
- **Medrol®** *see* MethylPREDNISolone *on page 141*

MedroxyPROGESTERone

(me DROKS ee proe JES te rone)

Genes of Interest

BRCA Genes *on page 240*

Prothrombin *on page 315*

U.S. Brand Names Depo-Provera® Contraceptive; Depo-Provera®; Provera®; depo-subQ provera 104™

Canadian Brand Names Alti-MPA; Apo-Medroxy®; Depo-Prevera®; Gen-Medroxy; Novo-Medrone; Provera®

Synonyms Acetoxymethylprogesterone; MPA; Medroxyprogesterone Acetate; Methylacetoxyprogesterone

Pharmacologic Class Contraceptive; Progestin

- **Medroxyprogesterone Acetate** *see* MedroxyPROGESTERone *on page 137*
- **Medroxyprogesterone and Estrogens (Conjugated)** *see* Estrogens (Conjugated/Equine) and Medroxyprogesterone *on page 102*

Mefenamic Acid (me fe NAM ik AS id)

Genes of Interest

Leukotriene C4 Synthase *on page 302*

U.S. Brand Names Ponstel®

Canadian Brand Names Apo-Mefenamic®; Nu-Mefenamic; PMS-Mefenamic Acid; Ponstel®

Pharmacologic Class Nonsteroidal Anti-inflammatory Drug (NSAID), Oral

Mefloquine (ME floe kwin)

Genes of Interest

ATP-Binding Cassette, Sub-Family B, Member 1 *on page 224*

CYP3A4 *on page 260*

U.S. Brand Names Lariam®

Canadian Brand Names Apo-Mefloquine®; Lariam®

Synonyms Mefloquine Hydrochloride

Pharmacologic Class Antimalarial Agent

- **Mefloquine Hydrochloride** *see* Mefloquine *on page 137*
- **Mellaril® (Can)** *see* Thioridazine *on page 193*

Meloxicam (mel OKS i kam)

Genes of Interest

Leukotriene C4 Synthase *on page 302*

U.S. Brand Names Mobic®

Canadian Brand Names Apo-Meloxicam®; CO Meloxicam; Gen-Meloxicam; Mobicox®; Mobic®; Novo-Meloxicam; pms-Meloxicam

Pharmacologic Class Nonsteroidal Anti-inflammatory Drug (NSAID), Oral

- **Menadol® [OTC] [DSC]** *see* Ibuprofen *on page 123*
- **Menest®** *see* Estrogens (Esterified) *on page 102*
- **Menostar™** *see* Estradiol *on page 101*

♦ **Mepergan** *see* Meperidine and Promethazine *on page 138*

Meperidine (me PER i deen)

Genes of Interest

COMT *on page 244*

U.S. Brand Names Demerol®; Meperitab®

Canadian Brand Names Demerol®

Synonyms Isonipecaine Hydrochloride; Meperidine Hydrochloride; Pethidine Hydrochloride

Pharmacologic Class Analgesic, Narcotic

Meperidine and Promethazine
(me PER i deen & proe METH a zeen)

Genes of Interest

COMT *on page 244*

Synonyms Mepergan; Promethazine and Meperidine

Pharmacologic Class Analgesic Combination (Narcotic)

♦ **Meperidine Hydrochloride** *see* Meperidine *on page 138*

♦ **Meperitab®** *see* Meperidine *on page 138*

Mephobarbital (me foe BAR bi tal)

Genes of Interest

CYP2C19 *on page 251*

U.S. Brand Names Mebaral®

Canadian Brand Names Mebaral®

Synonyms Methylphenobarbital

Pharmacologic Class Barbiturate

Mercaptopurine (mer kap toe PYOOR een)

Genes of Interest

Thiopurine Methyltransferase *on page 317*

U.S. Brand Names Purinethol®

Canadian Brand Names Purinethol®

Synonyms 6-MP; 6-Mercaptopurine; NSC-755

Pharmacologic Class Antineoplastic Agent, Antimetabolite

♦ **6-Mercaptopurine** *see* Mercaptopurine *on page 138*

♦ **Meridia®** *see* Sibutramine *on page 184*

♦ **M-Eslon® (Can)** *see* Morphine Sulfate *on page 146*

Mesoridazine (mez oh RID a zeen)

Genes of Interest

$Alpha_1$-Adrenergic Receptor *on page 210*

Cardiac Potassium Ion Channel *on page 241*

Cardiac Sodium Channel *on page 242*

D_2 Receptor *on page 263*

U.S. Brand Names Serentil® [DSC]
Canadian Brand Names Serentil®
Synonyms Mesoridazine Besylate
Pharmacologic Class Antipsychotic Agent, Typical, Phenothiazine

♦ **Mesoridazine Besylate** *see* Mesoridazine *on page 138*

Mestranol and Norethindrone

(MES tra nole & nor eth IN drone)

Genes of Interest
BRCA Genes *on page 240*
CYP2C8 *on page 248*
Prothrombin *on page 315*
U.S. Brand Names Necon® 1/50; Norinyl® 1+50; Ortho-Novum® 1/50
Canadian Brand Names Ortho-Novum® 1/50
Synonyms Norethindrone and Mestranol; Ortho Novum 1/50
Pharmacologic Class Contraceptive; Estrogen and Progestin Combination

♦ **Metadate® CD** *see* Methylphenidate *on page 141*
♦ **Metadate® ER** *see* Methylphenidate *on page 141*
♦ **Metadol™ (Can)** *see* Methadone *on page 140*

Metaproterenol (met a proe TER e nol)

Genes of Interest
$Beta_2$-Adrenergic Receptor *on page 233*
U.S. Brand Names Alupent®
Synonyms Metaproterenol Sulfate; Orciprenaline Sulfate
Pharmacologic Class $Beta_2$-Adrenergic Agonist

♦ **Metaproterenol Sulfate** *see* Metaproterenol *on page 139*

Metaxalone (me TAKS a lone)

Genes of Interest None known
U.S. Brand Names Skelaxin®
Canadian Brand Names Skelaxin®
Pharmacologic Class Skeletal Muscle Relaxant

Metformin (met FOR min)

Genes of Interest None known
U.S. Brand Names Fortamet™; Glucophage® XR; Glucophage®; Riomet™
Canadian Brand Names Alti-Metformin; Apo-Metformin®; Gen-Metformin; Glucophage®; Glycon; Novo-Metformin; Nu-Metformin; PMS-Metformin; Rho®-Metformin
Synonyms Metformin Hydrochloride
Pharmacologic Class Antidiabetic Agent, Biguanide

♦ **Metformin and Glyburide** *see* Glyburide and Metformin *on page 117*
♦ **Metformin Hydrochloride** *see* Metformin *on page 139*

Methadone (METH a done)

Genes of Interest

COMT *on page 244*
CYP2D6 *on page 254*
CYP3A4 *on page 260*

U.S. Brand Names Dolophine®; Methadone Diskets®; Methadone Intensol™; Methadose®

Canadian Brand Names Dolophine®; Metadol™; Methadose®

Synonyms Methadone Hydrochloride

Pharmacologic Class Analgesic, Narcotic

- ♦ **Methadone Diskets®** *see* Methadone *on page 140*
- ♦ **Methadone Hydrochloride** *see* Methadone *on page 140*
- ♦ **Methadone Intensol™** *see* Methadone *on page 140*
- ♦ **Methadose®** *see* Methadone *on page 140*
- ♦ **Methaminodiazepoxide Hydrochloride** *see* Chlordiazepoxide *on page 78*
- ♦ **Methergine®** *see* Methylergonovine *on page 141*

Methotrimeprazine (meth oh trye MEP ra zeen)

Genes of Interest

COMT *on page 244*

Canadian Brand Names Apo-Methoprazine®; Nozinan®

Synonyms Levomepromazine; Methotrimeprazine Hydrochloride

Pharmacologic Class Analgesic, Non-narcotic

- ♦ **Methotrimeprazine Hydrochloride** *see* Methotrimeprazine *on page 140*

Methsuximide (meth SUKS i mide)

Genes of Interest

CYP2C19 *on page 251*

U.S. Brand Names Celontin®

Canadian Brand Names Celontin®

Pharmacologic Class Anticonvulsant, Succinimide

Methyclothiazide (meth i kloe THYE a zide)

Genes of Interest

Alpha-Adducin *on page 212*
G-Protein Beta$_3$ Subunit *on page 286*

U.S. Brand Names Enduron® [DSC]

Canadian Brand Names Aquatensen®; Enduron®

Pharmacologic Class Diuretic, Thiazide

- ♦ **Methylacetoxyprogesterone** *see* MedroxyPROGESTERone *on page 137*

Methylene Blue (METH i leen bloo)

Genes of Interest

Glucose-6-Phosphate Dehydrogenase *on page 281*

U.S. Brand Names Urolene Blue®

Pharmacologic Class Antidote

- ♦ **Methylergometrine Maleate** *see* Methylergonovine *on page 141*

Methylergonovine (meth il er goe NOE veen)

Genes of Interest

CYP3A4 *on page 260*

U.S. Brand Names Methergine®

Canadian Brand Names Methergine®

Synonyms Methylergometrine Maleate; Methylergonovine Maleate

Pharmacologic Class Ergot Derivative

- ♦ **Methylergonovine Maleate** *see* Methylergonovine *on page 141*
- ♦ **Methylin®** *see* Methylphenidate *on page 141*
- ♦ **Methylin® ER** *see* Methylphenidate *on page 141*
- ♦ **Methylmorphine** *see* Codeine *on page 85*

Methylphenidate (meth il FEN i date)

Genes of Interest

Dopamine Transporter *on page 270*

U.S. Brand Names Concerta®; Metadate® ER; Metadate® CD; Methylin® ER; Methylin® ; Ritalin-SR®; Ritalin® LA; Ritalin®

Canadian Brand Names Concerta®; PMS-Methylphenidate; Riphenidate; Ritalin® SR; Ritalin®

Synonyms Methylphenidate Hydrochloride

Pharmacologic Class Central Nervous System Stimulant

- ♦ **Methylphenidate Hydrochloride** *see* Methylphenidate *on page 141*
- ♦ **Methylphenobarbital** *see* Mephobarbital *on page 138*
- ♦ **Methylphenoxy-Benzene Propanamine** *see* Atomoxetine *on page 66*

MethylPREDNISolone (meth il pred NIS oh lone)

Genes of Interest None known

U.S. Brand Names Depo-Medrol®; Medrol®; Solu-Medrol®

Canadian Brand Names Depo-Medrol®; Medrol®; Solu-Medrol®

Synonyms 6-α-Methylprednisolone; A-Methapred; Methylprednisolone Acetate; Methylprednisolone Sodium Succinate

Pharmacologic Class Corticosteroid, Systemic

- ♦ **6-α-Methylprednisolone** *see* MethylPREDNISolone *on page 141*
- ♦ **Methylprednisolone Acetate** *see* MethylPREDNISolone *on page 141*
- ♦ **Methylprednisolone Sodium Succinate** *see* MethylPREDNISolone *on page 141*

Metoclopramide (met oh kloe PRA mide)

Genes of Interest

D_2 Receptor *on page 263*

(Continued)

Metoclopramide *(Continued)*

U.S. Brand Names Reglan®

Canadian Brand Names Apo-Metoclop®; Nu-Metoclopramide

Pharmacologic Class Antiemetic; Gastrointestinal Agent, Prokinetic

Metolazone (me TOLE a zone)

Genes of Interest

Alpha-Adducin *on page 212*

G-Protein $Beta_3$ Subunit *on page 286*

U.S. Brand Names Zaroxolyn®

Canadian Brand Names Mykrox®; Zaroxolyn®

Pharmacologic Class Diuretic, Thiazide-Related

Metoprolol (me toe PROE lole)

Genes of Interest

Angiotensin-Converting Enzyme *on page 214*

Angiotensinogen *on page 219*

$Beta_1$-Adrenergic Receptor *on page 230*

Bradykinin B_2-Receptor *on page 237*

CYP2D6 *on page 254*

Gs Protein Alpha-Subunit *on page 288*

U.S. Brand Names Lopressor®; Toprol-XL®

Canadian Brand Names Apo-Metoprolol®; Betaloc® Durules®; Betaloc®; Lopressor®; Novo-Metoprolol; Nu-Metop; PMS-Metoprolol; Toprol-XL®

Synonyms Metoprolol Succinate; Metoprolol Tartrate

Pharmacologic Class Beta Blocker, $Beta_1$ Selective

- **Metoprolol Succinate** *see* Metoprolol *on page 142*
- **Metoprolol Tartrate** *see* Metoprolol *on page 142*
- **MetroCream®** *see* Metronidazole *on page 142*
- **MetroGel®** *see* Metronidazole *on page 142*
- **MetroGel-Vaginal®** *see* Metronidazole *on page 142*
- **MetroLotion®** *see* Metronidazole *on page 142*

Metronidazole (me troe NI da zole)

Genes of Interest None known

U.S. Brand Names Flagyl ER®; Flagyl® I.V. RTU™; Flagyl®; MetroCream®; MetroGel-Vaginal®; MetroGel®; MetroLotion®; Noritate®

Canadian Brand Names Apo-Metronidazole®; Flagyl®; Florazole® ER; MetroCream®; Metrogel®; Nidagel™; Noritate®; Trikacide

Synonyms Metronidazole Hydrochloride

Pharmacologic Class Amebicide; Antibiotic, Miscellaneous; Antibiotic, Topical; Antiprotozoal, Nitroimidazole

- **Metronidazole Hydrochloride** *see* Metronidazole *on page 142*
- **Mevacor®** *see* Lovastatin *on page 135*
- **Mevinolin** *see* Lovastatin *on page 135*

Mexiletine (MEKS i le teen)

Genes of Interest

CYP1A2 *on page 246*

CYP2D6 *on page 254*

U.S. Brand Names Mexitil® [DSC]

Canadian Brand Names Novo-Mexiletine

Pharmacologic Class Antiarrhythmic Agent, Class Ib

- **Mexitil® [DSC]** *see* Mexiletine *on page 143*
- **Micardis®** *see* Telmisartan *on page 190*
- **Microgestin™** *see* Ethinyl Estradiol and Norethindrone *on page 104*
- **Microgestin™ Fe** *see* Ethinyl Estradiol and Norethindrone *on page 104*
- **microK®** *see* Potassium Chloride *on page 169*
- **microK® 10** *see* Potassium Chloride *on page 169*
- **Micro-K Extencaps® (Can)** *see* Potassium Chloride *on page 169*
- **Micronase®** *see* GlyBURIDE *on page 117*
- **Micronor®** *see* Norethindrone *on page 151*
- **Microzide™** *see* Hydrochlorothiazide *on page 120*
- **Midamor® [DSC]** *see* Amiloride *on page 57*

Midazolam (MID aye zoe lam)

Genes of Interest

ATP-Binding Cassette, Sub-Family B, Member 1 *on page 224*

CYP3A4 *on page 260*

Canadian Brand Names Apo-Midazolam®

Synonyms Midazolam Hydrochloride; Versed

Pharmacologic Class Benzodiazepine

- **Midazolam Hydrochloride** *see* Midazolam *on page 143*
- **Midol® Cramp and Body Aches [OTC]** *see* Ibuprofen *on page 123*
- **Midol® Extended Relief** *see* Naproxen *on page 148*
- **Mifeprex®** *see* Mifepristone *on page 143*

Mifepristone (mi FE pris tone)

Genes of Interest

ATP-Binding Cassette, Sub-Family B, Member 1 *on page 224*

U.S. Brand Names Mifeprex®

Synonyms RU-38486; RU-486

Pharmacologic Class Abortifacient; Antineoplastic Agent, Hormone Antagonist; Antiprogestin

- **Migranal®** *see* Dihydroergotamine *on page 92*
- **Minestrin™ 1/20 (Can)** *see* Ethinyl Estradiol and Norethindrone *on page 104*
- **Minitran™** *see* Nitroglycerin *on page 151*
- **Minocin®** *see* Minocycline *on page 144*

Minocycline (mi noe SYE kleen)

Genes of Interest None known

U.S. Brand Names Dynacin®; Minocin®; myrac™

Canadian Brand Names Alti-Minocycline; Apo-Minocycline®; Gen-Minocycline; Minocin®; Novo-Minocycline; PMS-Minocycline; Rhoxal-minocycline

Synonyms Minocycline Hydrochloride

Pharmacologic Class Antibiotic, Tetracycline Derivative

- ♦ **Minocycline Hydrochloride** *see* Minocycline *on page 144*
- ♦ **Min-Ovral® (Can)** *see* Ethinyl Estradiol and Levonorgestrel *on page 104*
- ♦ **Mircette®** *see* Ethinyl Estradiol and Desogestrel *on page 103*
- ♦ **Mirena®** *see* Levonorgestrel *on page 130*

Mirtazapine (mir TAZ a peen)

Genes of Interest

Alpha$_1$-Adrenergic Receptor *on page 210*
CYP1A2 *on page 246*
CYP3A4 *on page 260*
G-Protein Beta$_3$ Subunit *on page 286*
Gs Protein Alpha-Subunit *on page 288*

U.S. Brand Names Remeron SolTab®; Remeron®

Canadian Brand Names Gen-Mirtazapine; Novo-Mirtazapine; Remeron® RD; Remeron®; Rhoxal-mirtazapine; pms-Mirtazapine

Pharmacologic Class Antidepressant, Alpha-2 Antagonist

- ♦ **Misoprostol and Diclofenac** *see* Diclofenac and Misoprostol *on page 91*

Mitomycin (mye toe MYE sin)

Genes of Interest

ATP-Binding Cassette, Sub-Family B, Member 1 *on page 224*
NAD(P)H Quinone Oxidoreductase *on page 309*

U.S. Brand Names Mutamycin®

Canadian Brand Names Mutamycin®

Synonyms MTC; Mitomycin-C; Mitomycin-X; NSC-26980

Pharmacologic Class Antineoplastic Agent, Antibiotic

- ♦ **Mitomycin-X** *see* Mitomycin *on page 144*
- ♦ **Mitomycin-C** *see* Mitomycin *on page 144*
- ♦ **MK383** *see* Tirofiban *on page 195*
- ♦ **MK594** *see* Losartan *on page 134*
- ♦ **MK 869** *see* Aprepitant *on page 64*
- ♦ **Moban®** *see* Molindone *on page 145*
- ♦ **Mobic®** *see* Meloxicam *on page 137*
- ♦ **Mobicox® (Can)** *see* Meloxicam *on page 137*

Moclobemide (moe KLOE be mide)

Genes of Interest

CYP2C19 *on page 251*

Canadian Brand Names Alti-Moclobemide; Apo-Moclobemide®; Manerix®; Novo-Moclobemide; Nu-Moclobemide; PMS-Moclobemide

Pharmacologic Class Antidepressant, Monoamine Oxidase Inhibitor, Reversible

Modafinil (moe DAF i nil)

Genes of Interest

CYP3A4 *on page 260*

U.S. Brand Names Provigil®

Canadian Brand Names Alertec®; Provigil®

Pharmacologic Class Stimulant

- ♦ **Modecate® (Can)** *see* Fluphenazine *on page 110*
- ♦ **Modicon®** *see* Ethinyl Estradiol and Norethindrone *on page 104*

Moexipril (mo EKS i pril)

Genes of Interest

Aldosterone Synthase *on page 208*
Angiotensin II Type 1 Receptor *on page 213*
Angiotensin-Converting Enzyme *on page 214*
Angiotensinogen *on page 219*
Bradykinin B_2-Receptor *on page 237*

U.S. Brand Names Univasc®

Synonyms Moexipril Hydrochloride

Pharmacologic Class Angiotensin-Converting Enzyme (ACE) Inhibitor

- ♦ **Moexipril Hydrochloride** *see* Moexipril *on page 145*

Molindone (moe LIN done)

Genes of Interest

Alpha$_1$-Adrenergic Receptor *on page 210*
D_2 Receptor *on page 263*

U.S. Brand Names Moban®

Canadian Brand Names Moban®

Synonyms Molindone Hydrochloride

Pharmacologic Class Antipsychotic Agent, Typical

- ♦ **Molindone Hydrochloride** *see* Molindone *on page 145*

Mometasone Furoate (moe MET a sone FYOOR oh ate)

Genes of Interest None known

U.S. Brand Names Asmanex® Twisthaler®; Elocon®; Nasonex®

Canadian Brand Names Elocom®; Nasonex®; ratio-Mometasone

Pharmacologic Class Corticosteroid, Inhalant (Oral); Corticosteroid, Nasal; Corticosteroid, Topical

- ♦ **Monacolin K** *see* Lovastatin *on page 135*
- ♦ **Monitan® (Can)** *see* Acebutolol *on page 52*
- ♦ **Monocor® (Can)** *see* Bisoprolol *on page 71*
- ♦ **Monodox®** *see* Doxycycline *on page 96*
- ♦ **MonoNessa™** *see* Ethinyl Estradiol and Norgestimate *on page 105*

- **Monopril®** *see* Fosinopril *on page 113*

Montelukast (mon te LOO kast)

Genes of Interest

Arachidonate 5-Lipoxygenase *on page 223*
CYP2C9 *on page 248*
Leukotriene C4 Synthase *on page 302*

U.S. Brand Names Singulair®

Canadian Brand Names Singulair®

Synonyms Montelukast Sodium

Pharmacologic Class Leukotriene-Receptor Antagonist

- **Montelukast Sodium** *see* Montelukast *on page 146*

Moricizine (mor I siz een)

Genes of Interest

CYP3A4 *on page 260*

U.S. Brand Names Ethmozine®

Canadian Brand Names Ethmozine®

Synonyms Moricizine Hydrochloride

Pharmacologic Class Antiarrhythmic Agent, Class I

- **Moricizine Hydrochloride** *see* Moricizine *on page 146*
- **Morning After Pill** *see* Ethinyl Estradiol and Norgestrel *on page 105*
- **Morphine HP® (Can)** *see* Morphine Sulfate *on page 146*
- **Morphine LP® Epidural (Can)** *see* Morphine Sulfate *on page 146*

Morphine Sulfate (MOR feen SUL fate)

Genes of Interest

COMT *on page 244*

U.S. Brand Names Astramorph/PF™; Avinza™; DepoDur™; Duramorph®; Infumorph®; Kadian®; MS Contin®; Oramorph SR®; RMS®; Roxanol 100™; Roxanol™-T; Roxanol™

Canadian Brand Names Kadian®; M-Eslon®; M.O.S.-Sulfate®; MS Contin®; MS-IR®; Morphine HP®; Morphine LP® Epidural; PMS-Morphine Sulfate SR; Statex®; ratio-Morphine SR

Synonyms MSO_4 (error-prone abbreviation)

Pharmacologic Class Analgesic, Narcotic

- **M.O.S.-Sulfate® (Can)** *see* Morphine Sulfate *on page 146*
- **Motilium® (Can)** *see* Domperidone *on page 94*
- **Motrin®** *see* Ibuprofen *on page 123*
- **Motrin® Children's [OTC]** *see* Ibuprofen *on page 123*
- **Motrin® IB [OTC]** *see* Ibuprofen *on page 123*
- **Motrin® Infants' [OTC]** *see* Ibuprofen *on page 123*
- **Motrin® Junior Strength [OTC]** *see* Ibuprofen *on page 123*

Moxifloxacin (moxs i FLOKS a sin)

Genes of Interest

Cardiac Potassium Ion Channel *on page 241*
Cardiac Sodium Channel *on page 242*

U.S. Brand Names Avelox® I.V.; Avelox®; Vigamox™

Canadian Brand Names Avelox®; Vigamox™

Synonyms Moxifloxacin Hydrochloride

Pharmacologic Class Antibiotic, Ophthalmic; Antibiotic, Quinolone

- **Moxifloxacin Hydrochloride** *see* Moxifloxacin *on page 146*
- **Moxilin®** *see* Amoxicillin *on page 59*
- **6-MP** *see* Mercaptopurine *on page 138*
- **MPA** *see* MedroxyPROGESTERone *on page 137*
- **MPA and Estrogens (Conjugated)** *see* Estrogens (Conjugated/Equine) and Medroxyprogesterone *on page 102*
- **MS Contin®** *see* Morphine Sulfate *on page 146*
- **MS-IR® (Can)** *see* Morphine Sulfate *on page 146*
- **MSO_4 (error-prone abbreviation)** *see* Morphine Sulfate *on page 146*
- **MTC** *see* Mitomycin *on page 144*

Mupirocin (myoo PEER oh sin)

Genes of Interest None known

U.S. Brand Names Bactroban® Nasal; Bactroban®; Centany™

Canadian Brand Names Bactroban®

Synonyms Mupirocin Calcium; Pseudomonic Acid A

Pharmacologic Class Antibiotic, Topical

- **Mupirocin Calcium** *see* Mupirocin *on page 147*
- **Mutamycin®** *see* Mitomycin *on page 144*
- **Mycobutin®** *see* Rifabutin *on page 179*
- **Mykrox® (Can)** *see* Metolazone *on page 142*
- **Myleran®** *see* Busulfan *on page 73*
- **myrac™** *see* Minocycline *on page 144*

Nabumetone (na BYOO me tone)

Genes of Interest

Leukotriene C4 Synthase *on page 302*

U.S. Brand Names Relafen®

Canadian Brand Names Apo-Nabumetone®; Gen-Nabumetone; Novo-Nabumetone; Relafen™; Rhoxal-nabumetone

Pharmacologic Class Nonsteroidal Anti-inflammatory Drug (NSAID), Oral

Nadolol (nay DOE lole)

Genes of Interest

$Beta_1$-Adrenergic Receptor *on page 230*
Gs Protein Alpha-Subunit *on page 288*

U.S. Brand Names Corgard®

Canadian Brand Names Alti-Nadolol; Apo-Nadol®; Corgard®; Novo-Nadolol

Pharmacologic Class Beta-Adrenergic Blocker, Nonselective

- **Nadopen-V® (Can)** *see* Penicillin V Potassium *on page 163*

Nalbuphine (NAL byoo feen)

Genes of Interest

COMT *on page 244*

U.S. Brand Names Nubain®

Synonyms Nalbuphine Hydrochloride

Pharmacologic Class Analgesic, Narcotic

- ♦ **Nalbuphine Hydrochloride** *see* Nalbuphine *on page 148*
- ♦ **Nalfon®** *see* Fenoprofen *on page 107*

Nalidixic Acid (nal i DIKS ik AS id)

Genes of Interest

Glucose-6-Phosphate Dehydrogenase *on page 281*

U.S. Brand Names NegGram®

Canadian Brand Names NegGram®

Synonyms Nalidixinic Acid

Pharmacologic Class Antibiotic, Quinolone

- ♦ **Nalidixinic Acid** *see* Nalidixic Acid *on page 148*
- ♦ **Naloxone and Buprenorphine** *see* Buprenorphine and Naloxone *on page 72*
- ♦ **Naloxone Hydrochloride and Pentazocine Hydrochloride** *see* Pentazocine *on page 163*
- ♦ **Naloxone Hydrochloride Dihydrate and Buprenorphine Hydrochloride** *see* Buprenorphine and Naloxone *on page 72*
- ♦ **Naprelan®** *see* Naproxen *on page 148*
- ♦ **Naprosyn®** *see* Naproxen *on page 148*

Naproxen (na PROKS en)

Genes of Interest

Leukotriene C4 Synthase *on page 302*

U.S. Brand Names Aleve® [OTC]; Anaprox® DS; Anaprox®; EC-Naprosyn®; Midol® Extended Relief; Naprelan®; Naprosyn®; Pamprin® Maximum Strength All Day Relief [OTC]

Canadian Brand Names Anaprox® DS; Anaprox®; Apo-Napro-Na DS®; Apo-Napro-Na®; Apo-Naproxen SR®; Apo-Naproxen®; Gen-Naproxen EC; Naprosyn®; Naxen®; Novo-Naproc EC; Novo-Naprox SR; Novo-Naprox Sodium DS; Novo-Naprox Sodium; Novo-Naprox; Nu-Naprox; Riva-Naproxen

Synonyms Naproxen Sodium

Pharmacologic Class Nonsteroidal Anti-inflammatory Drug (NSAID), Oral

- ♦ **Naproxen Sodium** *see* Naproxen *on page 148*
- ♦ **Nasacort® AQ** *see* Triamcinolone *on page 198*
- ♦ **Nasacort® HFA** *see* Triamcinolone *on page 198*
- ♦ **Nasonex®** *see* Mometasone Furoate *on page 145*

Nateglinide (na te GLYE nide)

Genes of Interest

CYP2C8 *on page 248*

CYP2C9 *on page 248*
CYP3A4 *on page 260*

U.S. Brand Names Starlix®

Canadian Brand Names Starlix®

Pharmacologic Class Antidiabetic Agent, Miscellaneous

- **Naturetin® [DSC]** *see* Bendroflumethiazide *on page 69*
- **Navane®** *see* Thiothixene *on page 193*
- **Navelbine®** *see* Vinorelbine *on page 203*
- **Naxen® (Can)** *see* Naproxen *on page 148*
- **NebuPent®** *see* Pentamidine *on page 163*
- **Necon® 0.5/35** *see* Ethinyl Estradiol and Norethindrone *on page 104*
- **Necon® 1/35** *see* Ethinyl Estradiol and Norethindrone *on page 104*
- **Necon® 1/50** *see* Mestranol and Norethindrone *on page 139*
- **Necon® 7/7/7** *see* Ethinyl Estradiol and Norethindrone *on page 104*
- **Necon® 10/11** *see* Ethinyl Estradiol and Norethindrone *on page 104*

Nefazodone (nef AY zoe done)

Genes of Interest

$Alpha_1$-Adrenergic Receptor *on page 210*
ATP-Binding Cassette, Sub-Family B, Member 1 *on page 224*
CYP3A4 *on page 260*
G-Protein $Beta_3$ Subunit *on page 286*
Gs Protein Alpha-Subunit *on page 288*

U.S. Brand Names Serzone® [DSC]

Synonyms Nefazodone Hydrochloride

Pharmacologic Class Antidepressant, Serotonin Reuptake Inhibitor/Antagonist

- **Nefazodone Hydrochloride** *see* Nefazodone *on page 149*
- **NegGram®** *see* Nalidixic Acid *on page 148*

Nelfinavir (nel FIN a veer)

Genes of Interest

ATP-Binding Cassette, Sub-Family B, Member 1 *on page 224*

U.S. Brand Names Viracept®

Canadian Brand Names Viracept®

Synonyms NFV

Pharmacologic Class Antiretroviral Agent, Protease Inhibitor

- **Neoral®** *see* CycloSPORINE *on page 87*
- **Neurontin®** *see* Gabapentin *on page 114*
- **Nexium®** *see* Esomeprazole *on page 101*
- **NFV** *see* Nelfinavir *on page 149*

NiCARdipine (nye KAR de peen)

Genes of Interest

ATP-Binding Cassette, Sub-Family B, Member 1 *on page 224*
CYP3A4 *on page 260*

(Continued)

NiCARdipine *(Continued)*

U.S. Brand Names Cardene® I.V.; Cardene® SR; Cardene®

Synonyms Nicardipine Hydrochloride

Pharmacologic Class Calcium Channel Blocker

- **Nicardipine Hydrochloride** *see* NiCARdipine *on page 149*
- **Nidagel™ (Can)** *see* Metronidazole *on page 142*
- **Nifediac™ CC** *see* NIFEdipine *on page 150*
- **Nifedical™ XL** *see* NIFEdipine *on page 150*

NIFEdipine (nye FED i peen)

Genes of Interest

ATP-Binding Cassette, Sub-Family B, Member 1 *on page 224*

CYP3A4 *on page 260*

U.S. Brand Names Adalat® CC; Afeditab™ CR; Nifediac™ CC; Nifedical™ XL; Procardia XL®; Procardia®

Canadian Brand Names Adalat® XL®; Apo-Nifed PA®; Apo-Nifed®; Novo-Nifedin; Nu-Nifed; Procardia®

Pharmacologic Class Calcium Channel Blocker

- **Niftolid** *see* Flutamide *on page 111*
- **Nilandron®** *see* Nilutamide *on page 150*

Nilutamide (ni LOO ta mide)

Genes of Interest

CYP2C19 *on page 251*

U.S. Brand Names Nilandron®

Canadian Brand Names Anandron®

Synonyms RU-23908

Pharmacologic Class Antiandrogen; Antineoplastic Agent, Antiandrogen

Nimodipine (nye MOE di peen)

Genes of Interest

CYP3A4 *on page 260*

U.S. Brand Names Nimotop®

Canadian Brand Names Nimotop®

Pharmacologic Class Calcium Channel Blocker

- **Nimotop®** *see* Nimodipine *on page 150*
- **Niravam™** *see* Alprazolam *on page 56*

Nisoldipine (NYE sole di peen)

Genes of Interest

CYP3A4 *on page 260*

U.S. Brand Names Sular®

Pharmacologic Class Calcium Channel Blocker

- **Nitalapram** *see* Citalopram *on page 81*
- **Nitrek®** *see* Nitroglycerin *on page 151*

Nitrendipine (NYE tren di peen)

Genes of Interest

ATP-Binding Cassette, Sub-Family B, Member 1 *on page 224*
CYP3A4 *on page 260*

Pharmacologic Class Calcium Channel Blocker

- **Nitro-Bid®** *see* Nitroglycerin *on page 151*
- **Nitro-Dur®** *see* Nitroglycerin *on page 151*

Nitrofurantoin (nye troe fyoor AN toyn)

Genes of Interest

Glucose-6-Phosphate Dehydrogenase *on page 281*

U.S. Brand Names Furadantin®; Macrobid®; Macrodantin®

Canadian Brand Names Apo-Nitrofurantoin®; Macrobid®; Macrodantin®; Novo-Furantoin

Pharmacologic Class Antibiotic, Miscellaneous

Nitroglycerin (nye troe GLI ser in)

Genes of Interest

G-Protein Beta$_3$ Subunit *on page 286*

U.S. Brand Names Minitran™; Nitrek®; Nitro-Bid®; Nitro-Dur®; Nitro-Tab®; NitroQuick®; NitroTime®; Nitrolingual®; Nitrostat®

Canadian Brand Names Gen-Nitro; Minitran™; Nitro-Dur®; Nitrol®; Nitrostat™; Rho-Nitro; Transderm-Nitro®

Synonyms Glyceryl Trinitrate; NTG; Nitroglycerol

Pharmacologic Class Vasodilator

- **Nitroglycerol** *see* Nitroglycerin *on page 151*
- **Nitrol® (Can)** *see* Nitroglycerin *on page 151*
- **Nitrolingual®** *see* Nitroglycerin *on page 151*
- **NitroQuick®** *see* Nitroglycerin *on page 151*
- **Nitrostat®** *see* Nitroglycerin *on page 151*
- **Nitro-Tab®** *see* Nitroglycerin *on page 151*
- **NitroTime®** *see* Nitroglycerin *on page 151*
- **4′-Nitro-3′-Trifluoromethylisobutyrantide** *see* Flutamide *on page 111*
- **Nizoral®** *see* Ketoconazole *on page 128*
- **Nizoral® A-D [OTC]** *see* Ketoconazole *on page 128*
- **Nolvadex®** *see* Tamoxifen *on page 190*
- **Nolvadex®-D (Can)** *see* Tamoxifen *on page 190*
- **Nora-BE™** *see* Norethindrone *on page 151*
- **Norco®** *see* Hydrocodone and Acetaminophen *on page 120*
- **Nordette®** *see* Ethinyl Estradiol and Levonorgestrel *on page 104*
- **Norelgestromin and Ethinyl Estradiol** *see* Ethinyl Estradiol and Norelgestromin *on page 104*

Norethindrone (nor eth IN drone)

Genes of Interest

BRCA Genes *on page 240*
Prothrombin *on page 315*

(Continued)

Norethindrone *(Continued)*

U.S. Brand Names Aygestin®; Camila™; Errin™; Jolivette™; Micronor®; Nor-QD®; Nora-BE™

Canadian Brand Names Micronor®

Synonyms Norethindrone Acetate; Norethisterone

Pharmacologic Class Contraceptive; Progestin

- **Norethindrone Acetate** *see* Norethindrone *on page 151*
- **Norethindrone Acetate and Ethinyl Estradiol** *see* Ethinyl Estradiol and Norethindrone *on page 104*
- **Norethindrone and Mestranol** *see* Mestranol and Norethindrone *on page 139*
- **Norethisterone** *see* Norethindrone *on page 151*
- **Norgestimate and Ethinyl Estradiol** *see* Ethinyl Estradiol and Norgestimate *on page 105*

Norgestrel (nor JES trel)

Genes of Interest

BRCA Genes *on page 240*
Prothrombin *on page 315*

U.S. Brand Names Ovrette® [DSC]

Canadian Brand Names Ovrette®

Pharmacologic Class Contraceptive; Progestin

- **Norgestrel and Ethinyl Estradiol** *see* Ethinyl Estradiol and Norgestrel *on page 105*
- **Norinyl® 1+35** *see* Ethinyl Estradiol and Norethindrone *on page 104*
- **Norinyl® 1+50** *see* Mestranol and Norethindrone *on page 139*
- **Noritate®** *see* Metronidazole *on page 142*
- **Norpace®** *see* Disopyramide *on page 93*
- **Norpace® CR** *see* Disopyramide *on page 93*
- **Norplant® Implant (Can)** *see* Levonorgestrel *on page 130*
- **Norpramin®** *see* Desipramine *on page 89*
- **Nor-QD®** *see* Norethindrone *on page 151*
- **Nortrel™** *see* Ethinyl Estradiol and Norethindrone *on page 104*
- **Nortrel™ 7/7/7** *see* Ethinyl Estradiol and Norethindrone *on page 104*

Nortriptyline (nor TRIP ti leen)

Genes of Interest

$Alpha_1$-Adrenergic Receptor *on page 210*
ATP-Binding Cassette, Sub-Family B, Member 1 *on page 224*
G-Protein $Beta_3$ Subunit *on page 286*
Gs Protein Alpha-Subunit *on page 288*

U.S. Brand Names Pamelor®

Canadian Brand Names Alti-Nortriptyline; Apo-Nortriptyline®; Aventyl®; Gen-Nortriptyline; Norventyl; Novo-Nortriptyline; Nu-Nortriptyline; PMS-Nortriptyline

Synonyms Nortriptyline Hydrochloride

Pharmacologic Class Antidepressant, Tricyclic (Secondary Amine)

- **Nortriptyline Hydrochloride** *see* Nortriptyline *on page 152*

- ♦ **Norvasc®** *see* Amlodipine *on page 58*
- ♦ **Norventyl (Can)** *see* Nortriptyline *on page 152*
- ♦ **Norvir®** *see* Ritonavir *on page 180*
- ♦ **Norvir® SEC (Can)** *see* Ritonavir *on page 180*
- ♦ **Novamoxin® (Can)** *see* Amoxicillin *on page 59*
- ♦ **Novasen (Can)** *see* Aspirin *on page 65*
- ♦ **Novo-Acebutolol (Can)** *see* Acebutolol *on page 52*
- ♦ **Novo-Alendronate (Can)** *see* Alendronate *on page 55*
- ♦ **Novo-Alprazol (Can)** *see* Alprazolam *on page 56*
- ♦ **Novo-Amiodarone (Can)** *see* Amiodarone *on page 57*
- ♦ **Novo-Atenol (Can)** *see* Atenolol *on page 66*
- ♦ **Novo-Azathioprine (Can)** *see* Azathioprine *on page 67*
- ♦ **Novo-Bromazepam (Can)** *see* Bromazepam *on page 72*
- ♦ **Novo-Bupropion SR (Can)** *see* BuPROPion *on page 73*
- ♦ **Novo-Buspirone (Can)** *see* BusPIRone *on page 73*
- ♦ **Novo-Captopril (Can)** *see* Captopril *on page 75*
- ♦ **Novo-Carbamaz (Can)** *see* Carbamazepine *on page 75*
- ♦ **Novo-Carvedilol (Can)** *see* Carvedilol *on page 76*
- ♦ **Novo-Chloroquine (Can)** *see* Chloroquine *on page 79*
- ♦ **Novo-Chlorpromazine (Can)** *see* ChlorproMAZINE *on page 79*
- ♦ **Novo-Cilazapril (Can)** *see* Cilazapril *on page 80*
- ♦ **Novo-Cimetidine (Can)** *see* Cimetidine *on page 80*
- ♦ **Novo-Ciprofloxacin (Can)** *see* Ciprofloxacin *on page 81*
- ♦ **Novo-Citalopram (Can)** *see* Citalopram *on page 81*
- ♦ **Novo-Clavamoxin (Can)** *see* Amoxicillin and Clavulanate Potassium *on page 59*
- ♦ **Novo-Clindamycin (Can)** *see* Clindamycin *on page 82*
- ♦ **Novo-Clobazam (Can)** *see* Clobazam *on page 83*
- ♦ **Novo-Clonazepam (Can)** *see* Clonazepam *on page 83*
- ♦ **Novo-Clonidine (Can)** *see* Clonidine *on page 83*
- ♦ **Novo-Clopate (Can)** *see* Clorazepate *on page 84*
- ♦ **Novo-Cycloprine (Can)** *see* Cyclobenzaprine *on page 87*
- ♦ **Novo-Difenac (Can)** *see* Diclofenac *on page 91*
- ♦ **Novo-Difenac K (Can)** *see* Diclofenac *on page 91*
- ♦ **Novo-Difenac-SR (Can)** *see* Diclofenac *on page 91*
- ♦ **Novo-Diflunisal (Can)** *see* Diflunisal *on page 91*
- ♦ **Novo-Digoxin (Can)** *see* Digoxin *on page 92*
- ♦ **Novo-Diltazem (Can)** *see* Diltiazem *on page 93*
- ♦ **Novo-Diltazem-CD (Can)** *see* Diltiazem *on page 93*
- ♦ **Novo-Dipam (Can)** *see* Diazepam *on page 90*
- ♦ **Novo-Divalproex (Can)** *see* Valproic Acid and Derivatives *on page 201*
- ♦ **Novo-Domperidone (Can)** *see* Domperidone *on page 94*
- ♦ **Novo-Doxazosin (Can)** *see* Doxazosin *on page 95*
- ♦ **Novo-Doxepin (Can)** *see* Doxepin *on page 95*
- ♦ **Novo-Doxylin (Can)** *see* Doxycycline *on page 96*

- ♦ **Novo-Naprox SR (Can)** *see* Naproxen *on page 148*
- ♦ **Novo-Nifedin (Can)** *see* NIFEdipine *on page 150*
- ♦ **Novo-Nortriptyline (Can)** *see* Nortriptyline *on page 152*
- ♦ **Novo-Ofloxacin (Can)** *see* Ofloxacin *on page 158*
- ♦ **Novo-Paroxetine (Can)** *see* Paroxetine *on page 162*
- ♦ **Novo-Pen-VK (Can)** *see* Penicillin V Potassium *on page 163*
- ♦ **Novo-Peridol (Can)** *see* Haloperidol *on page 118*
- ♦ **Novo-Pheniram (Can)** *see* Chlorpheniramine *on page 79*
- ♦ **Novo-Pirocam (Can)** *see* Piroxicam *on page 166*
- ♦ **Novo-Pramine (Can)** *see* Imipramine *on page 124*
- ♦ **Novo-Pranol (Can)** *see* Propranolol *on page 173*
- ♦ **Novo-Pravastatin (Can)** *see* Pravastatin *on page 169*
- ♦ **Novo-Prednisone (Can)** *see* PredniSONE *on page 169*
- ♦ **Novo-Profen (Can)** *see* Ibuprofen *on page 123*
- ♦ **Novo-Purol (Can)** *see* Allopurinol *on page 55*
- ♦ **Novo-Quinidin (Can)** *see* Quinidine *on page 174*
- ♦ **Novo-Quinine (Can)** *see* Quinine *on page 175*
- ♦ **Novo-Ranidine (Can)** *see* Ranitidine *on page 176*
- ♦ **NovoRapid (Can)** *see* Insulin Preparations *on page 125*
- ♦ **Novo-Rythro Estolate (Can)** *see* Erythromycin *on page 99*
- ♦ **Novo-Rythro Ethylsuccinate (Can)** *see* Erythromycin *on page 99*
- ♦ **Novo-Selegiline (Can)** *see* Selegiline *on page 183*
- ♦ **Novo-Semide (Can)** *see* Furosemide *on page 114*
- ♦ **Novo-Sertraline (Can)** *see* Sertraline *on page 183*
- ♦ **Novo-Simvastatin (Can)** *see* Simvastatin *on page 184*
- ♦ **Novo-Sorbide (Can)** *see* Isosorbide Dinitrate *on page 127*
- ♦ **Novo-Sotalol (Can)** *see* Sotalol *on page 185*
- ♦ **Novo-Soxazole (Can)** *see* SulfiSOXAZOLE *on page 188*
- ♦ **Novo-Spiroton (Can)** *see* Spironolactone *on page 186*
- ♦ **Novo-Sundac (Can)** *see* Sulindac *on page 188*
- ♦ **Novo-Tamoxifen (Can)** *see* Tamoxifen *on page 190*
- ♦ **Novo-Temazepam (Can)** *see* Temazepam *on page 191*
- ♦ **Novo-Terazosin (Can)** *see* Terazosin *on page 191*
- ♦ **Novo-Theophyl SR (Can)** *see* Theophylline *on page 192*
- ♦ **Novo-Tiaprofenic (Can)** *see* Tiaprofenic Acid *on page 194*
- ♦ **Novo-Ticlopidine (Can)** *see* Ticlopidine *on page 194*
- ♦ **Novo-Trazodone (Can)** *see* Trazodone *on page 197*
- ♦ **Novo-Trifluzine (Can)** *see* Trifluoperazine *on page 198*
- ♦ **Novo-Trimel (Can)** *see* Sulfamethoxazole and Trimethoprim *on page 187*
- ♦ **Novo-Trimel D.S. (Can)** *see* Sulfamethoxazole and Trimethoprim *on page 187*
- ♦ **Novo-Triptyn (Can)** *see* Amitriptyline *on page 57*
- ♦ **Novo-Veramil SR (Can)** *see* Verapamil *on page 201*
- ♦ **Novo-Zopiclone (Can)** *see* Zopiclone *on page 206*

- ♦ **Nu-Divalproex (Can)** *see* Valproic Acid and Derivatives *on page 201*
- ♦ **Nu-Domperidone (Can)** *see* Domperidone *on page 94*
- ♦ **Nu-Doxycycline (Can)** *see* Doxycycline *on page 96*
- ♦ **Nu-Erythromycin-S (Can)** *see* Erythromycin *on page 99*
- ♦ **Nu-Famotidine (Can)** *see* Famotidine *on page 106*
- ♦ **Nu-Fenofibrate (Can)** *see* Fenofibrate *on page 107*
- ♦ **Nu-Fluoxetine (Can)** *see* Fluoxetine *on page 109*
- ♦ **Nu-Flurprofen (Can)** *see* Flurbiprofen *on page 111*
- ♦ **Nu-Fluvoxamine (Can)** *see* Fluvoxamine *on page 112*
- ♦ **Nu-Gabapentin (Can)** *see* Gabapentin *on page 114*
- ♦ **Nu-Gemfibrozil (Can)** *see* Gemfibrozil *on page 115*
- ♦ **Nu-Glyburide (Can)** *see* GlyBURIDE *on page 117*
- ♦ **Nu-Hydral (Can)** *see* HydrALAZINE *on page 119*
- ♦ **Nu-Ibuprofen (Can)** *see* Ibuprofen *on page 123*
- ♦ **Nu-Indapamide (Can)** *see* Indapamide *on page 124*
- ♦ **Nu-Indo (Can)** *see* Indomethacin *on page 125*
- ♦ **Nu-Ketoprofen (Can)** *see* Ketoprofen *on page 128*
- ♦ **Nu-Ketoprofen-E (Can)** *see* Ketoprofen *on page 128*
- ♦ **Nu-Loraz (Can)** *see* Lorazepam *on page 134*
- ♦ **Nu-Lovastatin (Can)** *see* Lovastatin *on page 135*
- ♦ **Nu-Loxapine (Can)** *see* Loxapine *on page 135*
- ♦ **Nu-Mefenamic (Can)** *see* Mefenamic Acid *on page 137*
- ♦ **Nu-Metformin (Can)** *see* Metformin *on page 139*
- ♦ **Nu-Metoclopramide (Can)** *see* Metoclopramide *on page 141*
- ♦ **Nu-Metop (Can)** *see* Metoprolol *on page 142*
- ♦ **Nu-Moclobemide (Can)** *see* Moclobemide *on page 144*
- ♦ **Numorphan®** *see* Oxymorphone *on page 161*
- ♦ **Nu-Naprox (Can)** *see* Naproxen *on page 148*
- ♦ **Nu-Nifed (Can)** *see* NIFEdipine *on page 150*
- ♦ **Nu-Nortriptyline (Can)** *see* Nortriptyline *on page 152*
- ♦ **Nu-Pen-VK (Can)** *see* Penicillin V Potassium *on page 163*
- ♦ **Nupercainal® Hydrocortisone Cream [OTC]** *see* Hydrocortisone *on page 121*
- ♦ **Nu-Pirox (Can)** *see* Piroxicam *on page 166*
- ♦ **Nu-Prochlor (Can)** *see* Prochlorperazine *on page 171*
- ♦ **Nu-Propranolol (Can)** *see* Propranolol *on page 173*
- ♦ **Nu-Ranit (Can)** *see* Ranitidine *on page 176*
- ♦ **Nu-Selegiline (Can)** *see* Selegiline *on page 183*
- ♦ **Nu-Sertraline (Can)** *see* Sertraline *on page 183*
- ♦ **Nu-Sotalol (Can)** *see* Sotalol *on page 185*
- ♦ **Nu-Sulfinpyrazone (Can)** *see* Sulfinpyrazone *on page 188*
- ♦ **Nu-Sundac (Can)** *see* Sulindac *on page 188*
- ♦ **Nu-Temazepam (Can)** *see* Temazepam *on page 191*
- ♦ **Nu-Terazosin (Can)** *see* Terazosin *on page 191*
- ♦ **Nu-Tetra (Can)** *see* Tetracycline *on page 192*

- **Nu-Tiaprofenic (Can)** *see* Tiaprofenic Acid *on page 194*
- **Nu-Ticlopidine (Can)** *see* Ticlopidine *on page 194*
- **Nu-Timolol (Can)** *see* Timolol *on page 195*
- **Nutracort®** *see* Hydrocortisone *on page 121*
- **Nu-Trazodone (Can)** *see* Trazodone *on page 197*
- **Nu-Trimipramine (Can)** *see* Trimipramine *on page 199*
- **NuvaRing®** *see* Ethinyl Estradiol and Etonogestrel *on page 103*
- **Nu-Verap (Can)** *see* Verapamil *on page 201*
- **Nu-Zopiclone (Can)** *see* Zopiclone *on page 206*
- **NVB** *see* Vinorelbine *on page 203*
- **Nydrazid® [DSC]** *see* Isoniazid *on page 126*

Octreotide (ok TREE oh tide)

Genes of Interest

Cardiac Potassium Ion Channel *on page 241*
Cardiac Sodium Channel *on page 242*

U.S. Brand Names Sandostatin LAR®; Sandostatin®

Canadian Brand Names Octreotide Acetate Omega; Sandostatin LAR®; Sandostatin®

Synonyms Octreotide Acetate

Pharmacologic Class Antidiarrheal; Somatostatin Analog

- **Octreotide Acetate** *see* Octreotide *on page 158*
- **Octreotide Acetate Omega (Can)** *see* Octreotide *on page 158*
- **Ocufen®** *see* Flurbiprofen *on page 111*
- **Ocuflox®** *see* Ofloxacin *on page 158*
- **Oesclim® (Can)** *see* Estradiol *on page 101*

Ofloxacin (oh FLOKS a sin)

Genes of Interest

ATP-Binding Cassette, Sub-Family B, Member 1 *on page 224*

U.S. Brand Names Floxin®; Ocuflox®

Canadian Brand Names Apo-Ofloxacin® ; Apo-Oflox®; Floxin®; Novo-Ofloxacin; Ocuflox®; PMS-Ofloxacin

Synonyms Floxin Otic Singles

Pharmacologic Class Antibiotic, Quinolone

- **Ogen®** *see* Estropipate *on page 102*
- **Ogestrel®** *see* Ethinyl Estradiol and Norgestrel *on page 105*

Olanzapine (oh LAN za peen)

Genes of Interest

$Alpha_1$-Adrenergic Receptor *on page 210*
D_2 Receptor *on page 263*
D_3 Receptor *on page 266*
Histamine 1 and 2 Receptors *on page 289*
5-HT_{2A} Receptor *on page 291*
5-HT_{2C} Receptor *on page 294*
5-HT_6 Receptor *on page 297*
TNF-Alpha *on page 319*

U.S. Brand Names Zyprexa® Zydis®; Zyprexa®
Canadian Brand Names Zyprexa® Zydis®; Zyprexa®
Synonyms LY170053; Zyprexa Zydis
Pharmacologic Class Antipsychotic Agent, Atypical

Olmesartan (ole me SAR tan)

Genes of Interest
Adipocyte-Derived Leucine Aminopeptidase *on page 208*
Aldosterone Synthase *on page 208*
Angiotensin II Type 1 Receptor *on page 213*
Angiotensin-Converting Enzyme *on page 214*
Angiotensinogen *on page 219*
Bradykinin B_2-Receptor *on page 237*
CYP2C9 *on page 248*
U.S. Brand Names Benicar®
Synonyms Olmesartan Medoxomil
Pharmacologic Class Angiotensin II Receptor Blocker

♦ **Olmesartan Medoxomil** *see* Olmesartan *on page 159*

Olopatadine (oh loe pa TA deen)

Genes of Interest None known
U.S. Brand Names Patanol®
Canadian Brand Names Patanol®
Pharmacologic Class Antihistamine; Ophthalmic Agent, Miscellaneous

Omeprazole (oh ME pray zol)

Genes of Interest
CYP2C19 *on page 251*
U.S. Brand Names Prilosec OTC™ [OTC]; Prilosec®; Zegerid™
Canadian Brand Names Apo-Omeprazole®; Losec MUPS®; Losec®
Pharmacologic Class Proton Pump Inhibitor; Substituted Benzimidazole

♦ **Omnicef®** *see* Cefdinir *on page 77*
♦ **Onxol™** *see* Paclitaxel *on page 162*
♦ **OPC-13013** *see* Cilostazol *on page 80*
♦ **OPC-14597** *see* Aripiprazole *on page 64*
♦ **Opium and Belladonna** *see* Belladonna and Opium *on page 68*

Opium Tincture (OH pee um TING chur)

Genes of Interest
COMT *on page 244*
Synonyms DTO (error-prone abbreviation); Opium Tincture, Deodorized
Pharmacologic Class Analgesic, Narcotic; Antidiarrheal

♦ **Opium Tincture, Deodorized** *see* Opium Tincture *on page 159*
♦ **Optivar®** *see* Azelastine *on page 67*
♦ **Oracort (Can)** *see* Triamcinolone *on page 198*
♦ **Oramorph SR®** *see* Morphine Sulfate *on page 146*

- **Orap®** *see* Pimozide *on page 166*
- **Orciprenaline Sulfate** *see* Metaproterenol *on page 139*
- **Ortho® 0.5/35 (Can)** *see* Ethinyl Estradiol and Norethindrone *on page 104*
- **Ortho® 1/35 (Can)** *see* Ethinyl Estradiol and Norethindrone *on page 104*
- **Ortho® 7/7/7 (Can)** *see* Ethinyl Estradiol and Norethindrone *on page 104*
- **Ortho-Cept®** *see* Ethinyl Estradiol and Desogestrel *on page 103*
- **Ortho-Cyclen®** *see* Ethinyl Estradiol and Norgestimate *on page 105*
- **Ortho-Est®** *see* Estropipate *on page 102*
- **Ortho Evra™** *see* Ethinyl Estradiol and Norelgestromin *on page 104*
- **Ortho-Novum®** *see* Ethinyl Estradiol and Norethindrone *on page 104*
- **Ortho-Novum® 1/50** *see* Mestranol and Norethindrone *on page 139*
- **Ortho Tri-Cyclen®** *see* Ethinyl Estradiol and Norgestimate *on page 105*
- **Ortho Tri-Cyclen® Lo** *see* Ethinyl Estradiol and Norgestimate *on page 105*
- **Orudis® KT [OTC] [DSC]** *see* Ketoprofen *on page 128*
- **Oruvail® (Can)** *see* Ketoprofen *on page 128*
- **Ovace™** *see* Sulfacetamide *on page 187*
- **Ovcon®** *see* Ethinyl Estradiol and Norethindrone *on page 104*
- **Ovral® [DSC]** *see* Ethinyl Estradiol and Norgestrel *on page 105*
- **Ovrette® [DSC]** *see* Norgestrel *on page 152*

Oxaliplatin (ox AL i pla tin)

Genes of Interest

Excision Repair Cross-Complementing Rodent Repair Deficiency, Complementation Group 1 *on page 274*

Excision Repair Cross-Complementing Rodent Repair Deficiency, Complementation Group 2 *on page 277*

XRCC1 *on page 331*

U.S. Brand Names Eloxatin™

Synonyms Diaminocyclohexane Oxalatoplatinum; L-OHP; NSC-266046

Pharmacologic Class Antineoplastic Agent, Alkylating Agent

Oxaprozin (oks a PROE zin)

Genes of Interest

Leukotriene C4 Synthase *on page 302*

U.S. Brand Names Daypro®

Canadian Brand Names Apo-Oxaprozin®; Daypro®

Pharmacologic Class Nonsteroidal Anti-inflammatory Drug (NSAID), Oral

- **Oxeze® Turbuhaler® (Can)** *see* Formoterol *on page 112*
- **Oxilapine Succinate** *see* Loxapine *on page 135*
- **Oxycocet® (Can)** *see* Oxycodone and Acetaminophen *on page 161*
- **Oxycodan® (Can)** *see* Oxycodone and Aspirin *on page 161*

Oxycodone (oks i KOE done)

Genes of Interest

COMT *on page 244*

CYP2D6 *on page 254*

U.S. Brand Names OxyContin®; OxyFast®; OxyIR®; Oxydose™; Roxicodone™ Intensol™; Roxicodone™

Canadian Brand Names Oxy.IR®; OxyContin®; Supeudol®

Synonyms Dihydrohydroxycodeinone; Oxycodone Hydrochloride

Pharmacologic Class Analgesic, Narcotic

Oxycodone and Acetaminophen

(oks i KOE done & a seet a MIN oh fen)

Genes of Interest

COMT *on page 244*

CYP2D6 *on page 254*

U.S. Brand Names Endocet®; Percocet®; Roxicet™ 5/500; Roxicet™; Tylox®

Canadian Brand Names Endocet®; Oxycocet®; PMS-Oxycodone-Acetaminophen; Percocet®-Demi; Percocet®

Synonyms Acetaminophen and Oxycodone

Pharmacologic Class Analgesic, Narcotic

Oxycodone and Aspirin (oks i KOE done & AS pir in)

Genes of Interest

COMT *on page 244*

CYP2D6 *on page 254*

Glycoprotein IIIa Receptor *on page 285*

Leukotriene C4 Synthase *on page 302*

U.S. Brand Names Endodan®; Percodan®

Canadian Brand Names Endodan®; Oxycodan®; Percodan®

Synonyms Aspirin and Oxycodone

Pharmacologic Class Analgesic, Narcotic

- **Oxycodone Hydrochloride** *see* Oxycodone *on page 161*
- **OxyContin®** *see* Oxycodone *on page 161*
- **Oxydose™** *see* Oxycodone *on page 161*
- **OxyFast®** *see* Oxycodone *on page 161*
- **OxyIR®** *see* Oxycodone *on page 161*

Oxymorphone (oks i MOR fone)

Genes of Interest

COMT *on page 244*

U.S. Brand Names Numorphan®

Synonyms Oxymorphone Hydrochloride

Pharmacologic Class Analgesic, Narcotic

- **Oxymorphone Hydrochloride** *see* Oxymorphone *on page 161*
- **P-071** *see* Cetirizine *on page 78*
- **Pacerone®** *see* Amiodarone *on page 57*

Paclitaxel (PAK li taks el)

Genes of Interest

ATP-Binding Cassette, Sub-Family B, Member 1 *on page 224*
CYP2C8 *on page 248*
CYP2C9 *on page 248*
CYP3A4 *on page 260*

U.S. Brand Names Onxol™; Taxol®

Canadian Brand Names Taxol®

Synonyms NSC-125973

Pharmacologic Class Antineoplastic Agent, Antimicrotubular; Antineoplastic Agent, Natural Source (Plant) Derivative

- ♦ **Palladone™** *see* Hydromorphone *on page 122*
- ♦ **Pamelor®** *see* Nortriptyline *on page 152*
- ♦ **Pamprin® Maximum Strength All Day Relief [OTC]** *see* Naproxen *on page 148*
- ♦ **Pandel®** *see* Hydrocortisone *on page 121*
- ♦ **Panixine DisperDose™** *see* Cephalexin *on page 78*
- ♦ **Panto™ IV (Can)** *see* Pantoprazole *on page 162*
- ♦ **Pantoloc™ (Can)** *see* Pantoprazole *on page 162*

Pantoprazole (pan TOE pra zole)

Genes of Interest None known

U.S. Brand Names Protonix®

Canadian Brand Names Pantoloc™; Panto™ IV; Protonix®

Pharmacologic Class Proton Pump Inhibitor; Substituted Benzimidazole

- ♦ **Paraplatin®** *see* Carboplatin *on page 76*
- ♦ **Paraplatin-AQ (Can)** *see* Carboplatin *on page 76*

Paregoric (par e GOR ik)

Genes of Interest

COMT *on page 244*

Synonyms Camphorated Tincture of Opium (error-prone synonym)

Pharmacologic Class Analgesic, Narcotic

- ♦ **Pariet® (Can)** *see* Rabeprazole *on page 175*
- ♦ **Pariprazole** *see* Rabeprazole *on page 175*
- ♦ **Parlodel®** *see* Bromocriptine *on page 72*

Paroxetine (pa ROKS e teen)

Genes of Interest

CYP2D6 *on page 254*
D_2 Receptor *on page 263*
D_4 Receptor *on page 268*
G-Protein $Beta_3$ Subunit *on page 286*
Gs Protein Alpha-Subunit *on page 288*
5-HT_{2A} Receptor *on page 291*
5-HT Transporter *on page 297*
Monoamine Oxidase A *on page 307*

TNF-Alpha *on page 319*
Tryptophan Hydroxylase *on page 321*

U.S. Brand Names Paxil CR™; Paxil®; Pexeva™

Canadian Brand Names Apo-Paroxetine®; CO Paroxetine; Gen-Paroxetine; Novo-Paroxetine; PMS-Paroxetine; Paxil CR™; Paxil®; Rhoxal-paroxetine; ratio-Paroxetine

Synonyms Paroxetine Hydrochloride; Paroxetine Mesylate

Pharmacologic Class Antidepressant, Selective Serotonin Reuptake Inhibitor

- **Paroxetine Hydrochloride** *see* Paroxetine *on page 162*
- **Paroxetine Mesylate** *see* Paroxetine *on page 162*
- **Patanol®** *see* Olopatadine *on page 159*
- **Paxil®** *see* Paroxetine *on page 162*
- **Paxil CR™** *see* Paroxetine *on page 162*
- **PCA (error-prone abbreviation)** *see* Procainamide *on page 170*
- **PCE®** *see* Erythromycin *on page 99*
- **PCP** *see* Phencyclidine *on page 165*
- **Pediazole®** *see* Erythromycin and Sulfisoxazole *on page 100*

Penicillin V Potassium (pen i SIL in vee poe TASS ee um)

Genes of Interest None known

U.S. Brand Names Veetids®

Canadian Brand Names Apo-Pen VK®; Nadopen-V®; Novo-Pen-VK; Nu-Pen-VK; PVF® K

Synonyms Pen VK; Phenoxymethyl Penicillin

Pharmacologic Class Antibiotic, Penicillin

- **Pennsaid® (Can)** *see* Diclofenac *on page 91*
- **Pentam-300®** *see* Pentamidine *on page 163*

Pentamidine (pen TAM i deen)

Genes of Interest

Cardiac Potassium Ion Channel *on page 241*
Cardiac Sodium Channel *on page 242*
CYP2C19 *on page 251*

U.S. Brand Names NebuPent®; Pentam-300®

Synonyms Pentamidine Isethionate

Pharmacologic Class Antibiotic, Miscellaneous

- **Pentamidine Isethionate** *see* Pentamidine *on page 163*
- **Pentamycetin® (Can)** *see* Chloramphenicol *on page 78*

Pentazocine (pen TAZ oh seen)

Genes of Interest COMT *on page 244*

U.S. Brand Names Talwin® NX; Talwin®

Canadian Brand Names Talwin®

Synonyms Naloxone Hydrochloride and Pentazocine Hydrochloride; Pentazocine Hydrochloride and Naloxone Hydrochloride; Pentazocine Hydrochloride; Pentazocine Lactate

Pharmacologic Class Analgesic, Narcotic

- **Pentazocine Hydrochloride** *see* Pentazocine *on page 163*
- **Pentazocine Hydrochloride and Naloxone Hydrochloride** *see* Pentazocine *on page 163*
- **Pentazocine Lactate** *see* Pentazocine *on page 163*
- **Pen VK** *see* Penicillin V Potassium *on page 163*
- **Pepcid®** *see* Famotidine *on page 106*
- **Pepcid® AC [OTC]** *see* Famotidine *on page 106*
- **Pepcid® I.V. (Can)** *see* Famotidine *on page 106*
- **Percocet®** *see* Oxycodone and Acetaminophen *on page 161*
- **Percocet®-Demi (Can)** *see* Oxycodone and Acetaminophen *on page 161*
- **Percodan®** *see* Oxycodone and Aspirin *on page 161*
- **Percogesic® [OTC]** *see* Acetaminophen and Phenyltoloxamine *on page 53*

Pergolide (PER go lide)

Genes of Interest

CYP2D6 *on page 254*
CYP3A4 *on page 260*

U.S. Brand Names Permax®

Canadian Brand Names Permax®

Synonyms Pergolide Mesylate

Pharmacologic Class Anti-Parkinson's Agent, Dopamine Agonist; Ergot Derivative

- **Pergolide Mesylate** *see* Pergolide *on page 164*
- **Peridol (Can)** *see* Haloperidol *on page 118*

Perindopril Erbumine (per IN doe pril er BYOO meen)

Genes of Interest

Aldosterone Synthase *on page 208*
Angiotensin II Type 1 Receptor *on page 213*
Angiotensin-Converting Enzyme *on page 214*
Angiotensinogen *on page 219*
Bradykinin B_2-Receptor *on page 237*

U.S. Brand Names Aceon®

Canadian Brand Names Coversyl®

Pharmacologic Class Angiotensin-Converting Enzyme (ACE) Inhibitor

- **Periostat®** *see* Doxycycline *on page 96*
- **Permax®** *see* Pergolide *on page 164*

Perphenazine (per FEN a zeen)

Genes of Interest

$Alpha_1$-Adrenergic Receptor *on page 210*
CYP2D6 *on page 254*
D_2 Receptor *on page 263*

Canadian Brand Names Apo-Perphenazine®

Pharmacologic Class Antipsychotic Agent, Typical, Phenothiazine

- **Perphenazine and Amitriptyline** *see* Amitriptyline and Perphenazine *on page 58*
- **Persantine®** *see* Dipyridamole *on page 93*
- **Pethidine Hydrochloride** *see* Meperidine *on page 138*
- **Pexeva™** *see* Paroxetine *on page 162*
- **Pexicam® (Can)** *see* Piroxicam *on page 166*
- **PFA** *see* Foscarnet *on page 112*
- **Phenadoz™** *see* Promethazine *on page 171*

Phencyclidine (fen SYE kli deen)

Genes of Interest

CYP3A4 *on page 260*

Synonyms PCP

Pharmacologic Class General Anesthetic

- **Phenergan®** *see* Promethazine *on page 171*

Phenobarbital (fee noe BAR bi tal)

Genes of Interest

CYP2C19 *on page 251*

U.S. Brand Names Luminal® Sodium

Canadian Brand Names PMS-Phenobarbital

Synonyms Phenobarbital Sodium; Phenobarbitone; Phenylethylmalonylurea

Pharmacologic Class Anticonvulsant, Barbiturate; Barbiturate

- **Phenobarbital Sodium** *see* Phenobarbital *on page 165*
- **Phenobarbitone** *see* Phenobarbital *on page 165*
- **Phenoxymethyl Penicillin** *see* Penicillin V Potassium *on page 163*
- **Phenylethylmalonylurea** *see* Phenobarbital *on page 165*
- **Phenylgesic® [OTC]** *see* Acetaminophen and Phenyltoloxamine *on page 53*
- **Phenyltoloxamine and Acetaminophen** *see* Acetaminophen and Phenyltoloxamine *on page 53*
- **Phenytek™** *see* Phenytoin *on page 165*

Phenytoin (FEN i toyn)

Genes of Interest

ATP-Binding Cassette, Sub-Family B, Member 1 *on page 224*
CYP2C8 *on page 248*
CYP2C9 *on page 248*
CYP2C19 *on page 251*

U.S. Brand Names Dilantin®; Phenytek™

Canadian Brand Names Dilantin®

Synonyms DPH; Diphenylhydantoin; Phenytoin Sodium, Extended; Phenytoin Sodium, Prompt; Phenytoin Sodium

Pharmacologic Class Antiarrhythmic Agent, Class Ib; Anticonvulsant, Hydantoin

- **Phenytoin Sodium** *see* Phenytoin *on page 165*
- **Phenytoin Sodium, Extended** *see* Phenytoin *on page 165*
- **Phenytoin Sodium, Prompt** *see* Phenytoin *on page 165*
- **Phosphonoformate** *see* Foscarnet *on page 112*
- **Phosphonoformic Acid** *see* Foscarnet *on page 112*
- **Phoxal-timolol (Can)** *see* Timolol *on page 195*
- **Phrenilin® With Caffeine and Codeine** *see* Butalbital, Aspirin, Caffeine, and Codeine *on page 74*
- ***p*-Hydroxyampicillin** *see* Amoxicillin *on page 59*
- **Phyllocontin® (Can)** *see* Aminophylline *on page 57*
- **Phyllocontin®-350 (Can)** *see* Aminophylline *on page 57*

Pimozide (PI moe zide)

Genes of Interest

Alpha$_1$-Adrenergic Receptor *on page 210*
Cardiac Potassium Ion Channel *on page 241*
Cardiac Sodium Channel *on page 242*
CYP1A2 *on page 246*
CYP2D6 *on page 254*
CYP3A4 *on page 260*
D$_2$ Receptor *on page 263*

U.S. Brand Names Orap®
Canadian Brand Names Apo-Pimozide®; Orap®
Pharmacologic Class Antipsychotic Agent, Typical

Pioglitazone (pye oh GLI ta zone)

Genes of Interest

CYP2C8 *on page 248*
CYP2C9 *on page 248*
CYP3A4 *on page 260*

U.S. Brand Names Actos®
Canadian Brand Names Actos®
Pharmacologic Class Antidiabetic Agent, Thiazolidinedione

- **Piperazine Estrone Sulfate** *see* Estropipate *on page 102*

Pirbuterol (peer BYOO ter ole)

Genes of Interest Beta$_2$-Adrenergic Receptor *on page 233*
U.S. Brand Names Maxair™ Autohaler™
Synonyms Pirbuterol Acetate
Pharmacologic Class Beta$_2$-Adrenergic Agonist

- **Pirbuterol Acetate** *see* Pirbuterol *on page 166*

Piroxicam (peer OKS i kam)

Genes of Interest Leukotriene C4 Synthase *on page 302*
U.S. Brand Names Feldene®
Canadian Brand Names Apo-Piroxicam®; Gen-Piroxicam; Novo-Pirocam; Nu-Pirox; Pexicam®
Pharmacologic Class Nonsteroidal Anti-inflammatory Drug (NSAID), Oral

- ♦ **PMS-Lorazepam (Can)** *see* Lorazepam *on page 134*
- ♦ **PMS-Lovastatin (Can)** *see* Lovastatin *on page 135*
- ♦ **PMS-Loxapine (Can)** *see* Loxapine *on page 135*
- ♦ **PMS-Mefenamic Acid (Can)** *see* Mefenamic Acid *on page 137*
- ♦ **PMS-Meloxicam (Can)** *see* Meloxicam *on page 137*
- ♦ **PMS-Metformin (Can)** *see* Metformin *on page 139*
- ♦ **PMS-Methylphenidate (Can)** *see* Methylphenidate *on page 141*
- ♦ **PMS-Metoprolol (Can)** *see* Metoprolol *on page 142*
- ♦ **PMS-Minocycline (Can)** *see* Minocycline *on page 144*
- ♦ **PMS-Mirtazapine (Can)** *see* Mirtazapine *on page 144*
- ♦ **PMS-Moclobemide (Can)** *see* Moclobemide *on page 144*
- ♦ **PMS-Morphine Sulfate SR (Can)** *see* Morphine Sulfate *on page 146*
- ♦ **PMS-Nortriptyline (Can)** *see* Nortriptyline *on page 152*
- ♦ **PMS-Ofloxacin (Can)** *see* Ofloxacin *on page 158*
- ♦ **PMS-Oxycodone-Acetaminophen (Can)** *see* Oxycodone and Acetaminophen *on page 161*
- ♦ **PMS-Paroxetine (Can)** *see* Paroxetine *on page 162*
- ♦ **PMS-Phenobarbital (Can)** *see* Phenobarbital *on page 165*
- ♦ **PMS-Pravastatin (Can)** *see* Pravastatin *on page 169*
- ♦ **PMS-Ranitidine (Can)** *see* Ranitidine *on page 176*
- ♦ **PMS-Salbutamol (Can)** *see* Albuterol *on page 54*
- ♦ **PMS-Sertraline (Can)** *see* Sertraline *on page 183*
- ♦ **PMS-Simvastatin (Can)** *see* Simvastatin *on page 184*
- ♦ **PMS-Sotalol (Can)** *see* Sotalol *on page 185*
- ♦ **PMS-Temazepam (Can)** *see* Temazepam *on page 191*
- ♦ **PMS-Terazosin (Can)** *see* Terazosin *on page 191*
- ♦ **PMS-Theophylline (Can)** *see* Theophylline *on page 192*
- ♦ **PMS-Tiaprofenic (Can)** *see* Tiaprofenic Acid *on page 194*
- ♦ **PMS-Timolol (Can)** *see* Timolol *on page 195*
- ♦ **PMS-Trazodone (Can)** *see* Trazodone *on page 197*
- ♦ **PMS-Trifluoperazine (Can)** *see* Trifluoperazine *on page 198*
- ♦ **PMS-Valproic Acid (Can)** *see* Valproic Acid and Derivatives *on page 201*
- ♦ **PMS-Valproic Acid E.C. (Can)** *see* Valproic Acid and Derivatives *on page 201*
- ♦ **PMS-Zopiclone (Can)** *see* Zopiclone *on page 206*

Polythiazide (pol i THYE a zide)

Genes of Interest

Alpha-Adducin *on page 212*

G-Protein Beta$_3$ Subunit *on page 286*

U.S. Brand Names Renese®

Pharmacologic Class Diuretic, Thiazide

- ♦ **Ponstel®** *see* Mefenamic Acid *on page 137*
- ♦ **Portia™** *see* Ethinyl Estradiol and Levonorgestrel *on page 104*
- ♦ **Post Peel Healing Balm [OTC]** *see* Hydrocortisone *on page 121*

Potassium Chloride (poe TASS ee um KLOR ide)

Genes of Interest None known

U.S. Brand Names K+ Potassium; K-Dur® 10; K-Dur® 20; K-Lor®; K-Tab®; Kaon-Cl-10®; Kaon-Cl® 20; Kay Ciel®; Klor-Con® 10; Klor-Con® 8; Klor-Con® M; Klor-Con®/25; Klor-Con®; Rum-K®; microK® 10; microK®

Canadian Brand Names Apo-K®; K-10®; K-Dur®; K-Lor®; K-Lyte®/Cl; Micro-K Extencaps®; Roychlor®; Slow-K®

Synonyms KCl

Pharmacologic Class Electrolyte Supplement, Oral; Electrolyte Supplement, Parenteral

- **Prandin®** *see* Repaglinide *on page 177*
- **Pravachol®** *see* Pravastatin *on page 169*

Pravastatin (PRA va stat in)

Genes of Interest

Angiotensin-Converting Enzyme *on page 214*
Apolipoprotein E *on page 220*
Beta-Fibrinogen *on page 236*
Cholesteryl Ester Transfer Protein *on page 243*
Glycoprotein IIIa Receptor *on page 285*
HMG-CoA Reductase *on page 290*
Low-Density Lipoprotein Receptor *on page 304*
Stromelysin-1 *on page 316*

U.S. Brand Names Pravachol®

Canadian Brand Names Apo-Pravastatin®; CO Pravastatin; Novo-Pravastatin; PMS-Pravastatin; Pravachol®; ratio-Pravastatin

Synonyms Pravastatin Sodium

Pharmacologic Class Antilipemic Agent, HMG-CoA Reductase Inhibitor

- **Pravastatin Sodium** *see* Pravastatin *on page 169*
- **Precedex™** *see* Dexmedetomidine *on page 90*

PredniSONE (PRED ni sone)

Genes of Interest None known

U.S. Brand Names Prednisone Intensol™; Sterapred® DS; Sterapred®

Canadian Brand Names Apo-Prednisone®; Novo-Prednisone; Winpred™

Synonyms Deltacortisone; Deltadehydrocortisone

Pharmacologic Class Corticosteroid, Systemic

- **Prednisone Intensol™** *see* PredniSONE *on page 169*
- **Pregnenedione** *see* Progesterone *on page 171*
- **Premarin®** *see* Estrogens (Conjugated/Equine) *on page 102*
- **Premjact® [OTC]** *see* Lidocaine *on page 131*
- **Premphase®** *see* Estrogens (Conjugated/Equine) and Medroxyprogesterone *on page 102*
- **Premplus® (Can)** *see* Estrogens (Conjugated/Equine) and Medroxyprogesterone *on page 102*

- ♦ **Prempro™** *see* Estrogens (Conjugated/Equine) and Medroxyprogesterone *on page 102*
- ♦ **Preparation H® Hydrocortisone [OTC]** *see* Hydrocortisone *on page 121*
- ♦ **Prevacid®** *see* Lansoprazole *on page 129*
- ♦ **Prevacid® SoluTab™** *see* Lansoprazole *on page 129*
- ♦ **PREVEN®** *see* Ethinyl Estradiol and Levonorgestrel *on page 104*
- ♦ **Prevex® HC (Can)** *see* Hydrocortisone *on page 121*
- ♦ **Previfem™** *see* Ethinyl Estradiol and Norgestimate *on page 105*
- ♦ **Prilocaine and Lidocaine** *see* Lidocaine and Prilocaine *on page 131*
- ♦ **Prilosec®** *see* Omeprazole *on page 159*
- ♦ **Prilosec OTC™ [OTC]** *see* Omeprazole *on page 159*

Primaquine (PRIM a kween)

Genes of Interest

Glucose-6-Phosphate Dehydrogenase *on page 281*

Synonyms Primaquine Phosphate; Prymaccone

Pharmacologic Class Aminoquinoline (Antimalarial)

- ♦ **Primaquine Phosphate** *see* Primaquine *on page 170*
- ♦ **Primsol®** *see* Trimethoprim *on page 199*
- ♦ **Prinivil®** *see* Lisinopril *on page 132*
- ♦ **Prinzide®** *see* Lisinopril and Hydrochlorothiazide *on page 132*

Probenecid (proe BEN e sid)

Genes of Interest

ATP-Binding Cassette, Sub-Family B, Member 1 *on page 224*
Glucose-6-Phosphate Dehydrogenase *on page 281*

Canadian Brand Names Benuryl™

Synonyms Benemid [DSC]

Pharmacologic Class Uricosuric Agent

Procainamide (proe kane A mide)

Genes of Interest

Cardiac Potassium Ion Channel *on page 241*
Cardiac Sodium Channel *on page 242*
N-Acetyltransferase 2 Enzyme *on page 308*

U.S. Brand Names Procanbid®

Canadian Brand Names Apo-Procainamide®; Procan® SR; Pronestyl®-SR

Synonyms PCA (error-prone abbreviation); Procainamide Hydrochloride; Procaine Amide Hydrochloride

Pharmacologic Class Antiarrhythmic Agent, Class Ia

- ♦ **Procainamide Hydrochloride** *see* Procainamide *on page 170*
- ♦ **Procaine Amide Hydrochloride** *see* Procainamide *on page 170*
- ♦ **Procanbid®** *see* Procainamide *on page 170*
- ♦ **Procan® SR (Can)** *see* Procainamide *on page 170*
- ♦ **Procardia®** *see* NIFEdipine *on page 150*

- **Procardia XL**® *see* NIFEdipine *on page 150*
- **Procetofene** *see* Fenofibrate *on page 107*
- **Prochieve**™ *see* Progesterone *on page 171*

Prochlorperazine (proe klor PER a zeen)

Genes of Interest

Alpha$_1$-Adrenergic Receptor *on page 210*
ATP-Binding Cassette, Sub-Family B, Member 1 *on page 224*
D_2 Receptor *on page 263*

U.S. Brand Names Compazine® [DSC]; Compro™

Canadian Brand Names Apo-Prochlorperazine®; Compazine®; Nu-Prochlor; Stemetil®

Synonyms Chlormeprazine; Prochlorperazine Edisylate; Prochlorperazine Maleate

Pharmacologic Class Antiemetic; Antipsychotic Agent, Typical, Phenothiazine

- **Prochlorperazine Edisylate** *see* Prochlorperazine *on page 171*
- **Prochlorperazine Maleate** *see* Prochlorperazine *on page 171*
- **Proctocort**® *see* Hydrocortisone *on page 121*
- **ProctoCream® HC** *see* Hydrocortisone *on page 121*
- **Proctofene** *see* Fenofibrate *on page 107*
- **Procto-Kit**™ *see* Hydrocortisone *on page 121*
- **Procto-Pak**™ *see* Hydrocortisone *on page 121*
- **Proctosert** *see* Hydrocortisone *on page 121*
- **Proctosol-HC**® *see* Hydrocortisone *on page 121*
- **Proctozone-HC**™ *see* Hydrocortisone *on page 121*
- **Procytox® (Can)** *see* Cyclophosphamide *on page 87*

Progesterone (proe JES ter one)

Genes of Interest

ATP-Binding Cassette, Sub-Family B, Member 1 *on page 224*

U.S. Brand Names Crinone®; Prochieve™; Prometrium®

Canadian Brand Names Crinone®; Prometrium®

Synonyms Pregnenedione; Progestin

Pharmacologic Class Progestin

- **Progestin** *see* Progesterone *on page 171*
- **Prograf**® *see* Tacrolimus *on page 189*
- **Prolixin® [DSC]** *see* Fluphenazine *on page 110*
- **Prolixin Decanoate**® *see* Fluphenazine *on page 110*
- **Proloprim**® *see* Trimethoprim *on page 199*

Promethazine (proe METH a zeen)

Genes of Interest None known

U.S. Brand Names Phenadoz™; Phenergan®; Promethegan™

Canadian Brand Names Phenergan®

Synonyms Promethazine Hydrochloride

Pharmacologic Class Antiemetic; Antihistamine; Phenothiazine Derivative; Sedative

Promethazine and Codeine

(proe METH a zeen & KOE deen)

Genes of Interest

COMT *on page 244*

CYP2D6 *on page 254*

Synonyms Codeine and Promethazine

Pharmacologic Class Antihistamine/Antitussive

- **Promethazine and Meperidine** *see* Meperidine and Promethazine *on page 138*
- **Promethazine Hydrochloride** *see* Promethazine *on page 171*
- **Promethegan™** *see* Promethazine *on page 171*
- **Prometrium®** *see* Progesterone *on page 171*
- **Pronap-100®** *see* Propoxyphene and Acetaminophen *on page 172*
- **Pronestyl®-SR (Can)** *see* Procainamide *on page 170*

Propafenone (proe pa FEEN one)

Genes of Interest

ATP-Binding Cassette, Sub-Family B, Member 1 *on page 224*

CYP2D6 *on page 254*

U.S. Brand Names Rythmol® SR; Rythmol®

Canadian Brand Names Apo-Propafenone®; Rythmol® Gen-Propafenone

Synonyms Propafenone Hydrochloride

Pharmacologic Class Antiarrhythmic Agent, Class Ic

- **Propafenone Hydrochloride** *see* Propafenone *on page 172*

Propofol (PROE po fole)

Genes of Interest

CYP2C8 *on page 248*

CYP2C9 *on page 248*

U.S. Brand Names Diprivan®

Canadian Brand Names Diprivan®

Pharmacologic Class General Anesthetic

Propoxyphene (proe POKS i feen)

Genes of Interest

COMT *on page 244*

U.S. Brand Names Darvon-N®; Darvon®

Canadian Brand Names 642® Tablet; Darvon-N®

Synonyms Dextropropoxyphene; Propoxyphene Hydrochloride; Propoxyphene Napsylate

Pharmacologic Class Analgesic, Narcotic

Propoxyphene and Acetaminophen

(proe POKS i feen & a seet a MIN oh fen)

Genes of Interest

COMT *on page 244*

U.S. Brand Names Balacet 325™; Darvocet A500™; Darvocet-N® 100; Darvocet-N® 50; Pronap-100®

Canadian Brand Names Darvocet-N® 100; Darvocet-N® 50

Synonyms Propoxyphene Hydrochloride and Acetaminophen; Propoxyphene Napsylate and Acetaminophen

Pharmacologic Class Analgesic Combination (Narcotic)

- **Propoxyphene Hydrochloride** *see* Propoxyphene *on page 172*
- **Propoxyphene Hydrochloride and Acetaminophen** *see* Propoxyphene and Acetaminophen *on page 172*
- **Propoxyphene Napsylate** *see* Propoxyphene *on page 172*
- **Propoxyphene Napsylate and Acetaminophen** *see* Propoxyphene and Acetaminophen *on page 172*

Propranolol (proe PRAN oh lole)

Genes of Interest

ATP-Binding Cassette, Sub-Family B, Member 1 *on page 224*
Beta$_1$-Adrenergic Receptor *on page 230*
CYP1A2 *on page 246*
CYP2C19 *on page 251*
Gs Protein Alpha-Subunit *on page 288*

U.S. Brand Names Inderal® LA; Inderal®; InnoPran XL™

Canadian Brand Names Apo-Propranolol®; Inderal®-LA; Inderal®; Novo-Pranol; Nu-Propranolol

Synonyms Propranolol Hydrochloride

Pharmacologic Class Antiarrhythmic Agent, Class II; Beta-Adrenergic Blocker, Nonselective

- **Propranolol Hydrochloride** *see* Propranolol *on page 173*
- **Proprinal [OTC]** *see* Ibuprofen *on page 123*
- **Propulsid®** *see* Cisapride *on page 81*
- **2-Propylpentanoic Acid** *see* Valproic Acid and Derivatives *on page 201*
- **2-Propylvaleric Acid** *see* Valproic Acid and Derivatives *on page 201*
- **Proquin® XR** *see* Ciprofloxacin *on page 81*
- **Protonix®** *see* Pantoprazole *on page 162*
- **Protopic®** *see* Tacrolimus *on page 189*

Protriptyline (proe TRIP ti leen)

Genes of Interest

Alpha$_1$-Adrenergic Receptor *on page 210*
G-Protein Beta$_3$ Subunit *on page 286*
Gs Protein Alpha-Subunit *on page 288*

U.S. Brand Names Vivactil®

Synonyms Protriptyline Hydrochloride

Pharmacologic Class Antidepressant, Tricyclic (Secondary Amine)

- **Protriptyline Hydrochloride** *see* Protriptyline *on page 173*
- **Proventil®** *see* Albuterol *on page 54*
- **Proventil® HFA** *see* Albuterol *on page 54*
- **Proventil® Repetabs®** *see* Albuterol *on page 54*
- **Provera®** *see* MedroxyPROGESTERone *on page 137*

- **Provigil®** *see* Modafinil *on page 145*
- **Prozac®** *see* Fluoxetine *on page 109*
- **Prozac® Weekly™** *see* Fluoxetine *on page 109*
- **Prudoxin™** *see* Doxepin *on page 95*
- **Prymaccone** *see* Primaquine *on page 170*
- **Pseudomonic Acid A** *see* Mupirocin *on page 147*
- **Pulmicort® (Can)** *see* Budesonide *on page 72*
- **Pulmicort Respules®** *see* Budesonide *on page 72*
- **Pulmicort Turbuhaler®** *see* Budesonide *on page 72*
- **Pulmophylline (Can)** *see* Theophylline *on page 192*
- **Purinethol®** *see* Mercaptopurine *on page 138*
- **PVF® K (Can)** *see* Penicillin V Potassium *on page 163*
- **Pyrimethamine and Sulfadoxine** *see* Sulfadoxine and Pyrimethamine *on page 187*

Quetiapine (kwe TYE a peen)

Genes of Interest

Alpha$_1$-Adrenergic Receptor *on page 210*
Cardiac Potassium Ion Channel *on page 241*
Cardiac Sodium Channel *on page 242*
CYP3A4 *on page 260*
D_2 Receptor *on page 263*

U.S. Brand Names Seroquel®
Canadian Brand Names Seroquel®
Synonyms Quetiapine Fumarate
Pharmacologic Class Antipsychotic Agent, Atypical

- **Quetiapine Fumarate** *see* Quetiapine *on page 174*
- **Quibron®-T** *see* Theophylline *on page 192*
- **Quibron®-T/SR** *see* Theophylline *on page 192*

Quinapril (KWIN a pril)

Genes of Interest

Aldosterone Synthase *on page 208*
Angiotensin II Type 1 Receptor *on page 213*
Angiotensin-Converting Enzyme *on page 214*
Angiotensinogen *on page 219*
Bradykinin B_2-Receptor *on page 237*

U.S. Brand Names Accupril®
Canadian Brand Names Accupril®
Synonyms Quinapril Hydrochloride
Pharmacologic Class Angiotensin-Converting Enzyme (ACE) Inhibitor

- **Quinapril Hydrochloride** *see* Quinapril *on page 174*
- **Quinate® (Can)** *see* Quinidine *on page 174*

Quinidine (KWIN i deen)

Genes of Interest

ATP-Binding Cassette, Sub-Family B, Member 1 *on page 224*

Cardiac Potassium Ion Channel *on page 241*
Cardiac Sodium Channel *on page 242*
CYP2D6 *on page 254*
CYP3A4 *on page 260*
Glucose-6-Phosphate Dehydrogenase *on page 281*

Canadian Brand Names Apo-Quin-G®; Apo-Quinidine®; BioQuin® Durules™; Novo-Quinidin; Quinate®

Synonyms Quinidine Gluconate; Quinidine Polygalacturonate; Quinidine Sulfate

Pharmacologic Class Antiarrhythmic Agent, Class Ia

- ♦ **Quinidine Gluconate** *see* Quinidine *on page 174*
- ♦ **Quinidine Polygalacturonate** *see* Quinidine *on page 174*
- ♦ **Quinidine Sulfate** *see* Quinidine *on page 174*

Quinine (KWYE nine)

Genes of Interest

ATP-Binding Cassette, Sub-Family B, Member 1 *on page 224*
CYP2D6 *on page 254*
Glucose-6-Phosphate Dehydrogenase *on page 281*

Canadian Brand Names Apo-Quinine®; Novo-Quinine; Quinine-Odan™

Synonyms Quinine Sulfate

Pharmacologic Class Antimalarial Agent

- ♦ **Quinine-Odan™ (Can)** *see* Quinine *on page 175*
- ♦ **Quinine Sulfate** *see* Quinine *on page 175*
- ♦ **Quixin™** *see* Levofloxacin *on page 130*

Rabeprazole (ra BE pray zole)

Genes of Interest

CYP2C19 *on page 251*

U.S. Brand Names AcipHex®

Canadian Brand Names AcipHex®; Pariet®

Synonyms Pariprazole

Pharmacologic Class Proton Pump Inhibitor; Substituted Benzimidazole

- ♦ **R-albuterol** *see* Levalbuterol *on page 130*

Raloxifene (ral OKS i feen)

Genes of Interest None known

U.S. Brand Names Evista®

Canadian Brand Names Evista®

Synonyms Keoxifene Hydrochloride; Raloxifene Hydrochloride

Pharmacologic Class Selective Estrogen Receptor Modulator (SERM)

- ♦ **Raloxifene Hydrochloride** *see* Raloxifene *on page 175*

Raltitrexed (ral ti TREX ed)

Genes of Interest

5,10-Methylenetetrahydrofolate Reductase *on page 304*

(Continued)

Raltitrexed *(Continued)*

Canadian Brand Names Tomudex®

Synonyms ICI-D1694; NSC-639186; Raltitrexed Disodium; ZD1694

Pharmacologic Class Antineoplastic Agent, Antimetabolite

♦ **Raltitrexed Disodium** *see* Raltitrexed *on page 175*

Ramipril (ra MI pril)

Genes of Interest

Aldosterone Synthase *on page 208*
Angiotensin II Type 1 Receptor *on page 213*
Angiotensin-Converting Enzyme *on page 214*
Angiotensinogen *on page 219*
Bradykinin B_2-Receptor *on page 237*

U.S. Brand Names Altace®

Canadian Brand Names Altace®

Pharmacologic Class Angiotensin-Converting Enzyme (ACE) Inhibitor

Ranitidine (ra NI ti deen)

Genes of Interest

ATP-Binding Cassette, Sub-Family B, Member 1 *on page 224*

U.S. Brand Names Zantac 150™ [OTC]; Zantac 75® [OTC]; Zantac® EFFERdose®; Zantac®

Canadian Brand Names Alti-Ranitidine; Apo-Ranitidine®; CO Ranitidine; Gen-Ranidine; Novo-Ranidine; Nu-Ranit; PMS-Ranitidine; Rhoxal-ranitidine; Zantac 75®; Zantac®

Synonyms Ranitidine Hydrochloride

Pharmacologic Class Histamine H_2 Antagonist

♦ **Ranitidine Hydrochloride** *see* Ranitidine *on page 176*

♦ **Rapamune®** *see* Sirolimus *on page 185*

Rasburicase (ras BYOOR i kayse)

Genes of Interest

Glucose-6-Phosphate Dehydrogenase *on page 281*

U.S. Brand Names Elitek™

Canadian Brand Names Fasturtec®

Pharmacologic Class Enzyme; Enzyme, Urate-Oxidase (Recombinant)

♦ **ratio-Aclavulanate (Can)** *see* Amoxicillin and Clavulanate Potassium *on page 59*

♦ **ratio-Acyclovir (Can)** *see* Acyclovir *on page 54*

♦ **ratio-Carvedilol (Can)** *see* Carvedilol *on page 76*

♦ **ratio-Ciprofloxacin (Can)** *see* Ciprofloxacin *on page 81*

♦ **ratio-Citalopram (Can)** *see* Citalopram *on page 81*

♦ **ratio-Clarithromycin (Can)** *see* Clarithromycin *on page 82*

♦ **ratio-Diltiazem CD (Can)** *see* Diltiazem *on page 93*

♦ **ratio-Domperidone (Can)** *see* Domperidone *on page 94*

♦ **ratio-Emtec (Can)** *see* Acetaminophen and Codeine *on page 52*

- ♦ **ratio-Famotidine (Can)** *see* Famotidine *on page 106*
- ♦ **ratio-Fenofibrate MC (Can)** *see* Fenofibrate *on page 107*
- ♦ **ratio-Glyburide (Can)** *see* GlyBURIDE *on page 117*
- ♦ **ratio-Inspra-Sal (Can)** *see* Albuterol *on page 54*
- ♦ **ratio-Ketorolac (Can)** *see* Ketorolac *on page 129*
- ♦ **ratio-Lenoltec (Can)** *see* Acetaminophen and Codeine *on page 52*
- ♦ **ratio-Lovastatin (Can)** *see* Lovastatin *on page 135*
- ♦ **ratio-Mometasone (Can)** *see* Mometasone Furoate *on page 145*
- ♦ **ratio-Morphine SR (Can)** *see* Morphine Sulfate *on page 146*
- ♦ **ratio-Paroxetine (Can)** *see* Paroxetine *on page 162*
- ♦ **ratio-Pravastatin (Can)** *see* Pravastatin *on page 169*
- ♦ **ratio-Salbutamol (Can)** *see* Albuterol *on page 54*
- ♦ **ratio-Sertraline (Can)** *see* Sertraline *on page 183*
- ♦ **ratio-Simvastatin (Can)** *see* Simvastatin *on page 184*
- ♦ **ratio-Temazepam (Can)** *see* Temazepam *on page 191*
- ♦ **ratio-Theo-Bronc (Can)** *see* Theophylline *on page 192*
- ♦ **Razadyne™** *see* Galantamine *on page 114*
- ♦ **Razadyne™ ER** *see* Galantamine *on page 114*
- ♦ **Reactine™ (Can)** *see* Cetirizine *on page 78*
- ♦ **Reglan®** *see* Metoclopramide *on page 141*
- ♦ **Regular Iletin® II [DSC]** *see* Insulin Preparations *on page 125*
- ♦ **Regular, Insulin** *see* Insulin Preparations *on page 125*
- ♦ **Relafen®** *see* Nabumetone *on page 147*
- ♦ **Relpax®** *see* Eletriptan *on page 97*
- ♦ **Remeron®** *see* Mirtazapine *on page 144*
- ♦ **Remeron® RD (Can)** *see* Mirtazapine *on page 144*
- ♦ **Remeron SolTab®** *see* Mirtazapine *on page 144*

Remifentanil (rem i FEN ta nil)

Genes of Interest

COMT *on page 244*

U.S. Brand Names Ultiva®

Canadian Brand Names Ultiva®

Synonyms GI87084B

Pharmacologic Class Analgesic, Narcotic

- ♦ **Reminyl®** *see* Galantamine *on page 114*
- ♦ **Renedil® (Can)** *see* Felodipine *on page 106*
- ♦ **Renese®** *see* Polythiazide *on page 168*
- ♦ **ReoPro®** *see* Abciximab *on page 52*

Repaglinide (re pa GLI nide)

Genes of Interest

CYP2C8 *on page 248*

CYP3A4 *on page 260*

(Continued)

Repaglinide *(Continued)*

U.S. Brand Names Prandin®

Canadian Brand Names GlucoNorm®; Prandin®

Pharmacologic Class Antidiabetic Agent, Miscellaneous

- **Reprexain™** *see* Hydrocodone and Ibuprofen *on page 120*
- **Requip®** *see* Ropinirole *on page 181*

Reserpine (re SER peen)

Genes of Interest

ATP-Binding Cassette, Sub-Family B, Member 1 *on page 224*

Pharmacologic Class Central Monoamine-Depleting Agent; Rauwolfia Alkaloid

- **Restasis™** *see* CycloSPORINE *on page 87*
- **Restoril®** *see* Temazepam *on page 191*
- **Revatio™** *see* Sildenafil *on page 184*
- **Rhinocort® Aqua®** *see* Budesonide *on page 72*
- **Rhinocort® Turbuhaler® (Can)** *see* Budesonide *on page 72*
- **Rho-Clonazepam (Can)** *see* Clonazepam *on page 83*
- **Rhodacine® (Can)** *see* Indomethacin *on page 125*
- **Rhodis™ (Can)** *see* Ketoprofen *on page 128*
- **Rhodis-EC™ (Can)** *see* Ketoprofen *on page 128*
- **Rhodis SR™ (Can)** *see* Ketoprofen *on page 128*
- **Rho®-Metformin (Can)** *see* Metformin *on page 139*
- **Rho-Nitro (Can)** *see* Nitroglycerin *on page 151*
- **Rho®-Sotalol (Can)** *see* Sotalol *on page 185*
- **Rhotral (Can)** *see* Acebutolol *on page 52*
- **Rhotrimine® (Can)** *see* Trimipramine *on page 199*
- **Rhovane® (Can)** *see* Zopiclone *on page 206*
- **Rhoxal-acebutolol (Can)** *see* Acebutolol *on page 52*
- **Rhoxal-amiodarone (Can)** *see* Amiodarone *on page 57*
- **Rhoxal-atenolol (Can)** *see* Atenolol *on page 66*
- **Rhoxal-ciprofloxacin (Can)** *see* Ciprofloxacin *on page 81*
- **Rhoxal-citalopram (Can)** *see* Citalopram *on page 81*
- **Rhoxal-cyclosporine (Can)** *see* CycloSPORINE *on page 87*
- **Rhoxal-diltiazem CD (Can)** *see* Diltiazem *on page 93*
- **Rhoxal-diltiazem SR (Can)** *see* Diltiazem *on page 93*
- **Rhoxal-fluoxetine (Can)** *see* Fluoxetine *on page 109*
- **Rhoxal-fluvoxamine (Can)** *see* Fluvoxamine *on page 112*
- **Rhoxal-minocycline (Can)** *see* Minocycline *on page 144*
- **Rhoxal-mirtazapine (Can)** *see* Mirtazapine *on page 144*
- **Rhoxal-nabumetone (Can)** *see* Nabumetone *on page 147*
- **Rhoxal-paroxetine (Can)** *see* Paroxetine *on page 162*
- **Rhoxal-ranitidine (Can)** *see* Ranitidine *on page 176*
- **Rhoxal-salbutamol (Can)** *see* Albuterol *on page 54*
- **Rhoxal-sertraline (Can)** *see* Sertraline *on page 183*
- **Rhoxal-ticlopidine (Can)** *see* Ticlopidine *on page 194*

- **Rhoxal-valproic (Can)** *see* Valproic Acid and Derivatives *on page 201*
- **Rhoxal-zopiclone (Can)** *see* Zopiclone *on page 206*

Rifabutin (rif a BYOO tin)

Genes of Interest
CYP1A2 *on page 246*
U.S. Brand Names Mycobutin®
Canadian Brand Names Mycobutin®
Synonyms Ansamycin
Pharmacologic Class Antibiotic, Miscellaneous; Antitubercular Agent

- **Rifadin®** *see* Rifampin *on page 179*
- **Rifampicin** *see* Rifampin *on page 179*

Rifampin (RIF am pin)

Genes of Interest
ATP-Binding Cassette, Sub-Family B, Member 1 *on page 224*
CYP2C9 *on page 248*
U.S. Brand Names Rifadin®
Canadian Brand Names Rifadin®; Rofact™
Synonyms Rifampicin
Pharmacologic Class Antibiotic, Miscellaneous; Antitubercular Agent

- **Rilutek®** *see* Riluzole *on page 179*

Riluzole (RIL yoo zole)

Genes of Interest
CYP1A2 *on page 246*
U.S. Brand Names Rilutek®
Canadian Brand Names Rilutek®
Synonyms 2-Amino-6-Trifluoromethoxy-benzothiazole; RP-54274
Pharmacologic Class Glutamate Inhibitor

- **Riomet™** *see* Metformin *on page 139*
- **Riphenidate (Can)** *see* Methylphenidate *on page 141*
- **Ripserdal® M-Tab™ (Can)** *see* Risperidone *on page 180*

Risedronate (ris ED roe nate)

Genes of Interest None known
U.S. Brand Names Actonel®
Canadian Brand Names Actonel®
Synonyms Risedronate Sodium
Pharmacologic Class Bisphosphonate Derivative

- **Risedronate Sodium** *see* Risedronate *on page 179*
- **Risperdal®** *see* Risperidone *on page 180*
- **Risperdal® M-Tabs™** *see* Risperidone *on page 180*
- **Risperdal® Consta™** *see* Risperidone *on page 180*

Risperidone (ris PER i done)

Genes of Interest

Alpha$_1$-Adrenergic Receptor *on page 210*
Cardiac Potassium Ion Channel *on page 241*
Cardiac Sodium Channel *on page 242*
CYP2D6 *on page 254*
D_2 Receptor *on page 263*
D_3 Receptor *on page 266*
D_4 Receptor *on page 268*
5-HT$_{2A}$ Receptor *on page 291*
5-HT$_{2C}$ Receptor *on page 294*

U.S. Brand Names Risperdal® Consta™; Risperdal® M-Tabs™; Risperdal®

Canadian Brand Names Ripserdal® M-Tab™; Risperdal® Consta™; Risperdal®

Pharmacologic Class Antipsychotic Agent, Atypical

- **Ritalin®** *see* Methylphenidate *on page 141*
- **Ritalin® LA** *see* Methylphenidate *on page 141*
- **Ritalin-SR®** *see* Methylphenidate *on page 141*

Ritonavir (ri TOE na veer)

Genes of Interest

ATP-Binding Cassette, Sub-Family B, Member 1 *on page 224*
CYP2D6 *on page 254*

U.S. Brand Names Norvir®

Canadian Brand Names Norvir® SEC; Norvir®

Pharmacologic Class Antiretroviral Agent, Protease Inhibitor

- **Riva-Diclofenac (Can)** *see* Diclofenac *on page 91*
- **Riva-Diclofenac-K (Can)** *see* Diclofenac *on page 91*
- **Riva-Famotidine (Can)** *see* Famotidine *on page 106*
- **Riva-Lorazepam (Can)** *see* Lorazepam *on page 134*
- **Riva-Naproxen (Can)** *see* Naproxen *on page 148*
- **Riva-Simvastatin (Can)** *see* Simvastatin *on page 184*

Rivastigmine (ri va STIG meen)

Genes of Interest

Apolipoprotein E *on page 220*

U.S. Brand Names Exelon®

Canadian Brand Names Exelon®

Synonyms ENA 713; Rivastigmine Tartrate; SDZ ENA 713

Pharmacologic Class Acetylcholinesterase Inhibitor (Central)

- **Rivastigmine Tartrate** *see* Rivastigmine *on page 180*
- **Rivotril® (Can)** *see* Clonazepam *on page 83*
- **RMS®** *see* Morphine Sulfate *on page 146*
- **Rofact™ (Can)** *see* Rifampin *on page 179*

Rofecoxib (roe fe COX ib)

Genes of Interest

Leukotriene C4 Synthase *on page 302*

U.S. Brand Names Vioxx® [DSC]

Pharmacologic Class Nonsteroidal Anti-inflammatory Drug (NSAID), COX-2 Selective

♦ **Romycin®** *see* Erythromycin *on page 99*

Ropinirole (roe PIN i role)

Genes of Interest

CYP1A2 *on page 246*
CYP2D6 *on page 254*

U.S. Brand Names Requip®

Canadian Brand Names ReQuip™

Synonyms Ropinirole Hydrochloride

Pharmacologic Class Anti-Parkinson's Agent, Dopamine Agonist

♦ **Ropinirole Hydrochloride** *see* Ropinirole *on page 181*

Rosiglitazone (roh si GLI ta zone)

Genes of Interest

CYP2C8 *on page 248*
CYP2C9 *on page 248*

U.S. Brand Names Avandia®

Canadian Brand Names Avandia®

Pharmacologic Class Antidiabetic Agent, Thiazolidinedione

Rosuvastatin (roe SOO va sta tin)

Genes of Interest

Angiotensin-Converting Enzyme *on page 214*
Apolipoprotein E *on page 220*
Beta-Fibrinogen *on page 236*
Cholesteryl Ester Transfer Protein *on page 243*
Glycoprotein IIIa Receptor *on page 285*
Low-Density Lipoprotein Receptor *on page 304*
Stromelysin-1 *on page 316*

U.S. Brand Names Crestor®

Canadian Brand Names Crestor®

Synonyms Rosuvastatin Calcium

Pharmacologic Class Antilipemic Agent, HMG-CoA Reductase Inhibitor

♦ **Rosuvastatin Calcium** *see* Rosuvastatin *on page 181*
♦ **Roxanol™** *see* Morphine Sulfate *on page 146*
♦ **Roxanol 100™** *see* Morphine Sulfate *on page 146*
♦ **Roxanol™-T** *see* Morphine Sulfate *on page 146*
♦ **Roxicet™** *see* Oxycodone and Acetaminophen *on page 161*
♦ **Roxicet™ 5/500** *see* Oxycodone and Acetaminophen *on page 161*
♦ **Roxicodone™** *see* Oxycodone *on page 161*
♦ **Roxicodone™ Intensol™** *see* Oxycodone *on page 161*

- **Roychlor® (Can)** *see* Potassium Chloride *on page 169*
- **RP-54274** *see* Riluzole *on page 179*
- **RP-6976** *see* Docetaxel *on page 94*
- **RU-486** *see* Mifepristone *on page 143*
- **RU-23908** *see* Nilutamide *on page 150*
- **RU-38486** *see* Mifepristone *on page 143*
- **Rubex®** *see* DOXOrubicin *on page 95*
- **Rum-K®** *see* Potassium Chloride *on page 169*
- **Rythmodan® (Can)** *see* Disopyramide *on page 93*
- **Rythmodan®-LA (Can)** *see* Disopyramide *on page 93*
- **Rythmol®** *see* Propafenone *on page 172*
- **Rythmol® Gen-Propafenone (Can)** *see* Propafenone *on page 172*
- **Rythmol® SR** *see* Propafenone *on page 172*
- **Salazopyrin® (Can)** *see* Sulfasalazine *on page 188*
- **Salazopyrin En-Tabs® (Can)** *see* Sulfasalazine *on page 188*
- **Salbu-2 (Can)** *see* Albuterol *on page 54*
- **Salbu-4 (Can)** *see* Albuterol *on page 54*
- **Salbutamol** *see* Albuterol *on page 54*
- **Salicylazosulfapyridine** *see* Sulfasalazine *on page 188*

Salmeterol (sal ME te role)

Genes of Interest

Beta$_2$-Adrenergic Receptor *on page 233*

U.S. Brand Names Serevent® Diskus®

Canadian Brand Names Serevent®

Synonyms Salmeterol Xinafoate

Pharmacologic Class Beta$_2$-Adrenergic Agonist

- **Salmeterol and Fluticasone** *see* Fluticasone and Salmeterol *on page 111*
- **Salmeterol Xinafoate** *see* Salmeterol *on page 182*
- **Saluron® [DSC]** *see* Hydroflumethiazide *on page 121*
- **Sandimmune®** *see* CycloSPORINE *on page 87*
- **Sandimmune® I.V. (Can)** *see* CycloSPORINE *on page 87*
- **Sandostatin®** *see* Octreotide *on page 158*
- **Sandostatin LAR®** *see* Octreotide *on page 158*
- **Sans Acne® (Can)** *see* Erythromycin *on page 99*

Saquinavir (sa KWIN a veer)

Genes of Interest

ATP-Binding Cassette, Sub-Family B, Member 1 *on page 224*

U.S. Brand Names Fortovase® [DSC]; Invirase®

Canadian Brand Names Fortovase®; Invirase®

Synonyms Saquinavir Mesylate

Pharmacologic Class Antiretroviral Agent, Protease Inhibitor

- **Saquinavir Mesylate** *see* Saquinavir *on page 182*
- **Sarafem™** *see* Fluoxetine *on page 109*
- **Sarna® HC (Can)** *see* Hydrocortisone *on page 121*

- **Sarnol®-HC [OTC]** *see* Hydrocortisone *on page 121*
- **SCH 13521** *see* Flutamide *on page 111*
- **S-Citalopram** *see* Escitalopram *on page 100*
- **SDZ ENA 713** *see* Rivastigmine *on page 180*
- **Seasonale®** *see* Ethinyl Estradiol and Levonorgestrel *on page 104*
- **Sectral®** *see* Acebutolol *on page 52*
- **Select™ 1/35 (Can)** *see* Ethinyl Estradiol and Norethindrone *on page 104*

Selegiline (se LE ji leen)

Genes of Interest

CYP2C8 *on page 248*
CYP2C9 *on page 248*

U.S. Brand Names Eldepryl®

Canadian Brand Names Apo-Selegiline®; Gen-Selegiline; Novo-Selegiline; Nu-Selegiline

Synonyms Deprenyl; L-Deprenyl; Selegiline Hydrochloride

Pharmacologic Class Anti-Parkinson's Agent, MAO Type B Inhibitor; Antidepressant, Monoamine Oxidase Inhibitor

- **Selegiline Hydrochloride** *see* Selegiline *on page 183*
- **Septra®** *see* Sulfamethoxazole and Trimethoprim *on page 187*
- **Septra® DS** *see* Sulfamethoxazole and Trimethoprim *on page 187*
- **Septra® Injection (Can)** *see* Sulfamethoxazole and Trimethoprim *on page 187*
- **Serentil® [DSC]** *see* Mesoridazine *on page 138*
- **Serevent® (Can)** *see* Salmeterol *on page 182*
- **Serevent® Diskus®** *see* Salmeterol *on page 182*
- **Seroquel®** *see* Quetiapine *on page 174*

Sertraline (SER tra leen)

Genes of Interest

CYP2C8 *on page 248*
CYP2C9 *on page 248*
CYP2C19 *on page 251*
CYP3A4 *on page 260*
G-Protein Beta$_3$ Subunit *on page 286*
Gs Protein Alpha-Subunit *on page 288*
5-HT$_{2A}$ Receptor *on page 291*
5-HT Transporter *on page 297*
Monoamine Oxidase A *on page 307*

U.S. Brand Names Zoloft®

Canadian Brand Names Apo-Sertraline®; Gen-Sertraline; Novo-Sertraline; Nu-Sertraline; PMS-Sertraline; Rhoxal-sertraline; Zoloft®; ratio-Sertraline

Synonyms Sertraline Hydrochloride

Pharmacologic Class Antidepressant, Selective Serotonin Reuptake Inhibitor

- **Sertraline Hydrochloride** *see* Sertraline *on page 183*
- **Serzone® [DSC]** *see* Nefazodone *on page 149*

Sibutramine (si BYOO tra meen)

Genes of Interest

Beta$_3$-Adrenergic Receptor *on page 236*
CYP3A4 *on page 260*
G-Protein Beta$_3$ Subunit *on page 286*

U.S. Brand Names Meridia®

Canadian Brand Names Meridia®

Synonyms Sibutramine Hydrochloride Monohydrate

Pharmacologic Class Anorexiant

- **Sibutramine Hydrochloride Monohydrate** *see* Sibutramine *on page 184*

Sildenafil (sil DEN a fil)

Genes of Interest

CYP3A4 *on page 260*

U.S. Brand Names Revatio™; Viagra®

Canadian Brand Names Viagra®

Synonyms UK92480

Pharmacologic Class Phosphodiesterase-5 Enzyme Inhibitor

- **Silvadene®** *see* Silver Sulfadiazine *on page 184*

Silver Sulfadiazine (SIL ver sul fa DYE a zeen)

Genes of Interest

Glucose-6-Phosphate Dehydrogenase *on page 281*

U.S. Brand Names SSD® AF; SSD®; Silvadene®; Thermazene®

Canadian Brand Names Flamazine®

Pharmacologic Class Antibiotic, Topical

Simvastatin (SIM va stat in)

Genes of Interest

Angiotensin-Converting Enzyme *on page 214*
Apolipoprotein E *on page 220*
ATP-Binding Cassette, Sub-Family B, Member 1 *on page 224*
Beta-Fibrinogen *on page 236*
Cholesteryl Ester Transfer Protein *on page 243*
CYP3A4 *on page 260*
Glycoprotein IIIa Receptor *on page 285*
Low-Density Lipoprotein Receptor *on page 304*
Stromelysin-1 *on page 316*

U.S. Brand Names Zocor®

Canadian Brand Names Apo-Simvastatin®; CO Simvastatin; Gen-Simvastatin; Novo-Simvastatin; PMS-Simvastatin; Riva-Simvastatin; Zocor®; ratio-Simvastatin

Pharmacologic Class Antilipemic Agent, HMG-CoA Reductase Inhibitor

- **Sinequan®** *see* Doxepin *on page 95*
- **Singulair®** *see* Montelukast *on page 146*
- **Sirdalud®** *see* Tizanidine *on page 195*

Sirolimus (sir OH li mus)

Genes of Interest

CYP3A4 *on page 260*

U.S. Brand Names Rapamune®

Canadian Brand Names Rapamune®

Pharmacologic Class Immunosuppressant Agent

- **Skelaxin®** *see* Metaxalone *on page 139*
- **Slow FE® [OTC]** *see* Ferrous Sulfate *on page 108*
- **Slow-K® (Can)** *see* Potassium Chloride *on page 169*
- **SMZ-TMP** *see* Sulfamethoxazole and Trimethoprim *on page 187*
- **Sodium Sulfacetamide** *see* Sulfacetamide *on page 187*
- **Solaraze™** *see* Diclofenac *on page 91*
- **Solarcaine® Aloe Extra Burn Relief [OTC]** *see* Lidocaine *on* **page 131**
- **Solia™** *see* Ethinyl Estradiol and Desogestrel *on page 103*
- **Solu-Cortef®** *see* Hydrocortisone *on page 121*
- **Solu-Medrol®** *see* MethylPREDNISolone *on page 141*
- **Soma®** *see* Carisoprodol *on page 76*
- **Sorine®** *see* Sotalol *on page 185*
- **Sotacor® (Can)** *see* Sotalol *on page 185*

Sotalol (SOE ta lole)

Genes of Interest

Beta$_1$-Adrenergic Receptor *on page 230*
Cardiac Potassium Ion Channel *on page 241*
Cardiac Sodium Channel *on page 242*
Gs Protein Alpha-Subunit *on page 288*

U.S. Brand Names Betapace AF®; Betapace®; Sorine®

Canadian Brand Names Alti-Sotalol; Apo-Sotalol®; Betapace AF™; Gen-Sotalol; Lin-Sotalol; Novo-Sotalol; Nu-Sotalol; PMS-Sotalol; Rho®-Sotalol; Sotacor®

Synonyms Sotalol Hydrochloride

Pharmacologic Class Antiarrhythmic Agent, Class II; Antiarrhythmic Agent, Class III; Beta-Adrenergic Blocker, Nonselective

- **Sotalol Hydrochloride** *see* Sotalol *on page 185*

Sparfloxacin (spar FLOKS a sin)

Genes of Interest

Cardiac Potassium Ion Channel *on page 241*
Cardiac Sodium Channel *on page 242*

U.S. Brand Names Zagam® [DSC]

Pharmacologic Class Antibiotic, Quinolone

- **SPD417** *see* Carbamazepine *on page 75*

Spiramycin (speer a MYE sin)

Genes of Interest

CYP3A4 *on page 260*

Pharmacologic Class Antibiotic, Macrolide

Spirapril (SPYE ra pril)

Genes of Interest

Aldosterone Synthase *on page 208*
Angiotensin II Type 1 Receptor *on page 213*
Angiotensin-Converting Enzyme *on page 214*
Angiotensinogen *on page 219*
Bradykinin B_2-Receptor *on page 237*

Pharmacologic Class Angiotensin-Converting Enzyme (ACE) Inhibitor

Spironolactone (speer on oh LAK tone)

Genes of Interest None known

U.S. Brand Names Aldactone®

Canadian Brand Names Aldactone®; Novo-Spiroton

Pharmacologic Class Diuretic, Potassium-Sparing; Selective Aldosterone Blocker

- **Sporanox®** *see* Itraconazole *on page 127*
- **Sprintec™** *see* Ethinyl Estradiol and Norgestimate *on page 105*
- **SSD®** *see* Silver Sulfadiazine *on page 184*
- **SSD® AF** *see* Silver Sulfadiazine *on page 184*
- **Stadol®** *see* Butorphanol *on page 74*
- **Stadol® NS [DSC]** *see* Butorphanol *on page 74*
- **Stagesic®** *see* Hydrocodone and Acetaminophen *on page 120*
- **Starlix®** *see* Nateglinide *on page 148*
- **Statex® (Can)** *see* Morphine Sulfate *on page 146*
- **Staticin® [DSC]** *see* Erythromycin *on page 99*
- **Stemetil® (Can)** *see* Prochlorperazine *on page 171*
- **Sterapred®** *see* PredniSONE *on page 169*
- **Sterapred® DS** *see* PredniSONE *on page 169*
- **STI571** *see* Imatinib *on page 123*
- **St. Joseph® Adult Aspirin [OTC]** *see* Aspirin *on page 65*
- **Strattera®** *see* Atomoxetine *on page 66*
- **Striant®** *see* Testosterone *on page 192*
- **Stromectol®** *see* Ivermectin *on page 127*
- **Sublimaze®** *see* Fentanyl *on page 107*
- **Suboxone®** *see* Buprenorphine and Naloxone *on page 72*
- **Subutex®** *see* Buprenorphine *on page 72*
- **Sufenta®** *see* Sufentanil *on page 186*

Sufentanil (soo FEN ta nil)

Genes of Interest

COMT *on page 244*
CYP3A4 *on page 260*

U.S. Brand Names Sufenta®

Canadian Brand Names Sufenta®

Synonyms Sufentanil Citrate

Pharmacologic Class Analgesic, Narcotic; General Anesthetic

- **Sufentanil Citrate** *see* Sufentanil *on page 186*
- **Sular®** *see* Nisoldipine *on page 150*

Sulfacetamide (sul fa SEE ta mide)

Genes of Interest

Glucose-6-Phosphate Dehydrogenase *on page 281*

N-Acetyltransferase 2 Enzyme *on page 308*

U.S. Brand Names Bleph®-10; Carmol® Scalp; Klaron®; Ovace™

Canadian Brand Names Cetamide™; Diosulf™

Synonyms Sodium Sulfacetamide; Sulfacetamide Sodium

Pharmacologic Class Antibiotic, Ophthalmic; Antibiotic, Sulfonamide Derivative

- **Sulfacetamide Sodium** *see* Sulfacetamide *on page 187*

SulfaDIAZINE (sul fa DYE a zeen)

Genes of Interest

CYP2C9 *on page 248*

Glucose-6-Phosphate Dehydrogenase *on page 281*

N-Acetyltransferase 2 Enzyme *on page 308*

Pharmacologic Class Antibiotic, Sulfonamide Derivative

Sulfadoxine and Pyrimethamine

(sul fa DOKS een & peer i METH a meen)

Genes of Interest

Glucose-6-Phosphate Dehydrogenase *on page 281*

U.S. Brand Names Fansidar®

Synonyms Pyrimethamine and Sulfadoxine

Pharmacologic Class Antimalarial Agent

Sulfamethoxazole and Trimethoprim

(sul fa meth OKS a zole & trye METH oh prim)

Genes of Interest

CYP2C9 *on page 248*

Glucose-6-Phosphate Dehydrogenase *on page 281*

N-Acetyltransferase 2 Enzyme *on page 308*

U.S. Brand Names Bactrim™ DS; Bactrim™; Septra® DS; Septra®

Canadian Brand Names Apo-Sulfatrim®; Novo-Trimel D.S.; Novo-Trimel; Nu-Cotrimox; Septra® Injection

Synonyms Co-Trimoxazole; SMZ-TMP; Sulfatrim; TMP-SMZ; Trimethoprim and Sulfamethoxazole

Pharmacologic Class Antibiotic, Miscellaneous; Antibiotic, Sulfonamide Derivative

- **Sulfamylon®** *see* Mafenide *on page 136*

Sulfasalazine (sul fa SAL a zeen)

Genes of Interest

Glucose-6-Phosphate Dehydrogenase *on page 281*

U.S. Brand Names Azulfidine® EN-tabs®; Azulfidine®; Sulfazine EC; Sulfazine

Canadian Brand Names Alti-Sulfasalazine; Salazopyrin En-Tabs®; Salazopyrin®

Synonyms Salicylazosulfapyridine

Pharmacologic Class 5-Aminosalicylic Acid Derivative

♦ **Sulfatrim** *see* Sulfamethoxazole and Trimethoprim *on page 187*

♦ **Sulfazine** *see* Sulfasalazine *on page 188*

♦ **Sulfazine EC** *see* Sulfasalazine *on page 188*

Sulfinpyrazone (sul fin PEER a zone)

Genes of Interest

CYP2C9 *on page 248*

Canadian Brand Names Apo-Sulfinpyrazone®; Nu-Sulfinpyrazone

Synonyms Anturane

Pharmacologic Class Uricosuric Agent

SulfiSOXAZOLE (sul fi SOKS a zole)

Genes of Interest

CYP2C9 *on page 248*

Glucose-6-Phosphate Dehydrogenase *on page 281*

N-Acetyltransferase 2 Enzyme *on page 308*

U.S. Brand Names Gantrisin®

Canadian Brand Names Novo-Soxazole; Sulfizole®

Synonyms Sulfisoxazole Acetyl; Sulphafurazole

Pharmacologic Class Antibiotic, Sulfonamide Derivative

♦ **Sulfisoxazole Acetyl** *see* SulfiSOXAZOLE *on page 188*

♦ **Sulfisoxazole and Erythromycin** *see* Erythromycin and Sulfisoxazole *on page 100*

♦ **Sulfizole® (Can)** *see* SulfiSOXAZOLE *on page 188*

Sulindac (sul IN dak)

Genes of Interest

Leukotriene C4 Synthase *on page 302*

U.S. Brand Names Clinoril®

Canadian Brand Names Apo-Sulin®; Novo-Sundac; Nu-Sundac

Pharmacologic Class Nonsteroidal Anti-inflammatory Drug (NSAID), Oral

♦ **Sulphafurazole** *see* SulfiSOXAZOLE *on page 188*

Sumatriptan (soo ma TRIP tan SUKS i nate)

Genes of Interest None known

U.S. Brand Names Imitrex®

Canadian Brand Names Imitrex® DF

Synonyms Sumatriptan Succinate

Pharmacologic Class Serotonin 5-HT_{1D} Receptor Agonist

- **Sumatriptan Succinate** *see* Sumatriptan *on page 189*
- **Summer's Eve® SpecialCare™ Medicated Anti-Itch Cream [OTC]** *see* Hydrocortisone *on page 121*
- **Sumycin®** *see* Tetracycline *on page 192*
- **Supeudol® (Can)** *see* Oxycodone *on page 161*
- **Sureprin 81™ [OTC]** *see* Aspirin *on page 65*
- **Surgam® (Can)** *see* Tiaprofenic Acid *on page 194*
- **Surgam® SR (Can)** *see* Tiaprofenic Acid *on page 194*
- **Surmontil®** *see* Trimipramine *on page 199*
- **Synalgos®-DC** *see* Dihydrocodeine, Aspirin, and Caffeine *on page 92*
- **Syn-Diltiazem® (Can)** *see* Diltiazem *on page 93*
- **Synphasic® (Can)** *see* Ethinyl Estradiol and Norethindrone *on page 104*
- **Synthroid®** *see* Levothyroxine *on page 131*
- **T_4** *see* Levothyroxine *on page 131*
- **642® Tablet (Can)** *see* Propoxyphene *on page 172*
- **Tabloid®** *see* Thioguanine *on page 193*

Tacrine (TAK reen)

Genes of Interest

Apolipoprotein E *on page 220*
CYP1A2 *on page 246*
Glutathione-S-Transferase *on page 281*

U.S. Brand Names Cognex®

Synonyms THA; Tacrine Hydrochloride; Tetrahydroaminoacrine

Pharmacologic Class Acetylcholinesterase Inhibitor (Central)

- **Tacrine Hydrochloride** *see* Tacrine *on page 189*

Tacrolimus (ta KROE li mus)

Genes of Interest

ATP-Binding Cassette, Sub-Family B, Member 1 *on page 224*
CYP2C19 *on page 251*
CYP3A4 *on page 260*

U.S. Brand Names Prograf®; Protopic®

Canadian Brand Names Prograf®; Protopic®

Synonyms FK506

Pharmacologic Class Immunosuppressant Agent; Topical Skin Product

- **Tagamet®** *see* Cimetidine *on page 80*
- **Tagamet® HB (Can)** *see* Cimetidine *on page 80*

- **Tagamet® HB 200 [OTC]** *see* Cimetidine *on page 80*
- **Talwin®** *see* Pentazocine *on page 163*
- **Talwin® NX** *see* Pentazocine *on page 163*
- **TAM** *see* Tamoxifen *on page 190*
- **Tambocor™** *see* Flecainide *on page 108*
- **Tamofen® (Can)** *see* Tamoxifen *on page 190*

Tamoxifen (ta MOKS i fen)

Genes of Interest

ATP-Binding Cassette, Sub-Family B, Member 1 *on page 224*
CYP2C8 *on page 248*
CYP2C9 *on page 248*

U.S. Brand Names Nolvadex®

Canadian Brand Names Apo-Tamox®; Gen-Tamoxifen; Nolvadex®-D; Nolvadex®; Novo-Tamoxifen; Tamofen®

Synonyms ICI-46474; NSC-180973; TAM; Tamoxifen Citrate

Pharmacologic Class Antineoplastic Agent, Estrogen Receptor Antagonist

- **Tamoxifen Citrate** *see* Tamoxifen *on page 190*

Tamsulosin (tam SOO loe sin)

Genes of Interest

CYP3A4 *on page 260*

U.S. Brand Names Flomax®

Canadian Brand Names Flomax®

Synonyms Tamsulosin Hydrochloride

Pharmacologic Class $Alpha_1$ Blocker

- **Tamsulosin Hydrochloride** *see* Tamsulosin *on page 190*
- **Taro-Carbamazepine Chewable (Can)** *see* Carbamazepine *on page 75*
- **Taro-Warfarin (Can)** *see* Warfarin *on page 203*
- **Tavist® Allergy [OTC]** *see* Clemastine *on page 82*
- **Tavist® ND [OTC]** *see* Loratadine *on page 133*
- **Taxol®** *see* Paclitaxel *on page 162*
- **Taxotere®** *see* Docetaxel *on page 94*
- **Taztia XT™** *see* Diltiazem *on page 93*
- **TCN** *see* Tetracycline *on page 192*
- **Tecnal C 1/2 (Can)** *see* Butalbital, Aspirin, Caffeine, and Codeine *on page 74*
- **Tecnal C 1/4 (Can)** *see* Butalbital, Aspirin, Caffeine, and Codeine *on page 74*
- **Tegretol®** *see* Carbamazepine *on page 75*
- **Tegretol®-XR** *see* Carbamazepine *on page 75*
- **Teldrin® HBP [OTC]** *see* Chlorpheniramine *on page 79*

Telmisartan (tel mi SAR tan)

Genes of Interest

Adipocyte-Derived Leucine Aminopeptidase *on page 208*

Aldosterone Synthase *on page 208*
Angiotensin II Type 1 Receptor *on page 213*
Angiotensin-Converting Enzyme *on page 214*
Angiotensinogen *on page 219*
Bradykinin B_2-Receptor *on page 237*
CYP2C9 *on page 248*

U.S. Brand Names Micardis®

Canadian Brand Names Micardis®

Pharmacologic Class Angiotensin II Receptor Blocker

Temazepam (te MAZ e pam)

Genes of Interest None known

U.S. Brand Names Restoril®

Canadian Brand Names Apo-Temazepam®; CO Temazepam; Gen-Temazepam; Novo-Temazepam; Nu-Temazepam; PMS-Temazepam; Restoril®; ratio-Temazepam

Pharmacologic Class Benzodiazepine

♦ **Temodal™ (Can)** *see* Temozolomide *on page 191*

♦ **Temodar®** *see* Temozolomide *on page 191*

Temozolomide (te moe ZOE loe mide)

Genes of Interest

Methylguanine-DNA Methyltransferase *on page 305*

U.S. Brand Names Temodar®

Canadian Brand Names Temodal™; Temodar®

Synonyms NSC-362856; TMZ

Pharmacologic Class Antineoplastic Agent, Alkylating Agent

Teniposide (ten i POE side)

Genes of Interest

CYP3A4 *on page 260*

U.S. Brand Names Vumon®

Canadian Brand Names Vumon®

Synonyms EPT; VM-26

Pharmacologic Class Antineoplastic Agent, Miscellaneous

♦ **Tenolin (Can)** *see* Atenolol *on page 66*

♦ **Tenormin®** *see* Atenolol *on page 66*

♦ **Tequin®** *see* Gatifloxacin *on page 114*

Terazosin (ter AY zoe sin)

Genes of Interest None known

U.S. Brand Names Hytrin®

Canadian Brand Names Alti-Terazosin; Apo-Terazosin®; Hytrin®; Novo-Terazosin; Nu-Terazosin; PMS-Terazosin

Pharmacologic Class $Alpha_1$ Blocker

Terbutaline (ter BYOO ta leen)

Genes of Interest

$Beta_2$-Adrenergic Receptor *on page 233*

(Continued)

Terbutaline *(Continued)*

U.S. Brand Names Brethine®
Canadian Brand Names Bricanyl®
Synonyms Brethaire [DSC]; Bricanyl [DSC]
Pharmacologic Class Beta$_2$-Adrenergic Agonist

- **Terfluzine (Can)** *see* Trifluoperazine *on page 198*
- **Tessalon®** *see* Benzonatate *on page 69*
- **Testim®** *see* Testosterone *on page 192*
- **Testopel®** *see* Testosterone *on page 192*

Testosterone (tes TOS ter one)

Genes of Interest
ATP-Binding Cassette, Sub-Family B, Member 1 *on page 224*
U.S. Brand Names AndroGel®; Androderm®; Delatestryl®; Depo®-Testosterone; First® Testosterone MC; First® Testosterone; Striant®; Testim®; Testopel®
Canadian Brand Names Andriol®; AndroGel®; Androderm®; Andropository; Delatestryl®; Depotest® 100; Everone® 200; Virilon® IM
Synonyms Testosterone Cypionate; Testosterone Enanthate
Pharmacologic Class Androgen

- **Testosterone Cypionate** *see* Testosterone *on page 192*
- **Testosterone Enanthate** *see* Testosterone *on page 192*

Tetracycline (tet ra SYE kleen)

Genes of Interest None known
U.S. Brand Names Sumycin®
Canadian Brand Names Apo-Tetra®; Nu-Tetra
Synonyms Achromycin; TCN; Tetracycline Hydrochloride
Pharmacologic Class Antibiotic, Tetracycline Derivative

- **Tetracycline Hydrochloride** *see* Tetracycline *on page 192*
- **Tetrahydroaminoacrine** *see* Tacrine *on page 189*
- **Teveten®** *see* Eprosartan *on page 98*
- **Texacort®** *see* Hydrocortisone *on page 121*
- **TG** *see* Thioguanine *on page 193*
- **6-TG (error-prone abbreviation)** *see* Thioguanine *on page 193*
- **THA** *see* Tacrine *on page 189*
- **Thalitone®** *see* Chlorthalidone *on page 79*
- **Theo-24®** *see* Theophylline *on page 192*
- **Theochron®** *see* Theophylline *on page 192*
- **Theochron® SR (Can)** *see* Theophylline *on page 192*
- **Theolair™** *see* Theophylline *on page 192*
- **Theolair-SR® [DSC]** *see* Theophylline *on page 192*

Theophylline (thee OFF i lin)

Genes of Interest
CYP1A2 *on page 246*
CYP3A4 *on page 260*

U.S. Brand Names Elixophyllin®; Quibron®-T/SR; Quibron®-T; T-Phyl®; Theo-24®; Theochron®; Theolair-SR® [DSC]; Theolair™; Uniphyl®

Canadian Brand Names Apo-Theo LA®; Novo-Theophyl SR; PMS-Theophylline; Pulmophylline; Theochron® SR; Theolair™; Uniphyl® SRT; ratio-Theo-Bronc

Synonyms Theophylline Anhydrous

Pharmacologic Class Theophylline Derivative

- **Theophylline Anhydrous** *see* Theophylline *on page 192*
- **Theophylline Ethylenediamine** *see* Aminophylline *on page 57*
- **Theramycin Z®** *see* Erythromycin *on page 99*
- **Thermazene®** *see* Silver Sulfadiazine *on page 184*

Thioguanine (thye oh GWAH neen)

Genes of Interest

Thiopurine Methyltransferase *on page 317*

U.S. Brand Names Tabloid®

Canadian Brand Names Lanvis®

Synonyms 2-Amino-6-Mercaptopurine; 6-TG (error-prone abbreviation); 6-Thioguanine (error-prone abbreviation); NSC-752; TG; Tioguanine

Pharmacologic Class Antineoplastic Agent, Antimetabolite (Purine Antagonist)

- **6-Thioguanine (error-prone abbreviation)** *see* Thioguanine *on page 193*

Thioridazine (thye oh RID a zeen)

Genes of Interest

Alpha$_1$-Adrenergic Receptor *on page 210*
Cardiac Potassium Ion Channel *on page 241*
Cardiac Sodium Channel *on page 242*
CYP2D6 *on page 254*
D_2 Receptor *on page 263*

Canadian Brand Names Apo-Thioridazine®; Mellaril®

Synonyms Thioridazine Hydrochloride

Pharmacologic Class Antipsychotic Agent, Typical, Phenothiazine

- **Thioridazine Hydrochloride** *see* Thioridazine *on page 193*

Thiothixene (thye oh THIKS een)

Genes of Interest

Alpha$_1$-Adrenergic Receptor *on page 210*
Cardiac Potassium Ion Channel *on page 241*
Cardiac Sodium Channel *on page 242*
CYP1A2 *on page 246*
D_2 Receptor *on page 263*

(Continued)

Thiothixene *(Continued)*

U.S. Brand Names Navane®

Canadian Brand Names Navane®

Synonyms Tiotixene

Pharmacologic Class Antipsychotic Agent, Typical

♦ **Thorazine® [DSC]** *see* ChlorproMAZINE *on page 79*

Tiagabine (tye AG a been)

Genes of Interest

CYP3A4 *on page 260*

U.S. Brand Names Gabitril®

Canadian Brand Names Gabitril®

Synonyms Tiagabine Hydrochloride

Pharmacologic Class Anticonvulsant, Miscellaneous

♦ **Tiagabine Hydrochloride** *see* Tiagabine *on page 194*

♦ **Tiaprofenic-200 (Can)** *see* Tiaprofenic Acid *on page 194*

♦ **Tiaprofenic-300 (Can)** *see* Tiaprofenic Acid *on page 194*

Tiaprofenic Acid (tye ah PRO fen ik AS id)

Genes of Interest

Leukotriene C4 Synthase *on page 302*

Canadian Brand Names Albert® Tiafen; Apo-Tiaprofenic®; Dom-Tiaprofenic®; Novo-Tiaprofenic; Nu-Tiaprofenic; PMS-Tiaprofenic; Surgam® SR; Surgam®; Tiaprofenic-200; Tiaprofenic-300

Pharmacologic Class Nonsteroidal Anti-inflammatory Drug (NSAID), Oral

♦ **Tiazac®** *see* Diltiazem *on page 93*

♦ **Tiazac® XC (Can)** *see* Diltiazem *on page 93*

♦ **Ticlid®** *see* Ticlopidine *on page 194*

Ticlopidine (tye KLOE pi deen)

Genes of Interest

Glycoprotein IIIa Receptor *on page 285*

P2RY12 *on page 310*

U.S. Brand Names Ticlid®

Canadian Brand Names Alti-Ticlopidine; Apo-Ticlopidine®; Gen-Ticlopidine; Novo-Ticlopidine; Nu-Ticlopidine; Rhoxal-ticlopidine; Ticlid®

Synonyms Ticlopidine Hydrochloride

Pharmacologic Class Antiplatelet Agent

♦ **Ticlopidine Hydrochloride** *see* Ticlopidine *on page 194*

♦ **Tikosyn™** *see* Dofetilide *on page 94*

♦ **Tim-AK (Can)** *see* Timolol *on page 195*

Timolol (TYE moe lole)

Genes of Interest

$Beta_1$-Adrenergic Receptor *on page 230*
CYP2D6 *on page 254*
Gs Protein Alpha-Subunit *on page 288*

U.S. Brand Names Betimol®; Blocadren®; Istalol™; Timoptic-XE®; Timoptic® OcuDose®; Timoptic®

Canadian Brand Names Alti-Timolol; Apo-Timol®; Apo-Timop®; Gen-Timolol; Nu-Timolol; PMS-Timolol; Phoxal-timolol; Tim-AK; Timoptic-XE®; Timoptic®

Synonyms Timolol Hemihydrate; Timolol Maleate

Pharmacologic Class Beta-Adrenergic Blocker, Nonselective; Ophthalmic Agent, Antiglaucoma

- ♦ **Timolol Hemihydrate** *see* Timolol *on page 195*
- ♦ **Timolol Maleate** *see* Timolol *on page 195*
- ♦ **Timoptic®** *see* Timolol *on page 195*
- ♦ **Timoptic® OcuDose®** *see* Timolol *on page 195*
- ♦ **Timoptic-XE®** *see* Timolol *on page 195*
- ♦ **Tioguanine** *see* Thioguanine *on page 193*
- ♦ **Tiotixene** *see* Thiothixene *on page 193*

Tirofiban (tye roe FYE ban)

Genes of Interest

Glycoprotein IIIa Receptor *on page 285*

U.S. Brand Names Aggrastat®

Canadian Brand Names Aggrastat®

Synonyms MK383; Tirofiban Hydrochloride

Pharmacologic Class Antiplatelet Agent, Glycoprotein IIb/IIIa Inhibitor

- ♦ **Tirofiban Hydrochloride** *see* Tirofiban *on page 195*

Tizanidine (tye ZAN i deen)

Genes of Interest

Cardiac Potassium Ion Channel *on page 241*
Cardiac Sodium Channel *on page 242*

U.S. Brand Names Zanaflex®

Canadian Brand Names Apo-Tizanidine®; Zanaflex®

Synonyms Sirdalud®

Pharmacologic Class $Alpha_2$-Adrenergic Agonist

- ♦ **TMP** *see* Trimethoprim *on page 199*
- ♦ **TMP-SMZ** *see* Sulfamethoxazole and Trimethoprim *on page 187*
- ♦ **TMZ** *see* Temozolomide *on page 191*
- ♦ **Tofranil®** *see* Imipramine *on page 124*
- ♦ **Tofranil-PM®** *see* Imipramine *on page 124*

TOLBUTamide (tole BYOO ta mide)

Genes of Interest

CYP2C8 *on page 248*
(Continued)

TOLBUTamide *(Continued)*

CYP2C9 *on page 248*

Canadian Brand Names Apo-Tolbutamide®

Synonyms Tolbutamide Sodium

Pharmacologic Class Antidiabetic Agent, Sulfonylurea

- ♦ **Tolbutamide Sodium** *see* TOLBUTamide *on page 195*
- ♦ **Tolectin®** *see* Tolmetin *on page 196*

Tolmetin (TOLE met in)

Genes of Interest

Leukotriene C4 Synthase *on page 302*

U.S. Brand Names Tolectin®

Synonyms Tolmetin Sodium

Pharmacologic Class Nonsteroidal Anti-inflammatory Drug (NSAID), Oral

- ♦ **Tolmetin Sodium** *see* Tolmetin *on page 196*

Tolterodine (tole TER oh deen)

Genes of Interest

CYP3A4 *on page 260*

U.S. Brand Names Detrol® LA; Detrol®

Canadian Brand Names Detrol®; Unidet®

Synonyms Tolterodine Tartrate

Pharmacologic Class Anticholinergic Agent

- ♦ **Tolterodine Tartrate** *see* Tolterodine *on page 196*
- ♦ **Tomoxetine** *see* Atomoxetine *on page 66*
- ♦ **Tomudex® (Can)** *see* Raltitrexed *on page 175*
- ♦ **Topamax®** *see* Topiramate *on page 196*
- ♦ **Topicaine® [OTC]** *see* Lidocaine *on page 131*

Topiramate (toe PYRE a mate)

Genes of Interest None known

U.S. Brand Names Topamax®

Canadian Brand Names Topamax®

Pharmacologic Class Anticonvulsant, Miscellaneous

- ♦ **Toposar®** *see* Etoposide *on page 106*
- ♦ **Toprol-XL®** *see* Metoprolol *on page 142*
- ♦ **Toradol®** *see* Ketorolac *on page 129*
- ♦ **Toradol® IM (Can)** *see* Ketorolac *on page 129*

Torsemide (TORE se mide)

Genes of Interest

Alpha-Adducin *on page 212*

CYP2C9 *on page 248*

U.S. Brand Names Demadex®

Pharmacologic Class Diuretic, Loop

- ♦ **T-Phyl®** *see* Theophylline *on page 192*

♦ **Tracleer®** *see* Bosentan *on page 71*

Tramadol (TRA ma dole)

Genes of Interest

COMT *on page 244*
CYP2D6 *on page 254*

U.S. Brand Names Ultram®

Canadian Brand Names Ultram®

Synonyms Tramadol Hydrochloride

Pharmacologic Class Analgesic, Non-narcotic

♦ **Tramadol Hydrochloride** *see* Tramadol *on page 197*

♦ **Tramadol Hydrochloride and Acetaminophen** *see* Acetaminophen and Tramadol *on page 53*

Trandolapril (tran DOE la pril)

Genes of Interest

Aldosterone Synthase *on page 208*
Angiotensin II Type 1 Receptor *on page 213*
Angiotensin-Converting Enzyme *on page 214*
Angiotensinogen *on page 219*
Bradykinin B_2-Receptor *on page 237*

U.S. Brand Names Mavik®

Canadian Brand Names Mavik™

Pharmacologic Class Angiotensin-Converting Enzyme (ACE) Inhibitor

♦ **Transderm-Nitro® (Can)** *see* Nitroglycerin *on page 151*

♦ **Tranxene®** *see* Clorazepate *on page 84*

♦ **Tranxene® SD™** *see* Clorazepate *on page 84*

♦ **Tranxene® SD™-Half Strength** *see* Clorazepate *on page 84*

♦ **Tranxene T-Tab®** *see* Clorazepate *on page 84*

Trazodone (TRAZ oh done)

Genes of Interest

$Alpha_1$-Adrenergic Receptor *on page 210*
CYP3A4 *on page 260*
G-Protein $Beta_3$ Subunit *on page 286*
Gs Protein Alpha-Subunit *on page 288*

U.S. Brand Names Desyrel®

Canadian Brand Names Alti-Trazodone; Apo-Trazodone D®; Apo-Trazodone®; Desyrel®; Gen-Trazodone; Novo-Trazodone; Nu-Trazodone; PMS-Trazodone

Synonyms Trazodone Hydrochloride

Pharmacologic Class Antidepressant, Serotonin Reuptake Inhibitor/Antagonist

♦ **Trazodone Hydrochloride** *see* Trazodone *on page 197*

♦ **Triaderm (Can)** *see* Triamcinolone *on page 198*

Triamcinolone (trye am SIN oh lone)

Genes of Interest None known

U.S. Brand Names Aristocort® A; Aristocort®; Aristospan®; Azmacort®; Kenalog-10®; Kenalog-40®; Kenalog®; Nasacort® AQ; Nasacort® HFA; Tri-Nasal®; Triderm®

Canadian Brand Names Aristocort®; Aristospan®; Azmacort®; Kenalog® in Orabase; Kenalog®; Nasacort® AQ; Oracort; Triaderm; Trinasal®

Synonyms Triamcinolone Acetonide, Aerosol; Triamcinolone Acetonide, Parenteral; Triamcinolone Diacetate, Oral; Triamcinolone Diacetate, Parenteral; Triamcinolone Hexacetonide; Triamcinolone, Oral

Pharmacologic Class Corticosteroid, Adrenal; Corticosteroid, Inhalant (Oral); Corticosteroid, Nasal; Corticosteroid, Systemic; Corticosteroid, Topical

- **Triamcinolone Acetonide, Aerosol** *see* Triamcinolone *on page 198*
- **Triamcinolone Acetonide, Parenteral** *see* Triamcinolone *on page 198*
- **Triamcinolone Diacetate, Oral** *see* Triamcinolone *on page 198*
- **Triamcinolone Diacetate, Parenteral** *see* Triamcinolone *on page 198*
- **Triamcinolone Hexacetonide** *see* Triamcinolone *on page 198*
- **Triamcinolone, Oral** *see* Triamcinolone *on page 198*
- **Triatec-8 (Can)** *see* Acetaminophen and Codeine *on page 52*
- **Triatec-8 Strong (Can)** *see* Acetaminophen and Codeine *on page 52*
- **Triatec-30 (Can)** *see* Acetaminophen and Codeine *on page 52*
- **Triavil®** *see* Amitriptyline and Perphenazine *on page 58*

Triazolam (trye AY zoe lam)

Genes of Interest

CYP3A4 *on page 260*

U.S. Brand Names Halcion®

Canadian Brand Names Apo-Triazo®; Gen-Triazolam; Halcion®

Pharmacologic Class Benzodiazepine

- **TriCor®** *see* Fenofibrate *on page 107*
- **Tri-Cyclen® (Can)** *see* Ethinyl Estradiol and Norgestimate *on page 105*
- **Tri-Cyclen® Lo (Can)** *see* Ethinyl Estradiol and Norgestimate *on page 105*
- **Triderm®** *see* Triamcinolone *on page 198*

Trifluoperazine (trye floo oh PER a zeen)

Genes of Interest

$Alpha_1$-Adrenergic Receptor *on page 210*

CYP1A2 *on page 246*

D_2 Receptor *on page 263*

Canadian Brand Names Apo-Trifluoperazine®; Novo-Trifluzine; PMS-Trifluoperazine; Terfluzine

Synonyms Trifluoperazine Hydrochloride
Pharmacologic Class Antipsychotic Agent, Typical, Phenothiazine

- **Trifluoperazine Hydrochloride** *see* Trifluoperazine *on page 198*
- **Triglide™** *see* Fenofibrate *on page 107*
- **Trikacide (Can)** *see* Metronidazole *on page 142*
- **Tri-Levlen®** *see* Ethinyl Estradiol and Levonorgestrel *on page 104*

Trimethoprim (trye METH oh prim)

Genes of Interest
CYP2C9 *on page 248*
U.S. Brand Names Primsol®; Proloprim®
Canadian Brand Names Apo-Trimethoprim®
Synonyms TMP
Pharmacologic Class Antibiotic, Miscellaneous

- **Trimethoprim and Sulfamethoxazole** *see* Sulfamethoxazole and Trimethoprim *on page 187*

Trimipramine (trye MI pra meen)

Genes of Interest
Alpha$_1$-Adrenergic Receptor *on page 210*
ATP-Binding Cassette, Sub-Family B, Member 1 *on page 224*
CYP2C19 *on page 251*
CYP3A4 *on page 260*
G-Protein Beta$_3$ Subunit *on page 286*
Gs Protein Alpha-Subunit *on page 288*
U.S. Brand Names Surmontil®
Canadian Brand Names Apo-Trimip®; Nu-Trimipramine; Rhotrimine®; Surmontil®
Synonyms Trimipramine Maleate
Pharmacologic Class Antidepressant, Tricyclic (Tertiary Amine)

- **Trimipramine Maleate** *see* Trimipramine *on page 199*
- **Trimox®** *see* Amoxicillin *on page 59*
- **Tri-Nasal®** *see* Triamcinolone *on page 198*
- **TriNessa™** *see* Ethinyl Estradiol and Norgestimate *on page 105*
- **Tri-Norinyl®** *see* Ethinyl Estradiol and Norethindrone *on page 104*
- **Triphasil®** *see* Ethinyl Estradiol and Levonorgestrel *on page 104*
- **Tri-Previfem™** *see* Ethinyl Estradiol and Norgestimate *on page 105*
- **Triquilar® (Can)** *see* Ethinyl Estradiol and Levonorgestrel *on page 104*
- **Trisenox™** *see* Arsenic Trioxide *on page 64*
- **Tri-Sprintec™** *see* Ethinyl Estradiol and Norgestimate *on page 105*
- **Trivora®** *see* Ethinyl Estradiol and Levonorgestrel *on page 104*
- **T-Stat® [DSC]** *see* Erythromycin *on page 99*
- **T-Tab®** *see* Clorazepate *on page 84*
- **Tucks® Anti-Itch [OTC]** *see* Hydrocortisone *on page 121*
- **Tylenol Elixir with Codeine (Can)** *see* Acetaminophen and Codeine *on page 52*
- **Tylenol No. 1 (Can)** *see* Acetaminophen and Codeine *on page 52*

- **Tylenol No. 1 Forte (Can)** *see* Acetaminophen and Codeine *on page 52*
- **Tylenol No. 2 with Codeine (Can)** *see* Acetaminophen and Codeine *on page 52*
- **Tylenol No. 3 with Codeine (Can)** *see* Acetaminophen and Codeine *on page 52*
- **Tylenol No. 4 with Codeine (Can)** *see* Acetaminophen and Codeine *on page 52*
- **Tylenol® With Codeine** *see* Acetaminophen and Codeine *on page 52*
- **Tylox®** *see* Oxycodone and Acetaminophen *on page 161*
- **UCB-P071** *see* Cetirizine *on page 78*
- **UK109496** *see* Voriconazole *on page 203*
- **UK92480** *see* Sildenafil *on page 184*
- **Ultiva®** *see* Remifentanil *on page 177*
- **Ultracet™** *see* Acetaminophen and Tramadol *on page 53*
- **Ultram®** *see* Tramadol *on page 197*
- **Ultraprin [OTC]** *see* Ibuprofen *on page 123*
- **Unidet® (Can)** *see* Tolterodine *on page 196*
- **Uniphyl®** *see* Theophylline *on page 192*
- **Uniphyl® SRT (Can)** *see* Theophylline *on page 192*
- **Unithroid®** *see* Levothyroxine *on page 131*
- **Univasc®** *see* Moexipril *on page 145*
- **Urolene Blue®** *see* Methylene Blue *on page 140*
- **Utradol™ (Can)** *see* Etodolac *on page 105*
- **Vagifem®** *see* Estradiol *on page 101*

Valacyclovir (val ay SYE kloe veer)

Genes of Interest None known

U.S. Brand Names Valtrex®

Canadian Brand Names Valtrex®

Synonyms Valacyclovir Hydrochloride

Pharmacologic Class Antiviral Agent, Oral

- **Valacyclovir Hydrochloride** *see* Valacyclovir *on page 200*

Valdecoxib (val de KOKS ib)

Genes of Interest

Leukotriene C4 Synthase *on page 302*

U.S. Brand Names Bextra®

Pharmacologic Class Nonsteroidal Anti-inflammatory Drug (NSAID), COX-2 Selective

- **Valium®** *see* Diazepam *on page 90*
- **Valproate Semisodium** *see* Valproic Acid and Derivatives *on page 201*
- **Valproate Sodium** *see* Valproic Acid and Derivatives *on page 201*
- **Valproic Acid** *see* Valproic Acid and Derivatives *on page 201*

Valproic Acid and Derivatives
(val PROE ik AS id & dah RIV ah tives)

Genes of Interest None known

U.S. Brand Names Depacon®; Depakene®; Depakote® Delayed Release; Depakote® ER; Depakote® Sprinkle®

Canadian Brand Names Alti-Divalproex; Apo-Divalproex®; Depakene®; Epival® I.V.; Gen-Divalproex; Novo-Divalproex; Nu-Divalproex; PMS-Valproic Acid E.C.; PMS-Valproic Acid; Rhoxal-valproic

Synonyms 2-Propylpentanoic Acid; 2-Propylvaleric Acid; DPA; Dipropylacetic Acid; Divalproex Sodium; Valproate Semisodium; Valproate Sodium; Valproic Acid

Pharmacologic Class Anticonvulsant, Miscellaneous

Valsartan (val SAR tan)

Genes of Interest

Adipocyte-Derived Leucine Aminopeptidase *on page 208*
Aldosterone Synthase *on page 208*
Angiotensin II Type 1 Receptor *on page 213*
Angiotensin-Converting Enzyme *on page 214*
Angiotensinogen *on page 219*
Bradykinin B_2-Receptor *on page 237*
CYP2C9 *on page 248*

U.S. Brand Names Diovan®

Canadian Brand Names Diovan®

Pharmacologic Class Angiotensin II Receptor Blocker

- **Valtrex®** *see* Valacyclovir *on page 200*
- **Vascor® [DSC]** *see* Bepridil *on page 69*
- **Vasotec®** *see* Enalapril *on page 97*
- **VCR** *see* VinCRIStine *on page 202*
- **Veetids®** *see* Penicillin V Potassium *on page 163*
- **Velivet™** *see* Ethinyl Estradiol and Desogestrel *on page 103*

Venlafaxine (VEN la faks een)

Genes of Interest

CYP3A4 *on page 260*

U.S. Brand Names Effexor® XR; Effexor®

Canadian Brand Names Effexor® XR

Pharmacologic Class Antidepressant, Serotonin/Norepinephrine Reuptake Inhibitor

- **Ventolin® (Can)** *see* Albuterol *on page 54*
- **Ventolin® Diskus (Can)** *see* Albuterol *on page 54*
- **Ventolin® HFA** *see* Albuterol *on page 54*
- **Ventrodisk (Can)** *see* Albuterol *on page 54*
- **VePesid®** *see* Etoposide *on page 106*

Verapamil (ver AP a mil)

Genes of Interest

ATP-Binding Cassette, Sub-Family B, Member 1 *on page 224*

(Continued)

Verapamil *(Continued)*

CYP3A4 *on page 260*

U.S. Brand Names Calan® SR; Calan®; Covera-HS®; Isoptin® SR; Verelan® PM; Verelan®

Canadian Brand Names Alti-Verapamil; Apo-Verap®; Calan®; Chronovera®; Covera®; Gen-Verapamil SR; Gen-Verapamil; Isoptin® SR; Novo-Veramil SR; Nu-Verap

Synonyms Iproveratril Hydrochloride; Verapamil Hydrochloride

Pharmacologic Class Antiarrhythmic Agent, Class IV; Calcium Channel Blocker

- ♦ **Verapamil Hydrochloride** *see* Verapamil *on page 201*
- ♦ **Verelan®** *see* Verapamil *on page 201*
- ♦ **Verelan® PM** *see* Verapamil *on page 201*
- ♦ **Versed** *see* Midazolam *on page 143*
- ♦ **VFEND®** *see* Voriconazole *on page 203*
- ♦ **Viagra®** *see* Sildenafil *on page 184*
- ♦ **Vibramycin®** *see* Doxycycline *on page 96*
- ♦ **Vibra-Tabs®** *see* Doxycycline *on page 96*
- ♦ **Vicodin®** *see* Hydrocodone and Acetaminophen *on page 120*
- ♦ **Vicodin® ES** *see* Hydrocodone and Acetaminophen *on page 120*
- ♦ **Vicodin® HP** *see* Hydrocodone and Acetaminophen *on page 120*
- ♦ **Vicoprofen®** *see* Hydrocodone and Ibuprofen *on page 120*
- ♦ **Vigamox™** *see* Moxifloxacin *on page 146*

VinBLAStine (vin BLAS teen)

Genes of Interest

ATP-Binding Cassette, Sub-Family B, Member 1 *on page 224*
CYP3A4 *on page 260*

Synonyms NSC-49842; VLB; Vinblastine Sulfate

Pharmacologic Class Antineoplastic Agent, Natural Source (Plant) Derivative; Antineoplastic Agent, Vinca Alkaloid

- ♦ **Vinblastine Sulfate** *see* VinBLAStine *on page 202*
- ♦ **Vincasar PFS®** *see* VinCRIStine *on page 202*

VinCRIStine (vin KRIS teen)

Genes of Interest

CYP3A4 *on page 260*

U.S. Brand Names Vincasar PFS®

Canadian Brand Names Vincasar® PFS®

Synonyms LCR; Leurocristine Sulfate; NSC-67574; VCR; Vincristine Sulfate

Pharmacologic Class Antineoplastic Agent, Natural Source (Plant) Derivative; Antineoplastic Agent, Vinca Alkaloid

- ♦ **Vincristine Sulfate** *see* VinCRIStine *on page 202*

Vinorelbine (vi NOR el been)

Genes of Interest

CYP3A4 *on page 260*

U.S. Brand Names Navelbine®

Canadian Brand Names Navelbine®

Synonyms Dihydroxydeoxynorvinkaleukoblastine; NVB; Vinorelbine Tartrate

Pharmacologic Class Antineoplastic Agent, Natural Source (Plant) Derivative; Antineoplastic Agent, Vinca Alkaloid

- **Vinorelbine Tartrate** *see* Vinorelbine *on page 203*
- **Vioxx® [DSC]** *see* Rofecoxib *on page 181*
- **Viracept®** *see* Nelfinavir *on page 149*
- **Virilon® IM (Can)** *see* Testosterone *on page 192*
- **Vistaril®** *see* HydrOXYzine *on page 122*
- **Vivactil®** *see* Protriptyline *on page 173*
- **Vivelle®** *see* Estradiol *on page 101*
- **Vivelle-Dot®** *see* Estradiol *on page 101*
- **VLB** *see* VinBLAStine *on page 202*
- **VM-26** *see* Teniposide *on page 191*
- **Volmax® [DSC]** *see* Albuterol *on page 54*
- **Voltaren®** *see* Diclofenac *on page 91*
- **Voltaren Ophtha® (Can)** *see* Diclofenac *on page 91*
- **Voltaren Ophthalmic®** *see* Diclofenac *on page 91*
- **Voltaren Rapide® (Can)** *see* Diclofenac *on page 91*
- **Voltaren®-XR** *see* Diclofenac *on page 91*

Voriconazole (vor i KOE na zole)

Genes of Interest

CYP2C9 *on page 248*

U.S. Brand Names VFEND®

Canadian Brand Names VFEND®

Synonyms UK109496

Pharmacologic Class Antifungal Agent, Oral; Antifungal Agent, Parenteral

- **VoSpire ER™** *see* Albuterol *on page 54*
- **VP-16** *see* Etoposide *on page 106*
- **VP-16-213** *see* Etoposide *on page 106*
- **Vumon®** *see* Teniposide *on page 191*

Warfarin (WAR far in)

Genes of Interest

CYP2C8 *on page 248*
CYP2C9 *on page 248*
Protein C *on page 313*
Protein S *on page 314*
Vitamin K Epoxide Reductase Complex, Subunit 1 *on page 329*

(Continued)

Warfarin *(Continued)*

U.S. Brand Names Coumadin®; Jantoven™

Canadian Brand Names Apo-Warfarin®; Coumadin®; Gen-Warfarin; Taro-Warfarin

Synonyms Warfarin Sodium

Pharmacologic Class Anticoagulant, Coumarin Derivative

- ♦ **Warfarin Sodium** *see* Warfarin *on page 203*
- ♦ **Wellbutrin®** *see* BuPROPion *on page 73*
- ♦ **Wellbutrin XL™** *see* BuPROPion *on page 73*
- ♦ **Wellbutrin SR®** *see* BuPROPion *on page 73*
- ♦ **Westcort®** *see* Hydrocortisone *on page 121*
- ♦ **Winpred™ (Can)** *see* PredniSONE *on page 169*
- ♦ **WR-139007** *see* Dacarbazine *on page 87*
- ♦ **WR-139021** *see* Carmustine *on page 76*
- ♦ **Wytensin® (Can)** *see* Guanabenz *on page 118*
- ♦ **Xalatan®** *see* Latanoprost *on page 130*
- ♦ **Xanax®** *see* Alprazolam *on page 56*
- ♦ **Xanax TS™ (Can)** *see* Alprazolam *on page 56*
- ♦ **Xanax XR®** *see* Alprazolam *on page 56*
- ♦ **Xeloda®** *see* Capecitabine *on page 75*
- ♦ **Xopenex®** *see* Levalbuterol *on page 130*
- ♦ **Xopenex HFA™** *see* Levalbuterol *on page 130*
- ♦ **Xylocaine®** *see* Lidocaine *on page 131*
- ♦ **Xylocaine® MPF** *see* Lidocaine *on page 131*
- ♦ **Xylocaine® Viscous** *see* Lidocaine *on page 131*
- ♦ **Xylocard® (Can)** *see* Lidocaine *on page 131*
- ♦ **Yasmin®** *see* Ethinyl Estradiol and Drospirenone *on page 103*
- ♦ **Z4942** *see* Ifosfamide *on page 123*

Zafirlukast (za FIR loo kast)

Genes of Interest

Arachidonate 5-Lipoxygenase *on page 223*
CYP2C9 *on page 248*
Leukotriene C4 Synthase *on page 302*

U.S. Brand Names Accolate®

Canadian Brand Names Accolate®

Synonyms ICI-204,219

Pharmacologic Class Leukotriene-Receptor Antagonist

- ♦ **Zagam® [DSC]** *see* Sparfloxacin *on page 185*
- ♦ **Zanaflex®** *see* Tizanidine *on page 195*
- ♦ **Zantac®** *see* Ranitidine *on page 176*
- ♦ **Zantac 75® [OTC]** *see* Ranitidine *on page 176*
- ♦ **Zantac 150™ [OTC]** *see* Ranitidine *on page 176*
- ♦ **Zantac® EFFERdose®** *see* Ranitidine *on page 176*
- ♦ **Zarontin®** *see* Ethosuximide *on page 105*
- ♦ **Zaroxolyn®** *see* Metolazone *on page 142*

- **Z-chlopenthixol** *see* Zuclopenthixol *on page 206*
- **ZD1694** *see* Raltitrexed *on page 175*
- **ZD1839** *see* Gefitinib *on page 114*
- **Zebeta®** *see* Bisoprolol *on page 71*
- **Zegerid™** *see* Omeprazole *on page 159*
- **Zeldox** *see* Ziprasidone *on page 205*
- **Zestoretic®** *see* Lisinopril and Hydrochlorothiazide *on page 132*
- **Zestril®** *see* Lisinopril *on page 132*
- **Ziagen®** *see* Abacavir *on page 52*
- **Zilactin® (Can)** *see* Lidocaine *on page 131*
- **Zilactin-L® [OTC]** *see* Lidocaine *on page 131*
- **Zinecard®** *see* Dexrazoxane *on page 90*

Ziprasidone (zi PRAY si done)

Genes of Interest

$Alpha_1$-Adrenergic Receptor *on page 210*
Cardiac Potassium Ion Channel *on page 241*
Cardiac Sodium Channel *on page 242*
D_2 Receptor *on page 263*
D_3 Receptor *on page 266*
5-HT_{1A} Receptor *on page 291*
5-HT_{2A} Receptor *on page 291*
5-HT_{2C} Receptor *on page 294*

U.S. Brand Names Geodon®

Synonyms Zeldox; Ziprasidone Hydrochloride; Ziprasidone Mesylate

Pharmacologic Class Antipsychotic Agent, Atypical

- **Ziprasidone Hydrochloride** *see* Ziprasidone *on page 205*
- **Ziprasidone Mesylate** *see* Ziprasidone *on page 205*
- **Zithromax®** *see* Azithromycin *on page 68*
- **Zithromax® TRI-PAK™** *see* Azithromycin *on page 68*
- **Zithromax® Z-PAK®** *see* Azithromycin *on page 68*
- **Zmax™** *see* Azithromycin *on page 68*
- **Zocor®** *see* Simvastatin *on page 184*
- **Zoloft®** *see* Sertraline *on page 183*

Zolpidem (zole PI dem)

Genes of Interest

CYP3A4 *on page 260*

U.S. Brand Names Ambien®

Canadian Brand Names Ambien®

Synonyms Zolpidem Tartrate

Pharmacologic Class Hypnotic, Nonbenzodiazepine

- **Zolpidem Tartrate** *see* Zolpidem *on page 205*
- **Zonalon®** *see* Doxepin *on page 95*
- **Zonegran®** *see* Zonisamide *on page 206*

Zonisamide (zoe NIS a mide)

Genes of Interest

CYP3A4 *on page 260*

U.S. Brand Names Zonegran®

Canadian Brand Names Zonegran®

Pharmacologic Class Anticonvulsant, Miscellaneous

Zopiclone (ZOE pi clone)

Genes of Interest

CYP2C8 *on page 248*

CYP2C9 *on page 248*

CYP3A4 *on page 260*

Canadian Brand Names Alti-Zopiclone; Apo-Zopiclone®; Gen-Zopiclone; Imovane®; Novo-Zopiclone; Nu-Zopiclone; PMS-Zopiclone; Rhovane®; Rhoxal-zopiclone

Pharmacologic Class Hypnotic, Nonbenzodiazepine

- ♦ **ZORprin®** *see* Aspirin *on page 65*
- ♦ **Zovia™** *see* Ethinyl Estradiol and Ethynodiol Diacetate *on page 103*
- ♦ **Zovirax®** *see* Acyclovir *on page 54*

Zuclopenthixol (zoo kloe pen THIX ol)

Genes of Interest

$Alpha_1$-Adrenergic Receptor *on page 210*

Cardiac Potassium Ion Channel *on page 241*

Cardiac Sodium Channel *on page 242*

D_2 Receptor *on page 263*

Canadian Brand Names Clopixol-Acuphase®; Clopixol® Depot; Clopixol®

Synonyms Z-chlopenthixol; Zuclopenthixol Acetate; Zuclopenthixol Decanoate; Zuclopenthixol Dihydrochloride

Pharmacologic Class Antipsychotic Agent, Typical

- ♦ **Zuclopenthixol Acetate** *see* Zuclopenthixol *on page 206*
- ♦ **Zuclopenthixol Decanoate** *see* Zuclopenthixol *on page 206*
- ♦ **Zuclopenthixol Dihydrochloride** *see* Zuclopenthixol *on page 206*
- ♦ **Zyban®** *see* BuPROPion *on page 73*
- ♦ **Zydone®** *see* Hydrocodone and Acetaminophen *on page 120*
- ♦ **Zyloprim®** *see* Allopurinol *on page 55*
- ♦ **Zymar™** *see* Gatifloxacin *on page 114*
- ♦ **Zyprexa®** *see* Olanzapine *on page 158*
- ♦ **Zyprexa® Zydis®** *see* Olanzapine *on page 158*
- ♦ **Zyrtec®** *see* Cetirizine *on page 78*

ALPHABETICAL LISTING OF POTENTIAL POLYMORPHISMS

♦ **ABC20** *see* ATP-Binding Cassette, Sub-Family B, Member 1 *on page 224*

♦ **ABCB1** *see* ATP-Binding Cassette, Sub-Family B, Member 1 *on page 224*

♦ **ACE** *see* Angiotensin-Converting Enzyme *on page 214*

♦ **ADDA** *see* Alpha-Adducin *on page 212*

Adipocyte-Derived Leucine Aminopeptidase

Synonyms ALAP

Chromosome Location 5q15

Clinically-Important Polymorphisms Lys528Arg

Discussion Adipocyte-derived leucine aminopeptidase (A-LAP) is a member of the M1 family of zinc metallopeptidases. This enzyme is involved in angiotensin II inactivation, cell migration, and antigen presentation. Over 33 mutations have been described. The *Arg528* allele has been associated with essential hypertension (Yamamoto, 2002).

Irbesartan:

In patients with essential hypertension and left ventricular hypertrophy, there was a marked difference in regression of left ventricular mass between the Arg/Arg and Lys/Arg genotypes following treatment with irbesartan. Those with the Arg/Arg genotype had nearly a two-fold greater regression of left ventricular mass index as compared to individuals with the Lys/Arg genotype.

May Alter Pharmacodynamics of Angiotensin II type I receptor blockers

References

Hallberg P, Lind L, Michaelsson K, et al, "Adipocyte-Derived Leucine Aminopeptidase Genotype and Response to Antihypertensive Therapy," *BMC Cardiovasc Disord*, 2003, 3(1):11.

Yamamoto N, Nakayama J, Yamakawa-Kobayashi K, et al, "Identification of 33 Polymorphisms in the Adipocyte-Derived Leucine Aminopeptidase (ALAP) Gene and Possible Association With Hypertension," *Hum Mutat*, 2002, 19(3):251-7.

♦ **ADRA2B** *see* Alpha$_{2B}$-Adrenergic Receptor *on page 211*

♦ **ADRA2L1** *see* Alpha$_{2B}$-Adrenergic Receptor *on page 211*

♦ **ADRA2RL1** *see* Alpha$_{2B}$-Adrenergic Receptor *on page 211*

♦ **ADRARL1** *see* Alpha$_{2B}$-Adrenergic Receptor *on page 211*

♦ **ADRB1** *see* Beta$_1$-Adrenergic Receptor *on page 230*

♦ **ADRB2** *see* Beta$_2$-Adrenergic Receptor *on page 233*

♦ **ADRB3** *see* Beta$_3$-Adrenergic Receptor *on page 236*

♦ **AGT** *see* Angiotensinogen *on page 219*

♦ **AG TR1** *see* Angiotensin II Type 1 Receptor *on page 213*

♦ **ALAP** *see* Adipocyte-Derived Leucine Aminopeptidase *on page 208*

Aldosterone Synthase

Synonyms CYP11B2; P-450 C18 11-Beta Hydroxylase

Chromosome Location 8q21-22

Clinically-Important Polymorphisms Synonymous SNP in the 5′-flanking region *(C-344T)*

Discussion The conversion of 11-deoxycorticosterone to aldosterone requires three enzymatic reactions. Aldosterone synthase, a member of the cytochrome P450 enzyme family, mediates these reactions. The *C-344T* polymorphism, or a functional variant in linkage disequilibrium with it, is believed to contribute to the abnormal regulation of aldosterone secretion which may play a role in idiopathic low-renin hypertension (Rossi, 2001). The CYP11B2 genotype may also influence the effect of risk factors for coronary events. Smoking and dyslipidemia have been shown to be more potent risk factors for nonfatal MI in males who carry the *-344C* allele (Hautanen, 1999).

The *-344C* allele of CYP11B2 gene has been associated with a genetic predisposition to develop essential hypertension and may interact with other genes to influence phenotype and/or drug response (Tsukada, 2002). A relationship between the intima-media thickness of the large muscular femoral artery and the ACE gene has been noted to be apparent only in the presence of either the alpha-adducin *460W* or the aldosterone synthase *-344T* allele (Balkestein, 2002). In hypertensive patients of African ancestry who had never received antihypertensive therapy, neither the ACE insertion/deletion nor the angiotensinogen gene polymorphisms were associated with systolic or diastolic blood pressure. However, the CYP11B2 *-344T* variant was found to have a clinically important association with systolic blood pressure elevations in this population. In comparison to subjects with at least one copy of the *-344C* allele, patients who were homozygous for the *-344T* allele had higher systolic blood pressures in both the ambulatory and office settings. The relationship between this genetic polymorphism and hypertension may be complex, as interactions between a number of genes, including angiotensin converting enzyme, alpha-adducin, and aldosterone synthase, appear to contribute to the prevalence and incidence of hypertension in Caucasians (Staessen, 2001).

ACE inhibitors:

During ACE inhibitor therapy for a mean duration of 17 months in 107 patients with dilated cardiomyopathy, improvement in left ventricular ejection fraction was greater with the *-344C* allele compared to the *TT* genotype (Tiago, 2002).

Angiotensin II type 1 receptor antagonists:

During treatment with irbesartan in patients with essential hypertension and left ventricular hypertrophy, systolic blood pressure reduction was greater with the *-344TT* genotype compared to *-344TC* and *CC* genotypes. There was no association between this genotype and diastolic blood pressure response (Kurland, 2002). The *C-344T* polymorphism was not associated with regression of left ventricular mass during irbesartan treatment in this population (Kurland, 2002).

May Alter Pharmacokinetics of Aldosterone synthase is not known to affect the metabolism of any drugs.

(Continued)

Aldosterone Synthase *(Continued)*

May Alter Pharmacodynamics of ACE inhibitors, angiotensin II type 1 receptor blockers, aldosterone antagonists

Clinical Recommendations Data with the CYP11B2 gene to date are inconsistent. The CYP11B2 gene may interact with other genes in the renin-angiotensin system to influence response to renin-angiotensin system antagonists. The association between the CYP11B2 gene alone and response to ACE inhibitors or angiotensin II type 1 receptor blockers may be difficult to establish.

Counseling Points Since hypertension is a disease with polygenic etiology, carrier status of the aldosterone synthase variant allele does not necessarily predispose a person to developing hypertension or its sequelae.

References

Balkestein EJ, Wang JG, Struijker-Boudier HA, et al, "Carotid and Femoral Intima-Media Thickness in Relation to Three Candidate Genes in a Caucasian Population," *J Hypertens*, 2002, 20(8):1551-61.

Hautanen A, Toivanen P, Manttari M, et al, "Joint Effects of an Aldosterone Synthase (CYP11B2) Gene Polymorphism and Classic Risk Factors on Risk of Myocardial Infarction," *Circulation*, 1999, 100(22):2213-8.

Kurland L, Melhus H, Karlsson J, et al, "Aldosterone Synthase (CYP11B2) -344 C/T Polymorphism Is Related to Antihypertensive Response: Result From the Swedish Irbesartan Left Ventricular Hypertrophy Investigation Versus Atenolol (SILVHIA) Trial," *Am J Hypertens*, 2002, 15(5):389-93.

Kurland L, Melhus H, Karlsson J, et al, "Polymorphisms in the Angiotensinogen and Angiotensin II Type 1 Receptor Gene Are Related to Change in Left Ventricular Mass During Antihypertensive Treatment: Results From the Swedish Irbesartan Left Ventricular Hypertrophy Investigation Versus Atenolol (SILVHIA) Trial," *J Hypertens*, 2002, 20(4):657-63.

Rossi E, Regolisti G, Perazzoli F, et al, "-344C/T Polymorphism of CYP11B2 Gene in Italian Patients With Idiopathic Low Renin Hypertension," *Am J Hypertens*, 2001, 14(9 Pt 1):934-41.

Staessen JA, Wang JG, Brand E, et al, "Effects of Three Candidate Genes on Prevalence and Incidence of Hypertension in a Caucasian Population," *J Hypertens*, 2001, 19(8):1349-58.

Tiago AD, Badenhorst D, Nkeh B, et al, "Impact of Renin-Angiotensin-Aldosterone System Gene Variants on the Severity of Hypertension in Patients With Newly Diagnosed Hypertension," *Am J Hypertens*, 2003, 16(12):1006-10.

Tiago AD, Badenhorst D, Skudicky D, et al, "An Aldosterone Synthase Gene Variant Is Associated With Improvement in Left Ventricular Ejection Fraction in Dilated Cardiomyopathy," *Cardiovasc Res*, 2002, 54(3):584-9.

Tsukada K, Ishimitsu T, Teranishi M, et al, "Positive Association of CYP11B2 Gene Polymorphism With Genetic Predisposition to Essential Hypertension," *J Hum Hypertens*, 2002, 16(11):789-93.

♦ **ALOX5** *see* Arachidonate 5-Lipoxygenase *on page 223*

Alpha$_1$-Adrenergic Receptor

Chromosome Location 8p21-p11.2

Clinically-Important Polymorphisms ADRA1A; Arg347Cys

Discussion There are three pharmacologically defined α_1-adrenergic receptors with distinct sequences and tissue distribution. These include the α_{1A}-, α_{1B}-, and α_{1D}-receptors. The distinct functional properties of these different α_1-adrenergic receptor subtypes have not been fully illuminated.

α_1-adrenergic receptors are one of the key first messengers in the uncoupling protein pathway. They have an overlapping distribution on white and brown adipose tissue and within the hypothalamic paraventricular nucleus. Clozapine, via α_1-adrenergic antagonism, may disrupt peripheral, as well as central energy homeostasis and cause weight gain (Bymaster, 1996).

Clozapine:

Individuals who are homozygous for the cysteine variant of the α_{1a}-adrenergic receptor were protected from clozapine-induced weight gain (Basile, 2001).

May Alter Pharmacodynamics of Clozapine and other agents that affect the α_1-adrenergic receptor

May Affect Disease Predisposition of Risk of coronary events

References

Basile VS, Masellis M, McIntyre RS, et al, "Genetic Dissection of Atypical Antipsychotic-Induced Weight Gain: Novel Preliminary Data on the Pharmacogenetic Puzzle," *J Clin Psychiatry*, 2001, 62(Suppl 23):45-66.

Bymaster FP, Hemrick-Luecke SK, Perry KW, et al, "Neurochemical Evidence for Antagonism by Olanzapine of Dopamine, Serotonin, Alpha$_1$-Adrenergic and Muscarinic Receptors *in vivo* in Rats," *Psychopharmacology (Berl)*, 1996, 124(1-2):87-94.

Alpha$_{2B}$-Adrenergic Receptor

Synonyms ADRA2B; ADRA2L1; ADRA2RL1; ADRARL1

Chromosome Location 2p13-q13

Clinically-Important Polymorphisms A polymorphic variant consists of a deletion of 3 glutamic acids (residues 301-303) in the third intracellular loop. This deletion *(D)* allele was found to be common in Caucasians (31%) and to a lesser extent in African-Americans (12%).

Discussion Alpha$_2$-adrenergic receptors are G protein-coupled receptors. There are 3 subtypes which are highly homologous: α_{2A}, α_{2B}, and α_{2C}. Alpha$_2$-adrenergic receptors regulate neurotransmitter release from nerves within the sympathetic nervous system. In addition, α_2 receptors may be found on neurons within the central nervous system. The α_{2B} subtype includes a polymorphic variant which lacks 3 glutamic acids from a glutamic acid repeat element. The deletion *(D)* variant corresponds to decreased signaling activity. It has been associated with reduced basal metabolic rate in obese subjects. The gene contains no introns in either its coding or untranslated sequences.

The α_{2B}-receptor is involved with vascular smooth muscle contraction and may induce coronary vasoconstriction in humans. In a cohort of middle-aged men, the *DD* genotype has been described as a novel risk factor for acute coronary events (Snapir, 2001). Middle-aged white men (<55 years of age) carrying the *DD* genotype of the α_{2B} adrenergic receptor had a significantly increased risk for both fatal myocardial infarction and sudden cardiac death (Snapir, 2003).

References

Small KM, Brown M, Forbes SL, et al, "Polymorphic Deletion of Three Intracellular Acidic Residues of the Alpha$_{2B}$-Adrenergic Receptor Diseases G Protein-Coupled Receptor Kinase-Mediated Phosphorylation and Desensitization," *J Biol Chem*, 2001, 276(7):4917-22.

(Continued)

Alpha$_{2B}$-Adrenergic Receptor *(Continued)*

Snapir A, Heinonen P, Tuomainen TP, et al, "An Insertion/Deletion Polymorphism in the Alpha$_{2B}$-Adrenergic Receptor Gene Is a Novel Genetic Ris Factor for Acute Coronary Events," *J Am Coll Cardiol*, 2001, 37(6):1516-22.

Snapir A, Mikkelsson J, Perola M, et al, "Variation in the Alpha$_{2B}$-Adrenoceptor Gene as a Risk Factor for Prehospital Fatal Myocardial Infarction and Sudden Cardiac Death," *J Am Coll Cardiol*, 2003, 41(2):190-4.

Alpha-Adducin

Synonyms ADDA

Chromosome Location 4p16.3

Clinically-Important Polymorphisms Nonsynonymous SNP at codon 460 *(Gly460Trp)*

Discussion Alpha-adducin is a cytoskeletal protein that is important in the assembly of the intracellular actin-spectrin network. It may also play a role in intracellular signaling and membrane ion transport. The alpha-adducin gene variant, *Gly460Trp*, has been associated with a salt-sensitive form of hypertension, renal sodium retention, and plasma renin activity (Manunta, 1999; Cusi, 1997). A relationship between the intima-media thickness of the large muscular femoral artery and the ACE gene has been noted to be apparent only in the presence of either the alpha-adducin *460Trp* allele or the aldosterone synthase *-344T* allele (Balkestein, 2002).

Hydrochlorothiazide:

Significantly greater reductions in mean blood pressure were observed in hypertensive individuals with the *460Trp* allele during 2-month treatment with hydrochlorothiazide (Glorioso, 1999). In a population-based-case-control study, treatment with a thiazide diuretic was associated with a significantly lower risk of the combined endpoint of myocardial infarction and stroke compared to other antihypertensive treatments among carriers of at least one *460Trp* allele (Psaty, 2002).

May Alter Pharmacokinetics of Alpha-adducin is not known to affect the metabolism of any drugs.

May Alter Pharmacodynamics of Thiazide diuretics, loop diuretics

Clinical Recommendations Genotyping for the *Gly460Trp* polymorphism may have a role in predicting the effects of diuretics on blood pressure and clinical outcomes in hypertensive patients.

Counseling Points Since hypertension is a disease with polygenic etiology, carrier status of the *460Trp* allele does not necessarily predispose a person to developing hypertension or its sequelae.

References

Balkestein EJ, Wang JG, Struijker-Boudier HA, et al, "Carotid and Femoral Intima-Media Thickness in Relation to Three Candidate Genes in a Caucasian Population," *J Hypertens*, 2002, 20(8):1551-61.

Cusi D, Barlassina C, Azzani T, et al, "Polymorphisms of Alpha-Adducin and Salt Sensitivity in Patients With Essential Hypertension," *Lancet*, 1997, 349(9062):1353-7.

Glorioso N, Manunta P, Filigheddu F, et al, "The Role of Alpha-Adducin Polymorphism in Blood Pressure and Sodium Handling Regulation May Not Be Excluded by a Negative Association Study," *Hypertension*, 1999, 34(4 Pt 1):649-54.

Manunta P, Burnier M, D'Amico M, et al, "Adducin Polymorphism Affects Renal Proximal Tubule Reabsorption in Hypertension," *Hypertension*, 1999, 33(2):694-7.

Psaty BM, Smith NL, Heckbert SR, et al, "Diuretic Therapy, the Alpha-Adducin Gene Variant, and the Risk of Myocardial Infarction or Stroke in Persons With Treated Hypertension," *JAMA*, 2002, 287(13):1680-9.

◆ **γ-Aminobutyric Acid (GABA) Type A Receptor Alpha$_1$ Subunit GABA** *see* Gamma-Aminobutyric Acid (GABA) Type A Receptor Alpha$_1$ Subunit *on page 280*

Angiotensin II Type 1 Receptor

Synonyms AG TR1; AT1; AT$_1$R

Chromosome Location 3q21-25

Clinically-Important Polymorphisms Synonymous SNP at nucleotide 1166 in the 3′ untranslated region *(A1166C)*

Discussion The angiotensin type 1 receptor mediates vasoconstriction, aldosterone secretion, and cardiac remodeling following stimulation by angiotensin II. The *1166C* allele has been shown to increase the arterial responsiveness to angiotensin II (VanGeel, 2000). It has also been associated with aortic stiffness in hypertensive patients (Benetos, 1996).

ACE inhibitors:

In hypertensive individuals, *1166C* allele carriers had threefold greater reductions in aortic stiffness with perindopril therapy compared to *1166AA* homozygotes (Benetos, Cambien, 1996).

Angiotensin II type 1 receptor antagonists:

In healthy volunteers, a single dose of losartan resulted in a greater reduction in mean arterial pressure in *1166C* allele carriers compared to *1166AA* homozygotes (Miller, 1999). However, in hypertensive patients treated with an ACE inhibitor, no association between the AT$_1$R gene and blood pressure reduction was found (Hingorani, 1995).

During treatment with irbesartan in patients with essential hypertension and left ventricular hypertrophy, reductions in left ventricular mass were greater with the *1166AC* genotype compared to the *1166AA* genotype (Kurland, 2002). However, the *1166AA* genotype did not remain an independent predictor of blood pressure response after regression analysis.

The *A1166C* polymorphism has been associated with increased synthesis of type I collagen and myocardial stiffness in hypertensive patients. Treatment with losartan resulted in a significant decrease in collagen synthesis and left ventricular chamber stiffness only in *1166AA* patients (Diez, 2003). No changes were noted in patients treated with atenolol.

May Alter Pharmacokinetics of AT$_1$R is not known to alter the metabolism of any drugs.

May Alter Pharmacodynamics of ACE inhibitors, angiotensin II type 1 receptor blockers

May Affect Disease Predisposition of Hypertension, hypertensive heart disease/CHF, left ventricular hypertrophy, anxiety, depression, Alzheimer's disease

(Continued)

Angiotensin II Type 1 Receptor *(Continued)*

Clinical Recommendations Data with the AT_1R gene are inconsistent. The AT_1R gene may interact with other genes in the renin-angiotensin system to influence response to renin-angiotensin system antagonists. The association between the AT_1R gene alone and response to ACE inhibitors or angiotensin II type 1 receptor blockers may be difficult to establish.

Counseling Points Since hypertension is a disease with polygenic etiology, carrier status of the AT_1R variant allele does not necessarily predispose a person to developing hypertension.

References

Benetos A and Safar ME, "Aortic Collagen, Aortic Stiffness, and AT1 Receptors in Experimental and Human Hypertension," *Can J Physiol Pharmacol*, 1996, 74(7):862-6.

Benetos A, Cambien F, Gautier S, et al, "Influence of the Angiotensin II Type 1 Receptor Gene Polymorphism on the Effects of Perindopril and Nitrendipine on Arterial Stiffness in Hypertensive Individuals," *Hypertension*, 1996, 28(6):1081-4.

Hingorani AD and Brown MJ, "A Simple Molecular Assay for the C1166 Variant of the Angiotensin II Type 1 Receptor Gene," *Biochem Biophys Res Commun*, 1995, 213(2):725-9.

Kurland L, Melhus H, Karlsson J, et al, "Aldosterone Synthase (CYP11B2) -344 C/T Polymorphism Is Related to Antihypertensive Response: Result From the Swedish Irbesartan Left Ventricular Hypertrophy Investigation Versus Atenolol (SILVHIA) Trial," *Am J Hypertens*, 2002, 15(5):389-93.

Miller JA, Thai K, and Scholey JW, "Angiotensin II Type 1 Receptor Gene Polymorphism Predicts Response to Losartan and Angiotensin II," *Kidney Int*, 1999, 56(6):2173-80.

van Geel PP, Pinto YM, Voors AA, et al, "Angiotensin II Type 1 Receptor A1166C Gene Polymorphism Is Associated With an Increased Response to Angiotensin II in Human Arteries," *Hypertension*, 2000, 35(3):717-21.

Angiotensin-Converting Enzyme

Synonyms ACE

Chromosome Location 17q22-24

Clinically-Important Polymorphisms The ACE insertion/deletion (I/D) polymorphism results in the presence or absence of a 287 base pair fragment in intron 16 of the ACE gene.

Discussion Angiotensin-converting enzyme (ACE) mediates the conversion of angiotensin I to angiotensin II. Polymorphism of the human ACE gene contributes to circulating ACE activity, as evidenced by the insertion/deletion (I/D) polymorphism accounting for nearly 50% of the variability in enzyme activity (Rigat, 1990). Genotype has been postulated to influence the development of hypertension and cardiovascular disease since the D allele is associated with higher ACE levels as compared to the I allele (Kohno, 1999; Ohmichi, 1997; Danser, 1995). Consistent with the observation of higher plasma and tissue levels of angiotensin II associated with the D variant (Diequez-Lucena, 1996), the ACE *DD* genotype has been associated with increased mortality and cardiac morbidity following coronary artery bypass grafting (Volzke, 2002). However, correlations between gene distribution and cardiovascular disease have been inconsistent. In large, randomized trial of hypertensive patients with cardiovascular risk factors, Arnett et al, reported no association between I/D genotype and the risk of fatal coronary heart disease or nonfatal myocardial infarction. Thus, the clinical significance of this polymorphism may be difficult to distinguish.

ACE inhibitors:

In early investigations, the ACE I/D genotype has been correlated with the clinical effects of ACE inhibitors including blood pressure lowering (Ohmichi, 1997; Stavroulakis; 2000), reductions in left ventricular hypertrophy (Sasaki, 1996; Kohno, 1999), and improvements in endothelial function (Prasad, 2000). However, data are inconsistent with some studies showing greater response to ACE inhibitors with the II genotype (Ohmichi, 1997; Kohno, 1999) and others showing greater response with the DD genotype (Stavroulakis, 2000; Li, 2003; Sasaki, 1996). Other studies found no association between the ACE gene and blood pressure reduction or regression of left ventricular hypertrophy with ACE inhibitors or angiotensin receptor blockers (Hingorani, 1995; Kurland, 2001). In an attempt to clarify these conflicting results, a majority of the patients who participated in the Antihypertensive and Lipid Lowering Treatment for the Prevention of Heart Attack Trial (ALLHAT) were subsequently enrolled in the Genetics of Hypertension-Associated Treatment (GenHAT) study, with hypertension and presence of ≥1 cardiovascular risk factors as criteria for inclusion. In this follow-up evaluation, 37,939 participants were assessed for the risk of fatal coronary heart disease (CHD), nonfatal myocardial infarction (primary endpoints) and a variety of secondary outcomes for up to 6 years as a function of ACE genotype and therapeutic intervention. The hypothesis of increased cardiovascular events in patients possessing the D/D variant was not supported. The relative risk for fatal and nonfatal CHD for D/D vs combined I/D and I/I patients was 0.99 (95% CI: 0.91-1.07). In fact, D/D patients randomized to receive lisinopril as first-line monotherapy exhibited a smaller blood pressure reduction at 6 months as compared to a composite of patients with the I/D and I/I genotypes. In addition, patients responded better overall to treatment with amlodipine, chlorthalidone or doxazosin ($p \leq 0.018$), regardless of genotype, as compared to lisinopril. These results are in general agreement with those of the PROGRESS trial, which demonstrated no significant benefit of ACE inhibitor therapy or improvement in cardio- or cerebrovascular risk as a function of I/D genotype (Harrap, 2003). At this time, data from the GenHAT and PROGRESS studies cast doubt as to the significance of the I/D polymorphism in assessing response to ACE inhibitor therapy and risk stratification.

Although the data on cardiovascular disease risk and drug response are inconsistent, the I/D polymorphism has been associated with ACE inhibitor-induced cough. In a healthy volunteer study, cough threshold following 4 weeks of ACE inhibitor therapy was significantly reduced in volunteers with the II genotype (Takahashi, 2001). However, a study in hypertensive subjects found no association between the ACE gene and the ACE inhibitor-induced cough (Zee, 1998).

(Continued)

Angiotensin-Converting Enzyme *(Continued)*

In patients with COPD, the DD genotype has been noted to correspond to a greater increase in pulmonary hypertension and diminished tissue oxygenation during exercise. In a small pilot study, captopril was associated with improvements in pulmonary hemodynamics and tissue oxygenation during exercise which were limited to the II genotype (Kanazawa, 2003).

The ACE I/D polymorphism may influence the rate of progression of nephropathy and antiproteinuric response to ACE inhibitors in diabetic patients. The II genotype has been correlated to a more rapid progression of microalbuminuria (Penno, 1998). The II genotype has also been associated with greater renoprotective effects from ACE inhibitors among both normotensive and hypertensive diabetic patients in some studies (Penno, 1998; Jacobsen, 1998). In contrast, other investigators reported greater reductions in proteinuria and albuminuria with the DD genotype (Ha, 2000).

Although activation of the ACE system has been associated with endothelial injury, the rate of restenosis following coronary stent implantation has not been consistently related to ACE genotype (Jorgensen, 2001; Ferrari, 2002). This is likely due to the fact that multiple factors may impact on the progression to this clinical event.

Angiotensin II type 1 receptor antagonists:

The II genotype was associated with greater diastolic blood pressure decline with 3-month treatment with irbesartan in 86 hypertensive European Caucasians compared to the ID and DD genotypes (Kurland, 2001).

Antipsychotics:

Having both low activity of the catechol-O-methyltransferase enzyme and high activity of the ACE genotypes has been associated with poor response to conventional antipsychotics (Illi, 2003).

β-blockers:

In a retrospective study of heart failure patients, the ACE D allele was associated with greater transplant-free survival with β-blocker therapy compared to the I allele (McNamara, 2001).

Spironolactone:

In a study of heart failure patients, only those with the non-DD genotype had significant improvements in echocardiographic parameters with spironolactone treatment (Cicoira, 2004).

Statins:

In a study of individuals with coronary atherosclerosis who were treated with fluvastatin for 2.5 years, reductions in total and LDL cholesterol were greater in those with the DD genotype compared to those with the ID and II genotypes (Marian, 2000).

In myocardial infarction survivors, the greatest reductions in fatal coronary heart disease or nonfatal myocardial infarction with pravastatin occurred in those with the Pl^{A2} allele of the glycoprotein IIIa subunit gene and either the ACE ID or DD genotype (Bray, 2001).

Fibrates:

In a small clinical study, the ACE DD genotype was associated with greater increases in HDL cholesterol levels with gemfibrozil (Bosse, 2002).

May Alter Pharmacokinetics of ACE is not known to alter the metabolism of any drugs.

May Alter Pharmacodynamics of ACE inhibitors, angiotensin II type 1 receptor blockers, β-blockers in heart failure, conventional antipsychotics, HMG CoA reductase inhibitors, fibrates

May Affect Disease Predisposition of In addition to cardiovascular disease, preliminary evidence suggests that the ACE-DD-genotype may be associated with other common adult diseases, including diabetes, psychiatric disease, depression, and some forms of cancer (Moskowitz, 2002).

Laboratory Evaluation Clinical testing available

Clinical Recommendations Data with the ACE gene are inconsistent and often conflicting. The ACE gene may interact with other genes in the renin-angiotensin system to influence response to renin-angiotensin system antagonists. The association between the ACE gene alone and response to ACE inhibitors or angiotensin II type 1 receptor blockers may be difficult to establish.

Counseling Points Since hypertension is a disease with polygenic etiology, carrier status of the ACE variant allele does not necessarily predispose a person to developing hypertension or its sequelae.

References

Arnett DK, Davis BR, Ford CE, et al, "Pharmacogenetic Association of the Angiotensin-Converting Enzyme Insertion/Deletion Polymorphism on Blood Pressure and Cardiovascular Risk in Relation to Antihypertensive Treatment: The Genetics of Hypertension-Associated Treatment (GenHAT) Study," *Circulation*, 2005, 111(25):3374-83.

Bosse Y, Pascot A, Dumont M, et al, "Influences of the PPAR Alpha-L162V Polymorphism on Plasma HDL(2)-Cholesterol Response of Abdominally Obese Men Treated With Gemfibrozil," *Genet Med*, 2002, 4(4):311-5.

Bray PF, Cannon CP, Goldschmidt-Clermont P, et al, "The Platelet PI(A2) and Angiotensin-Converting Enzyme (ACE) D Allele Polymorphisms and the Risk of Recurrent Events After Acute Myocardial Infarction," *Am J Cardiol*, 2001, 88(4):347-52.

Cicoira M, Rossi A, Bonapace S, et al, 'Effects of ACE Gene Insertion/Deletion Polymorphism on Response to Spironolactone in Patients With Chronic Heart Failure,' *Am J Med*, 2004, 116(10): 657-61.

Danser AH, Schalekamp MA, Bax WA, et al, "Angiotensin-Converting Enzyme in the Human Heart. Effect of the Deletion/Insertion Polymorphism," *Circulation*, 1995, 92(6):1387-8.

Ferrari M, Mudra H, Grip L, et al, "Angiotensin-Converting Enzyme Insertion/Deletion Polymorphism Does Not Influence the Restenosis Rate After Coronary Stent Implantation," *Cardiology*, 2002, 97(1):29-36.

Ha SK, Yong Lee S, Su Park H, et al, "ACE DD Genotype is More Susceptible Than ACE II and ID Genotypes to the Antiproteinuric Effect of ACE Inhibitors in Patients With Proteinuric Noninsulin-Dependent Diabetes Mellitus," *Nephrol Dial Transplant*, 2000, 15(10):1617-23.

Harrap SB, Tzourio C, Cambien F, et al, "The ACE Gene I/D Polymorphism is not Associated With the Blood Pressure and Cardiovascular Benefits of ACE Inhibition," *Hypertension*, 2003, 42(3):297-303.

Hingorani AD, Jia H, Stevens PA, et al, "Renin-Angiotensin System Gene Polymorphisms Influence Blood Pressure and the Response to Angiotensin-Converting Enzyme Inhibition," *J Hypertens*, 1995, 13(12 Pt 2):1602-9.

(Continued)

Angiotensin-Converting Enzyme *(Continued)*

Illi A, Kampman O, Anttila S, et al, "Interaction Between Angiotensin-Converting Enzyme and Catechol-O-Methyltransferase Genotypes in Schizophrenics With Poor Response to Conventional Neuroleptics," *Eur Neuropsychopharmacol*, 2003, 13(3):147-51.

Jacobsen P, Rossing K, Rossing P, et al, "Angiotensin-Converting Enzyme Gene Polymorphism and ACE Inhibition in Diabetic Nephropathy," *Kidney Int*, 1998, 53(4):1002-6.

Jorgensen E, Kelbaek H, Helqvist S, et al, "Predictors of Coronary In-Stent Restenosis: Importance of Angiotensin-Converting Enzyme Gene Polymorphism and Treatment With Angiotensin-Converting Enzyme Inhibitors," *J Am Coll Cardiol*, 2001, 38(5):1434-9.

Kanazawa H, Hirata K, and Yoshikawa J, "Effects of Captopril Administration on Pulmonary Haemodynamics and Tissue Oxygenation During Exercise in ACE Gene Subtypes in Patients With COPD: A Preliminary Study," *Thorax*, 2003, 58(7):629-31.

Kohno M, Yokokawa K, Minami M, et al, "Association Between Angiotensin-Converting Enzyme Gene Polymorphisms and Regression of Left Ventricular Hypertrophy in Patients Treated With Angiotensin-Converting Enzyme Inhibitors," *Am J Med*, 1999, 106(5):544-9.

Kurland LH, Melhus J, Karlsson T, et al, "Angiotensin-Converting Enzyme Gene Polymorphism Predicts Blood Pressure Response to Angiotensin II Receptor Type 1 Antagonist Treatment in Hypertensive Patients," *J Hypertens*, 2001, 19(10):1783-7.

Kurland LH, Melhus J, Karlsson T, et al, "Polymorphisms in the Angiotensinogen and Angiotensin II Type I Receptor Gene are Related to Change in Left Ventricular Mass During Antihypertensive Treatment: Results From the Swedish Irbesartan Left Ventricular Hypertrophy Investigation Versus Atenolol (SILVHIA) Trial," *J Hypertens*, 2002, 20(4):657-63.

Li X, Du Y, Du Y, et al, "Correlation of Angiotensin-Converting Enzyme Gene Polymorphisms With Effect of Antihypertensive Therapy by Angiotensin-Converting Enzyme Inhibitor," *J Cardiovasc Pharmacol Ther*, 2003, 8(1):25-30.

Marian AJ, Safavi F, Ferlic L, et al, "Interactions Between Angiotensin-I Converting Enzyme Insertion/Deletion Polymorphism and Response of Plasma Lipids and Coronary Atherosclerosis to Treatment With Fluvastatin: The Lipoprotein and Coronary Atherosclerosis Study," *J Am Coll Cardiol*, 2000, 35(1):89-95.

McNamara DM, Holubkov R, Janosko K, et al, "Pharmacogenetic Interactions Between Beta-Blocker Therapy and the Angiotensin-Converting Enzyme Deletion Polymorphism in Patients With Congestive Heart Failure," *Circulation*, 2001, 103(12):1644-8.

Moskowitz DW, "Is Angiotensin I-Converting Enzyme a "Master" Disease Gene?" *Diabetes Technol Ther*, 2002, 4(5):683-711.

Ohmichi N, Iwai N, Uchida Y, et al, "Relationship Between the Response to the Angiotensin Converting Enzyme Inhibitor Imidapril and the Angiotensin Converting Enzyme Genotype," *Am J Hypertens*, 1997, 10(8):951-5.

Penno G, Chaturvedi N, Talmud PJ, et al, "Effect of Angiotensin-Converting Enzyme (ACE) Gene Polymorphism on Progression of Renal Disease and the Influence of ACE Inhibition in IDDM Patients: Findings From the EUCLID Randomized Controlled Trial. EURODIAB Controlled Trial of Lisinopril in IDDM," *Diabetes*, 1998, 47(9):507-11.

Prasad A, Narayanan S, Husain S, et al, "Insertion-Deletion Polymorphism of the ACE Gene Modulates Reversibility of Endothelial Dysfunction With ACE Inhibition," *Circulation*, 2000, 102(1):35-41.

Rigat B, Hubert C, Alhenc-Gelas F, et al, "An Insertion/Deletion Polymorphism in the Angiotensin I-Converting Enzyme Gene Accounting for Half the Variance of Serum Enzyme Levels," *J Clin Invest*, 1990, 86(4):1343-6.

Sasaki M, Oki T, Iuchi A, et al, "Relationship Between the Angiotensin Converting Enzyme Gene Polymorphism and the Effects of Enalapril on Left Ventricular Hypertrophy and Impaired Diastolic Filling in Essential Hypertension: M-Mode and Pulsed Doppler Echocardiographic Studies," *J Hypertens*, 1996, 14(12):1403-8.

Stavroulakis GA, Makris TK, Krespi PG, et al, "Predicting Response to Chronic Antihypertensive Treatment With Fosinopril: The Role of Angiotensin-Converting Enzyme Gene Polymorphism," *Cardiovasc Drugs Ther*, 2000, 14(4):427-32.

Takahashi T, Yamaguchi E, Furuya K, et al, "The ACE Gene Polymorphism and Cough Threshold for Capsaicin After Cilazapril Usage," *Respir Med*, 2001, 95(2):130-5.

van der Kleij FG, de Jong PE, Henning RH, et al, "Enhanced Responses of Blood Pressure, Renal Function, and Aldosterone to Angiotensin I in the DD Genotype Are Blunted by Low Sodium Intake," *J Am Soc Nephrol*, 2002, 13(4):1025-33.

Volzke H, Engel J, Kleine V, et al, "Angiotensin I-Converting Enzyme Insertion/Deletion Polymorphism and Cardiac Mortality and Morbidity After Coronary Artery Bypass Graft Surgery," *Chest*, 2002, 122(1):31-6.

Zee RY, Rao VS, Paster RZ, et al, "Three Candidate Genes and Angiotensin-Converting Enzyme Inhibitor-Related Cough: A Pharmacogenetic Analysis," *Hypertension*, 1998, 31(4):925-8.

Angiotensinogen

Synonyms AGT

Chromosome Location 1q42-43

Clinically-Important Polymorphisms

Nonsynonymous SNP at codon 235 in exon 2 with a threonine instead of methionine *(Met235Thr)*

Nonsynonymous SNP at codon 174 in exon 2 with methionine rather than threonine *(Thr174Met)*

Discussion Angiotensinogen is the precursor to the formation of angiotensin I. Plasma angiotensinogen levels have been associated with the number of *235Thr* alleles (Winkelmann, 1999). Since the systems regulating blood pressure involve multiple factors, the association of any single polymorphism with the development of hypertension may be difficult to establish. Studies evaluating the role of AGT polymorphisms have yielded inconsistent results. However, polymorphisms of this protein have been associated with differential responses to antihypertensive therapy. In one study, the *235Thr* allele was associated with the need for multiple antihypertensive medications (Schunkert, 1997). In addition, the *Met235Thr* genotype has been correlated to carotid intima-media thickness, explaining 7% of the overall variance. Carotid intima-media thickness was higher in individuals with the *Thr* allele. Antihypertensive therapy, with either the ACE inhibitor, enalapril, or the β-blocker, celiprolol, resulted in a significantly greater reduction in carotid intima-media thickness in the *Thr/Thr* homozygotes, regardless of the drug used, in spite of the fact that blood pressure reductions were similar between genotype groups. The authors concluded that *Thr/Thr* genotype was a marker for early carotid atherosclerosis, and identified individuals more likely to experience regression during antihypertensive therapy.

ACE inhibitors:

The *235Thr* allele has been associated with enhanced blood pressure reduction during ACE inhibitor therapy compared to the *235Met* genotype (Hingorani, 1995).

The *Thr/Thr* genotype has also been correlated to a greater protective effect between ACE inhibitor use and risk of nonfatal stroke (Bis, 2003).

Angiotensin II type 1 receptor antagonists:

During treatment with irbesartan in patients with essential hypertension and left ventricular hypertrophy, the *174Thr/Met* genotype and the *235Thr* allele were associated with the greatest reductions in left ventricular mass (Kurland, 2002). The *174Thr/Met* genotype

(Continued)

Angiotensinogen *(Continued)*

remained an independent predictor of drug response after step-wise multiple regression analysis.

May Alter Pharmacokinetics of The AGT gene is not known to alter the metabolism of any drugs.

May Alter Pharmacodynamics of ACE inhibitors, angiotensin II type 1 receptor blockers, β-blockers

May Affect Disease Predisposition of Hypertension, left ventricular hypertrophy

Clinical Recommendations Data suggest that the AGT gene may be an important predictor of response to renin-angiotensin system therapy in hypertension. The AGT gene may interact with other renin-angiotensin genes to determine responses to renin-angiotensin system antagonists.

Counseling Points Since hypertension is a disease with polygenic etiology, carrier status of the AGT variant allele does not necessarily predispose a person to developing hypertension.

References

Bis JC, Smith NL, Psaty BM, et al, "Angiotensinogen Met235Thr Polymorphism, Angiotensin-Converting Enzyme Inhibitor Therapy, and the Risk of Nonfatal Stroke or Myocardial Infarction in Hypertensive Patients," *Am J Hypertens*, 2003, 16(12):1011-7.

Bozec E, Fassot C, Tropeano AI, et al, "Angiotensinogen Gene M235T Polymorphism and Reduction in Wall Thickness in Response to Antihypertensive Treatment," *Clin Sci (Lond)*, 2003, 105(5):637-44.

Hingorani AD, Jia H, Stevens PA, et al, "Renin-Angiotensin System Gene Polymorphisms Influence Blood Pressure and the Response to Angiotensin-Converting Enzyme Inhibition," *J Hypertens*, 1995, 13(12 Pt 2):1602-9.

Kurland L, Melhus H, Karlsson J, et al, "Aldosterone Synthase (CYP11B2) -344 C/T Polymorphism Is Related to Antihypertensive Response: Result From the Swedish Irbesartan Left Ventricular Hypertrophy Investigation Versus Atenolol (SILVHIA) Trial," *Am J Hypertens*, 2002, 15(5):389-93.

Schunkert H, Hense HW, Gimenez-Roqueplo AP, et al, "The Angiotensinogen T235 Variant and the Use of Antihypertensive Drugs in a Population-Based Cohort," *Hypertension*, 1997, 29(2):628-33.

Winkelmann BR, Russ AP, Nauck M, et al, "Angiotensinogen M235T Polymorphism Is Associated With Plasma Angiotensinogen and Cardiovascular Disease," *Am Heart J*, 1999, 137(4 Pt 1):698-705.

♦ **APOE** *see* Apolipoprotein E *on page 220*

Apolipoprotein E

Synonyms APOE

Chromosome Location 19q13.2

Clinically-Important Polymorphisms Human APOE has three common alleles, *APOE2*, *APOE3*, and *APOE4*, resulting from nonsynonymous SNPs at codons 112 and 158.

Discussion Apolipoprotein E modulates cholesterol and phospholipid transport between cells of different types. Apolipoprotein is involved in lipid transport in both the plasma and within the brain. It mediates the binding of lipoproteins to members of the low density lipoprotein (LDL) receptor family. Genetic variation has been associated with plasma lipid profiles (including LDL, high density lipoprotein (HDL) and triglyceride concentrations). The APOE locus has been found to be a significant genetic determinant of cardiovascular disease. Some of the variation in response to dietary modification has been reported to be associated with the *E4* allele. Additional variation in response to drug therapy are described under individual categories (below).

APOE and its receptors are expressed at high levels in the brain. The *APOE4* allele is associated with sporadic and late-onset familial Alzheimer disease. *APOE4* has been shown to correlate with the risk of developing Alzheimer's disease, age of onset, accumulation of plaques, and reduction of choline acetyltransferase activity in the hippocampus. *APOE4* allele copy number has an inverse relationship with residual brain choline acetyltransferase activity and nicotinic receptor binding sites in both the hippocampal formation and the temporal cortex of AD subjects. Individuals lacking the *APOE4* allele showed ChAT activities close or within age-matched normal control values. *APOE4* appears to play a crucial role in cholinergic transmission in Alzheimer's disease.

HMG CoA reductase inhibitors:

A relationship between the *APOE4* allele and response to statins has been described. In studies evaluating the effect of the *APOE* genotype on lipoprotein lipid changes during HMG CoA reductase therapy, the *E2* allele was associated with a more favorable drug response compared to other genotypes (Ordovas, 1995; Nestel, 1997). Other studies found no significant association between *APOE* genotype and lipoprotein response to HMG CoA reductase inhibitors (Sanllehy, 1998).

In a large clinical trial of simvastatin therapy in myocardial infarction survivors, the greatest benefit from simvastatin therapy, in terms of mortality reduction, has been observed in patients with the *E4* allele (Gerdes, 2000).

Cholinesterase inhibitors:

As a prognostic indicator, presence of the *APOE4* allele may signal the potential for a poor response to therapy with cholinesterase inhibitors. In a study of 40 patients with Alzheimer's disease, over 80% of *APOE4*-negative patients showed marked improvement in response to tacrine (ADAS scale). Deterioration of ADAS scores was noted in 60% of *APOE4* carriers (Poirier, 1995). From the studies done to date analyzing genotype correlations to drug response, it is evident that there is an effect of *APOE4* (Poirier, 1995; Farlow, 1998; MacGowan, 1998). The nature of this effect is well established for tacrine, with research showing that *E4* patients with AD respond poorer to this medication than those without an *E4* allele. Subsequent studies investigating galantamine, donepezil, and metrifonate have had mixed results depending on the agent studied, duration of treatment period, and primary outcome measure used (Wilcock, 2000; Greenberg, 2000; Farlow, 1999). Further long-term studies utilizing the ADAS-Cog scale to assess patient response will determine which agents will be most beneficial to patients with or without an *E4* allele. An intent to treat

(Continued)

Apolipoprotein E *(Continued)*

analysis of patients with Alzheimer's disease treated with donepezil did not reveal significant differences between the responses of *E4-* and *E4+* carriers according to the ADAS-Cog (p=0.28) (Rigaud, 2002).

May Alter Pharmacokinetics of APOE is not known to alter the metabolism of any drugs.

May Alter Pharmacodynamics of HMG-CoA reductase inhibitors, cholinesterase inhibitors

May Affect Disease Predisposition of Alzheimer's disease

Laboratory Evaluation Commercial testing available

Clinical Recommendations Data suggest that the *APOE* genotype may be useful in predicting clinical outcomes with HMG CoA reductase inhibitor therapy in patients with coronary heart disease. The *APOE* genotype may interact with the β-fibrinogen, stromelysin-1, ACE, and cholesterol ester transfer protein genes in predicting HMG CoA reductase inhibitor response. Data suggest that the *APOE* genotype may be related to response to the cholinesterase inhibitors. Some patients may have a better response to these medications based on their *APOE* genotype.

Counseling Points Carrier status for the *APOE4* allele has been associated with increased risk for developing coronary heart disease and Alzheimer's disease and for greater disease progression in individuals with coronary heart disease. Individuals who carry this allele should be encouraged to discuss the implications of their carrier status with their clinician or another healthcare professional.

References

Farlow MR, Cyrus PA, Nadel A, et al, "Metrifonate Treatment of AD: Influence of APOE Genotype," *Neurology*, 1999, 53(9):2010-6.

Farlow MR, Lahiri DK, Poirier J, et al, "Treatment Outcome of Tacrine Therapy Depends on Apolipoprotein Genotype and Gender of the Subjects With Alzheimer's Disease," *Neurology*, 1998, 50(3):669-77.

Gerdes LU, Gerdes C, Kervinen K, et al, "The Apolipoprotein Epsilon4 Allele Determines Prognosis and the Effect on Prognosis of Simvastatin in Survivors of Myocardial Infarction: A Substudy of the Scandinavian Simvastatin Survival Study," *Circulation*, 2000, 28;101(12):1366-71.

Greenberg SM, Tennis MK, Brown LB, et al, "Donepezil Therapy in Clinical Practice: A Randomized Crossover Study," *Arch Neurol*, 2000, 57(1):94-9.

MacGowan SH, Wilcock GK, and Scott M, "Effect of Gender and Apolipoprotein E Genotype on Response to Anticholinesterase in Alzheimer's Disease," *Int J Geriatr Psychiatry*, 1998, 13(9):625-30.

Nestel P, Simons L, Barter P, et al, "A Comparative Study of the Efficacy of Simvastatin and Gemfibrozil in Combined Hyperlipoproteinemia: Prediction of Response by Baseline Lipids, Apo E Genotype, Lipoprotein(a) and Insulin," *Atherosclerosis*, 1997, 21;129(2):231-9.

Ordovas JM, Lopez-Miranda J, Perez-Jimenez F, et al, "Effect of Apolipoprotein E and A-IV Phenotypes on the Low Density Lipoprotein Response to HMG CoA Reductase Inhibitor Therapy," *Atherosclerosis*, 1995, 113(2):157-66.

Poirier J, Delisle MC, Quirion R, et al, "Apolipoprotein E4 Allele as a Predictor of Cholinergic Deficits and Treatment Outcome in Alzheimer Disease," *Proc Natl Acad Sci U S A*, 1995, 92(26):12260-4.

Rigaud AS, Traykov L, Latour F et al, "Presence or Absence of at Least One Epsilon 4 Allele and Gender Are Not Predictive for the Response to Donepezil Treatment in Alzheimer's Disease," *Pharmacogenetics*, 2002, 12(5):415-20.

Sanllehy C, Casals E, Rodriguez-Villar C, et al, "Lack of Interaction of Apolipoprotein E Phenotype With the Lipoprotein Response to Lovastatin or Gemfibrozil in Patients With Primary Hypercholesterolemia," *Metabolism*, 1998, 47(5):560-5.

Wilcock GK, Lilienfeld S, and Gaens E, "Efficacy and Safety of Galantamine in Patients With Mild to Moderate Alzheimer's Disease: Multicentre Randomised Controlled Trial. Galantamine International-1 Study Group," *BMJ*, 2000, 321(7274):1445-9.

Arachidonate 5-Lipoxygenase

Synonyms 5-LO; 5-LOX; 5LPG; ALOX5; LOG5

Chromosome Location 10q11.2

Clinically-Important Polymorphisms The promoter region of the arachidonate 5-lipoxygenase gene contains an Sp-1 transcription factor binding motif designated as GGGCGG. Three to six tandem repeats of this motif have been identified, with 5 repeats recognized as the wild-type genotype. Variant genotypes (ie, 3, 4, or 6 repeats) have been reported to occur in up to 45% and 23% of Korean and Caucasian sample populations, respectively.

Discussion Arachidonate 5-lipoxygenase (ALOX5) in association with the activator protein (ALOX5AP or FLAP) is a critical enzyme complex responsible for the synthesis of leukotrienes from arachidonic acid. Leukotrienes mediate a number of smooth muscle effects, including bronchoconstriction. Increased expression of 5-lipoxygenase in pulmonary artery endothelial cells has been observed in pulmonary hypertension and has been associated with allergenic stimuli. Variant alleles encoding ALOX5 are associated with reduced transcription factor binding and hence diminished promoter region-driven expression of 5-lipoxygenase. Polymorphisms of the ALOX5AP protein have also been described; however, to date, no functional significance with respect to asthma severity has been attributed to these mutations.

A phenotype favoring allergic responses may be induced by increased or excessive leukotriene production. Leukotrienes synthesized by ALOX5 clearly play a role in the pathogenesis of asthma, given the clinical efficacy of drugs which inhibit the syntheses or activity of leucotrienes. However, the association between genetic polymorphisms and the asthmatic phenotype has not been adequately defined. In fact, studies by Kim et al and Sayers et al reported no significant difference in the frequency of mutant alleles and the incidence of asthma among Asian, American, or British sample populations. Nevertheless, the pathogenesis of asthma is undoubtedly recognized as a complex, multifactorial process involving a number of potential inflammatory pathways, suggesting the possibility of leukotriene-dependent and independent phenotypes. Consistent with this notion, Palmer et al suggested that asthmatic patients harboring mutant variant alleles may be less responsive to pharmacologic intervention targeting the leukotriene pathway, presumably reflecting disease processes in these patients involving other inflammatory mediators.

Arachidonate 5-lipoxygenase antagonists:

In a study of 221 asthmatic patients (American Thoracic Society [ATS] criteria), a change in forced expiratory volume in 1 second (FEV1) was assessed after 84 days of treatment with ABT-761 (selective ALOX5 inhibitor derived from zileuton) or placebo, and

(Continued)

Arachidonate 5-Lipoxygenase *(Continued)*

analyzed with respect to promoter region status. Patients exhibiting the wild-type (n=64) or heterozygous (n=40) status showed a statistically significant improvement in FEV1 (19% to 23%) at the completion of the active treatment period compared to patients with homozygous variant alleles (-1.2%, n=10) (p<0.0001 and p=0.0006 compared to wild-type and heterozygous, respectively). There was no significant difference in response observed between wild-types and heterozygotes. As defined by the ATS, a threshold of 12% improvement in FEV1 defines a level of significant clinical improvement. Based on these criteria, none of the variant genotype patients exhibited a >12% FEV increase, while 52% of the wild-type patients exceeded this level (p=0.0016) (Drazen, 1999).

Zafirlukast:

In 52 asthmatic patients (40 homozygous wild type, 12 heterozygous), the influence of 5-lipoxygenase promoter region polymorphisms and response to a leukotriene receptor antagonist was evaluated. An analysis of genotype and response to zafirlukast failed to demonstrate a significant difference between homozygous wild types and heterozygotes in terms of bronchodilator response or bronchial hyper-responsiveness (Fowler, 2002). This lack of differentiation is consistent with the Drazen study. However, unlike the Drazen study, there were no patients exhibiting the homozygous variant genotype in this analysis, which may have precluded the observation of a meaningful difference in response.

May Alter Pharmacodynamics of Zafirlukast, montelukast, zileuton derivates

May Affect Disease Predisposition of Asthma

References

Drazen JM, Yandava CN, Dube L, et al, "Pharmacogenetic Association Between ALOX5 Promoter Genotype and the Response to Antiasthma Treatment," *Nat Genet*, 1999, 22(2):168-70.

Fowler SJ, Hall IP, Wilson AM, et al, "5-Lipoxygenase Polymorphism and *in vivo* Response to Leukotriene Receptor Antagonists," *Eur J Clin Pharmacol*, 2002, 58(3):187-90.

Kedda Ma, Worsley P, Shi J, et al, "Polymorphisms in the 5-Lipoxygenase Activating Protein (ALOX5AP) Gene are Not Associated With Asthma in an Australian Population," *Clin Exp Allergy*, 2005, 35(3):332-8.

Kim SH, Bae JS, Suh CH, et al, "Polymorphism of Tandem Repeat in Promoter of 5-Lipoxygenase in ASA-Intolerant Asthma: A Positive Association With Airway Hyperresponsiveness," *Allergy*, 2005, 60(6):760-5.

Palmer LJ, Silverman ES, Weiss ST, et al, "Pharmacogenetics of Asthma," *Am J Respir Crit Care Med*, 2002, 165(7):861-66.

Sayers I, Barton S, Rorke S, et al, "Promoter Polymorphism in the 5-Lipoxygenase (ALOX5) and 5-Lipoxygenase-Activating Protein (ALOX5AP) Genes and Astham Susceptibility in a Caucasian Population," *Clin Exp Allergy*, 2003, 33(8):1103-10.

♦ **AT1** *see* Angiotensin II Type 1 Receptor *on page 213*

♦ **AT_1R** *see* Angiotensin II Type 1 Receptor *on page 213*

ATP-Binding Cassette, Sub-Family B, Member 1

Synonyms ABC20; ABCB1; CD243; CLCS; GP170; MDR-1; MDR1; Multidrug Resistance Gene; P-gp; PGP; PGY1

Chromosome Location 7q21.1

Clinically-Important Polymorphisms

At least 48 SNPs have been described for the ABCB1 gene. Three common SNPs are the synonymous *C3435T* polymorphism in exon 26, the nonsynonymous SNP *(G2677T)* in exon 21, and the synonymous SNP *(C1236T)* in exon 12. These SNPs appear to be in linkage disequilibrium. For the C3435T SNP, the occurrence of the wild-type C allele is quite common among white Caucasians (~50-60%) and African-American (~80-90%) populations studied. Frequency estimates suggest that 61% of African-Americans, 26% of Caucasians, and 34% of Japanese possess homozygosity for the 3435T allele (Schaeffeler, 2001).

Discussion ABCB1 (formerly MDR1) encodes for P-glycoprotein (PGP), a member of the ATP-binding cassette family of transporter proteins encoded by the multidrug resistance gene. These proteins are commonly located in the plasma membranes of intestinal, renal and hepatic epithelial cells, and primarily responsible for efflux of many natural compounds and xenobiotics. As such, the function of these proteins has a major influence on the pharmacokinetics/dynamics of many drugs.

Of the many polymorphisms identified for this gene, the C3435T, G2677T, and C1236T SNPs have been reported most commonly and appear to be associated in linkage disequilibrium. Of these, the 3435T variant has received much attention due to the association of this polymorphism with reduced expression of the glycoprotein (Hoffmeyer, 2000).

Antiepileptic agents:

Three hundred and fifteen patients with epilepsy were genotyped to determine if the *CC* genotype at the *ABCB1 C3435T* polymorphism alters the response to antiepileptic agents. Patients with drug-resistant epilepsy were more likely to have the *CC* genotype at *ABCB1 3453* than the *TT* genotype (Siddiqui, 2003).

Antiretroviral agents:

The influence of genotype on the efficacy of antiretroviral therapy was evaluated in 123 patients. Median drug concentrations in patients with the *MDR1 3435 TT*, *CT*, and *CC* genotypes were at the 30th, 50th, and 75th percentiles, respectively. Patients with the *MDR1 TT* genotype had a greater rise in CD4-cell count at 6 months after treatment than the *CT* or *CC* genotype, and the best recovery of naive CD4-cells. Therefore, the *MDR1* genotype appears to predict immune recovery after the initiation of antiretroviral treatment (Fellay, 2002).

Defective PGP expression in HIV-1 infection has been noted to increase with the progression of HIV-1 infection. Larger studies of patients with HIV-1 infection are needed to determine the effects of opportunistic infection and antiretroviral therapy on the expression of PGP. Potentially, the expression of PGP may serve as another surrogate marker for the progression of HIV-1 infection (Andreana, 1996).

(Continued)

ATP-Binding Cassette, Sub-Family B, Member 1 *(Continued)*

Corticosteroids:

Glucocorticoids are known Pgp substrates. Inflammatory bowel disease (IBD), which is poorly responsive to medical therapy, has been noted to correlate to MDR expression. This may be related to the role of Pgp in determining the response of IBD patients to glucocorticoid therapy (Farrell, 2000).

Cyclosporine:

Although PGP is suspected to influence cyclosporine concentrations, some data suggests that the *MDR-1 C3435T* mutation (in addition to the CYP3A4-V variant) is not a major determinant of cyclosporine A efficacy in renal transplant recipients (von Ahsen, 2001). Data from Min et al, supports this contention, finding no relationship between the pharmacokinetics of cyclosporine and *C3435T* genotype.

However, subsequent studies provide conflicting evidence. In a study of 44 European liver transplant patients receiving stable, weight-adjusted therapy with cyclosporine, homozygous patients (TT) had significantly higher concentration/dose ratios compared to wild-type patients (p= 0.012). After 1 month of therapy and dose adjustments to maintain equivalent plasma concentrations between groups, patients harboring the mutation required a significantly lower (50%) weight-adjusted dose compared to CC homozygotes (p=0.033) (Bonhomme-Faivre, 2004).

Apparently contradictory results were generated by Yates and colleagues. This study evaluated the oral clearance of cyclosporine in 19 renal transplant patients as a function of ABCB1 genotype. Carriers of at least one T allele exhibited a significantly higher clearance (40 ± 2.2 L/h) compared to homozygotic wild type patients (26.4 ± 3.1 L/h, p=0.007), with genotype accounting for approximately 43% of interindividual variability of drug clearance.

Unlike the Yates trial, the data from Bonhomme-Faivre's study suggest that African-American patients, who are more likely to possess the C allele, would be at risk of experiencing lower plasma drug levels with standard dosing of cyclosporine A. This provides a plausible explanation for the increased rate of renal graft failure observed in this ethnic group. However, as noted in the digoxin discussion, interpretation of isolated SNPs is likely to evoke flawed conclusions. Therefore, haplotype analysis would likely be more predictive and provide clarity of these apparently dichotomous results.

Digoxin:

In vitro studies demonstrated the *3435T* allele was associated with twofold lower *ABCB1* gene expression and reduced PGP activity compared to *3435C* allele (Hoffmeyer, 2000). In healthy volunteers, plasma digoxin levels were 4 times higher in those with the *3435TT* genotype than *CC* homozygotes after a single, oral digoxin dose (Hoffmeyer, 2000). However, these findings have not been consistently replicated.

The area under the plasma concentration-time curve from time zero to 4 hours [AUC(0-4)] and C_{max} values of digoxin were higher in subjects with the *3435TT* genotype than in those with the *3435CC*. Significant differences for AUC(0-4) and C_{max} were substantiated by haplotype analysis. Haplotype 12 (*2677G/3435T*), which had a frequency of 13.3% in a randomly drawn Caucasian sample (n=687), was associated with higher AUC(0-4) values than were found in noncarriers. Haplotype 11 (*2677G/3435C*) had lower AUC(0-4) values compared with those of noncarriers. Analysis of *ABCB1* haplotypes is superior to unphased SNP analysis to predict *ABCB1* (Johne, 2002).

The bioavailability of digoxin in *2677GG/3435CC*, *2677GT/3435CT*, and *2677TT/3435TT* subjects were 67.6% ±4.3%, 80.9% ±8.9%, and 87.1% ±8.4%, respectively, and the difference between *2677GG/3435CC* and *2677TT/3435TT* subjects was statistically significant ($p \leq 0.05$). The *ABCB1* variants were also associated with differences in disposition kinetics of digoxin, with the renal clearance being almost 32% lower in *2677TT/3435TT* subjects (1.9 ±0.1 mL/min/kg) than *2677GG/3435CC* subjects (2.8 ±0.3 mL/min/kg), and heterozygote subjects having an intermediate value (2.1 ±0.6 mL/min/kg).

Coadministration of clarithromycin did not consistently affect digoxin clearance or renal clearance. However, a significant increase in digoxin bioavailability was observed in *2677GG/3435CC* subjects (67.6% ±4.3% versus 85.4% ±6.1%; $p < 0.05$) but not in the other 2 genotype groups (Kurata, 2002).

Fexofenadine:

Kim et al, identified two haplotypes associated with differences in fexofenadine levels. The *MDR1*2* haplotype was defined as the co-linked polymorphic variants of 1236T, 3435T, and 2677T, while MDR1*1 represented the wild-type forms of these codons. Consistent with the *in vitro* data, with the area under the plasma level-time curve for fexofenadine was almost 40% greater in the **1/*1* genotype compared with the **2/*2* and the **1/*2* heterozygotes having an intermediate value, suggesting enhanced *in vivo* P-glycoprotein activity among subjects with the *MDR1*2* allele (Kim, 2001).

Morphine:

Eighteen healthy male volunteers participated in a double-blind, three-way crossover study to determine the pharmacokinetic and pharmacodynamic effects of morphine compared with and without acute inhibition of P-glycoprotein. Acute inhibition of P-glycoprotein did not result in clinically significant changes in pharmacokinetics or pharmacodynamic (Drewe, 2000).

Nortriptyline:

The multidrug resistance gene *ABCB1* encodes a P-glycoprotein that regulates passage of many substances across the blood-brain

(Continued)

ATP-Binding Cassette, Sub-Family B, Member 1 *(Continued)*

barrier. A significant association was noted between nortriptyline-induced postural hypotension and the *3435C/T* polymorphism. Homozygosity for *3435T* may be a risk factor for nortriptyline-induced postural hypotension (Roberts, 2002).

Paclitaxel:

Resistance to paclitaxel has been attributed to overexpression of P-glycoprotein (PGP) (Kao, 2000).

Phenytoin:

Although some of the interindividual differences in phenytoin metabolism can be attributed to polymorphisms in CYP2C9, a large component of individual variability remains still unexplained. A portion of this variability may be attributed to variable uptake by P-glycoprotein. Phenytoin plasma levels correlate with the *ABCB1 C3435T* polymorphism associated with intestinal PGP activity. The *CC* genotype was found to be more common in individuals with low phenytoin levels.

In a regression analysis which included CYP2C9, 2C19, and ABCB1, the number of variant CYP2C9 alleles was a major determinant, and the number of *ABCB1 T* alleles further contributed to the prediction of phenytoin plasma levels. CYP2C19*2 did not appear to contribute to individual variability. The regression equation explained 15.4% of the variability of phenytoin data (Kerb, 2001).

Statins:

In a study of 344 hypercholesterolemic patients treated with atorvastatin (10 mg/day), patients were evaluated for the G2677T/A and C3435T polymorphisms relative to cholesterol-lowering response after 1 year of treatment. In a gender-specific manner, a composite of female patients carrying 1 or 2 copies of the 3435T variant allele showed significantly greater reductions in both total and LDL cholesterol (p=0.031 and p=0.023, respectively) and significantly smaller increases in HDL cholesterol compared to wild-type homozygotes (Kajinami, 2004). There was no gene-response relationship associated with the 2677T/A variant. However, haplotype analysis confirmed the gender-specific response, showing a significantly lower drug-induced cholesterol reduction (total and LDL) in female patients homozygous for the GC haplotype, independent of individual polymorphism alone. In the multiple regression analysis, both pretreatment cholesterol levels and haplotype were predictors of cholesterol changes with atorvastatin. The investigators postulated that the enhanced cholesterol-reducing response may be related to increased serum levels of atorvastatin, as the 3435T allele has been associated with reduced expression of p-glycoprotein; however, drug levels and adverse reaction profiles were not determined in this study. The mechanism for a gender-specific effect is not clear. Interestingly, *in vitro* evidence has documented an allosteric progesterone binding site on p-glycoprotein, suggesting the possibility of a genotype-sensitive, hormonal influence on drug efflux (Shaprio, 1999).

Tacrolimus:

In a small series, the polymorphism at position 2677 in exon 21 of Pgp, as well as high tacrolimus concentrations and hepatic dysfunction were demonstrated as positive predictors of tacrolimus-induced neurotoxicity (Yamauchi, 2002).

However, no pharmacogenetic effect was observed on steady-state tacrolimus trough levels in a retrospective evaluation of 73 renal transplant patients study by Mai et al (2004). In this study, serum trough concentrations (corrected for dose) did not differ significantly among patient groups exhibiting 4 possible ABCB1 haplotypes (defined by G2677T and C3435T SNPs) or between groups differentiated by the presence of the CYP3A5 variant *1/*3.

May Alter Pharmacokinetics of Protease inhibitors, corticosteroids, cyclosporine, digoxin, fexofenadine, paclitaxel, tacrolimus, nortriptyline, phenytoin, statins, and other p-glycoprotein substrates

References

Andreana A, Aggarwal S, Gollapudi S, et al, "Abnormal Expression of a 170-Kilodalton P-Glycoprotein Encoded by MDR1 Gene, a Metabolically Active Efflux Pump, in CD4+ and CD8+ T Cells From Patients With Human Immunodeficiency Virus Type 1 Infection," *AIDS Res Hum Retroviruses*, 1996, 12(15):1457-62.

Bonhomme-Faivre L, Devocelle A, Saliba F, et al, "MDR-1 C3435T Polymorphism Influences Cyclosporine a Dose Requirement in Liver-Transplant Recipients," *Transplantation*, 2004, 78(1):21-5.

Drewe J, Ball HA, Beglinger C, et al, "Effect of P-Glycoprotein Modulation on the Clinical Pharmacokinetics and Adverse Effects of Morphine," *Br J Clin Pharmacol*, 2000, 50(3):237-46.

Farrell RJ, Murphy A, Long A, et al, "High Multidrug Resistance (P-Glycoprotein 170) Expression in Inflammatory Bowel Disease Patients Who Fail Medical Therapy," *Gastroenterology*, 2000, 118(2):279-88.

Fellay J, Marzolini C, Meaden ER, et al, "Response to Antiretroviral Treatment in HIV-1-Infected Individuals With Allelic Variants of the Multidrug Resistance Transporter 1: A Pharmacogenetics Study," *Lancet*, 2002, 359(9300):30-6.

Hoffmeyer S, Burk O, von Richter O, et al, "Functional Polymorphisms of the Human Multidrug-Resistance Gene: Multiple Sequence Variations and Correlation of One Allele With P-Glycoprotein Expression and Activity *in vivo*," *Proc Natl Acad Sci U S A*, 2000, 97(7):3473-8.

Johne A, Kopke K, Gerloff T, et al, "Modulation of Steady-State Kinetics of Digoxin by Haplotypes of the P-Glycoprotein MDR1 Gene," *Clin Pharmacol Ther*, 2002, 72(5):584-94.

Kajinami K, Brousseau ME, Ordovas JM, et al, "Polymorphisms in the Multidrug Resistance-1 (MDR1) Gene Influence the Response to Atorvastatin Treatment in a Gender-Specific Manner," *Am J Cardiol*, 2004, 93(8):1046-50.

Kao CH, Hsieh JF, Tsai SC, et al, "Quickly Predicting Chemotherapy Response to Paclitaxel-Based Therapy in Non-Small Cell Lung Cancer by Early Technetium-99m Methoxyisobutylisonitrile Chest Single-Photon-Emission Computed Tomography," *Clin Cancer Res*, 2000, 6(3):820-4.

Kerb R, Aynacioglu AS, Brockmoller J, et al, "The Predictive Value of MDR1, CYP2C9, and CYP2C19 Polymorphisms for Phenytoin Plasma Levels," *Pharmacogenomics J*, 2001, 1(3):204-10.

Kim RB, Leake BF, Choo EF, et al, "Identification of Functionally Variant MDR1 Alleles Among European Americans and African Americans," *Clin Pharmacol Ther*, 2001, 70(2):189-99.

Kurata Y, Ieiri I, Kimura M, et al, "Role of Human MDR1 Gene Polymorphism in Bioavailability and Interaction of Digoxin, a Substrate of P-Glycoprotein," *Clin Pharmacol Ther*, 2002, 72(2):209-19

(Continued)

ATP-Binding Cassette, Sub-Family B, Member 1 *(Continued)*

Mai I, Perloff ES, Bauer S, et al, "MDR1 Haplotypes Derived From Exons 21 and 26 Do Not Affect the Steady-State Pharmacokinetics of Tacrolimus in Renal Transplant Patients," *Br J Clin Pharmacol*, 2004, 58(5):548-53.

Min DI and Ellingrod VL, "C3435T Mutation in Exon 26 of the Human MDR1 Gene and Cyclosporine Pharmacokinetics in Healthy Subjects," *Ther Drug Monit*, 2002, 24(3):400-4.

Roberts RL, Joyce PR, Mulder RT, et al, "A Common P-Glycoprotein Polymorphism Is Associated With Nortriptyline-Induced Postural Hypotension in Patients Treated for Major Depression," *Pharmacogenomics J*, 2002, 2(3):191-6.

Schaeffeler E, Eichelbaum M, Brinkmann U, et al, "Frequency of C3435T Polymorphism of MDR1 Gene in African People," *Lancet*, 2001, 358(9279):383-4.

Shapiro AB, Fox K, Lam P, et al, "Stimulation of P-Glycoprotein-Mediated Drug Transport by Prazosin and Progesterone. Evidence for a Third Drug-Binding Site," *Eur J Biochem*, 1999, 259(3):841-50.

Siddiqui A, Kerb R, Weale ME, et al, "Association of Multidrug Resistance in Epilepsy With a Polymorphism in the Drug-Transporter Gene ABCB1," *N Engl J Med*, 2003, 348(15):1442-8.

von Ahsen N, Richter M, Grupp C, et al, "No Influence of the MDR-1 C3435T Polymorphism or a CYP3A4 Promoter Polymorphism (CYP3A4-V Allele) on Dose-Adjusted Cyclosporin A Trough Concentrations or Rejection Incidence in Stable Renal Transplant Recipients," *Clin Chem*, 2001, 47(6):1048-52.

Yamauchi A, Ieiri I, Kataoka Y, et al, "Neurotoxicity Induced by Tacrolimus After Liver Transplantation: Relation to Genetic Polymorphisms of the ABCB1 (MDR1) Gene," *Transplantation*, 2002, 74(4):571-2.

Yates CR, Zhang W, Song P, et al, "The Effect of CYP3A5 and MDR1 Polymorphic Expression on Cyclosporine Oral Disposition in Renal Transplant Patients," *J Clin Pharmacol*, 2003, 43(6):555-64.

♦ **B1AR** *see* Beta$_1$-Adrenergic Receptor *on page 230*

♦ **B2AR** *see* Beta$_2$-Adrenergic Receptor *on page 233*

♦ **B2BKR** *see* Bradykinin B$_2$-Receptor *on page 237*

♦ **B3AR** *see* Beta$_3$-Adrenergic Receptor *on page 236*

♦ **BDKRB2** *see* Bradykinin B$_2$-Receptor *on page 237*

♦ **BDNF** *see* Brain-Derived Neurotropic-Factor *on page 239*

Beta$_1$-Adrenergic Receptor

Synonyms ADRB1; B1AR; BETA1AR; RHR

Chromosome Location 10q24-26

Clinically-Important Polymorphisms Nonsynonymous SNPs at codon 49 in the amino terminus region *(Ser49Gly)* and codon 389 in the carboxy-terminus region *(Arg389Gly)*. Allelic frequencies for the 389 codon have been reported as 74% for *Arg389* and 26% for *Gly389* in a small sample population. Another report identified 15% of a mixed Caucasian/African-American cohort as carriers of the *Gly49* allele, and a differential distribution of the *Gly389* allele between Caucasians (42%) and African-Americans (27%) (Moore, 1999).

Discussion In site-directed mutagenesis studies, the *Ser49Gly* polymorphism was associated with B1AR down-regulation and increased basal and agonist-stimulated adenylyl cyclase activity (Levin, 2002; Rathz, 2002). The *Arg389Gly* polymorphism was associated with basal- and agonist-mediated decreases in adenylyl cyclase activities (Rathz, 2002; Mason 1999). The *Ser49* allele has been associated with increased hospitalizations and poorer survival in heart failure patients (Borjesson, 2000). The *389Arg/Arg* genotype has been associated with hypertension (Bengtsson, 2001).

Metoprolol:

The *389Arg/Arg* genotype and the combination of the *389Arg/Arg* and *49Ser/Ser* genotypes were associated with greater diastolic blood pressure response to metoprolol in hypertensive subjects (Johnson, 2003).

In a small study of Chinese males, statistically greater reductions in resting and exercise heart rate and systolic blood pressure following metoprolol were correlated with the Arg389 variant. No significant differences between groups were noted with respect to the decrease in diastolic blood pressure (Liu, 2001).

In a prospective study of 61 beta-blocker naïve patients with systolic failure, metoprolol oral therapy (extended release) was titrated up to 200 mg/day or maximal tolerated dose (Terra, 2005). Left ventricular (LV) ejection fraction and LV dimension, were evaluated via echocardiography at baseline and after 3 months of stable therapy. Change in LV ejection fraction and dimension were evaluated as a function of *Arg389Gly* and *Ser49Gly* genotype. Compared to carriers of the *Gly389* genotype, homozygous wild-type patients showed a significant reduction in LV end-diastolic diameter (-2 mm vs +2 mm relative to baseline, p = 0.03 between groups), end-systolic diameter (-3 mm vs +1 mm relative to baseline, p = 0.03 between groups) and increase in LVEF (+6% vs +1% relative to baseline, p = 0.04 between groups). Carriers of the variant Gly49 allele experienced significant reductions in end-diastolic diameter compared to Ser49Ser wild-types (-2 mm vs +1 mm relative to baseline, p = 0.003 between groups). Diplotype analysis revealed a significant association of lower end-diastolic diameter with carriers of at least one Arg389 allele in combination with carriers of the Gly49 allele.

These data in heart failure are consistent with the general concept of increased beta receptor sensitivity for the *Arg389* and/or *Gly49* variants. Heart failure patients with these genotypes are possibly likely to have a greater contribution to their overall decompensation of cardiac function mediated through adrenergic stimulation of the beta-1 receptor. A complementary evaluation of the study population reported in Terra et al, seems to support this hypothesis (Terra, 2005). During titration of metoprolol, patients were assessed for the need for additional heart failure medications (defined as one index of decompensation). Significantly more patients possessing either of the two "low sensitivity" genotypes (ie, *Gly389* or *Ser49*) required an increase in medication (eg, diuretics, ACEI/ARB, digoxin).

Atenolol:

ARG389 homozygotes have been demonstrated to have a larger reduction in resting mean arterial blood pressure, as well as resting systolic blood pressure, following atenolol (Sofowora, 2003).

Blood pressure and heart rate were evaluated relative to codon 389 and 49 polymorphisms in 101 hypertensive patients with verified

(Continued)

Beta$_1$-Adrenergic Receptor *(Continued)*

LV hypertrophy following 12 weeks treatment with atenolol or irbesartan (Karlsson, 2004). Changes in hemodynamic variables did not significantly correlate with either of the observed polymorphisms. However, there was a trend towards a greater reduction in heart rate associated with the *Gly49* allele.

May Alter Pharmacokinetics of The B1AR is not known to alter the metabolism of any drugs.

May Alter Pharmacodynamics of β-Blockers

May Affect Disease Predisposition of Hypertension, heart failure

Clinical Recommendations The data suggest that *B1AR* genotype may be an important determinant of blood pressure response to β-blocker therapy. Whether the *B1AR* gene interacts with intracellular signaling genes in determining β-blocker response remains to be determined.

Counseling Points Since hypertension is a disease with polygenic etiology, carrier status of the *389Arg/Arg* genotype does not necessarily predispose a person to developing hypertension or its sequelae. Heart failure patients with the *Ser49* allele should discuss the implications of carrier status with their clinician or another healthcare professional.

References

Bengtsson K, Melander O, Orho-Melander M, et al, "Polymorphism in the Beta(1)-Adrenergic Receptor Gene and Hypertension," *Circulation*, 2001, 104(2):187-90.

Borjesson M, Magnusson Y, Hjalmarson A, et al, "A Novel Polymorphism in the Gene Coding for the Beta$_1$-Adrenergic Receptor Associated With Survival in Patients With Heart Failure," *Eur Heart J*, 2000, 21(22):1853-8.

Johnson JA, Zineh I, Puckett BJ, et al, "Beta$_1$-Adrenergic Receptor Polymorphism and Antihypertensive Response to Metoprolol," *Clin Pharmacol Ther*, 2003, 74(1):444-52.

Karlsson J, Lind L, Hallberg P, et al, "Beta1-Adrenergic Receptor Gene Polymorphisms and Response to Beta$_1$-Adrenergic Receptor Blockade in Patients With Essential Hypertension," *Clin Cardiol*, 2004, 27(6):347-50.

Levin MC, Marullo S, Muntaner O, et al, "The Myocardium-Protective Gly-49 Variant of the Beta$_1$-Adrenergic Receptor Exhibits Constitutive Activity and Increased Desensitization and Down-Regulation," *J Biol Chem*, 2002, 277(34):30429-35.

Liu J, Liu ZQ, Tan ZR, et al, "Gly389Arg Polymorphism of Beta$_1$-Adrenergic Receptor Is Associated With the Cardiovascular Response to Metoprolol," *Clin Pharmacol Ther*, 2003, 74(4):372-9.

Mason DA, Moore JD, Green SA, et al, "A Gain-of-Function Polymorphism in a G-Protein Coupling Domain of the Human Beta$_1$-Adrenergic Receptor," *J Biol Chem*, 1999, 274(18):12670-4.

Moore JD, Mason DA, Green SA, et al, "Racial Differences in the Frequencies of Cardiac Beta$_1$-Adrenergic Receptor Polymorphisms: Analysis of c145A>G and c1165G>C," *Hum Mutat*, 1999, 14(3):271.

Rathz DA, Brown KM, Kramer LA, et al, "Amino Acid 49 Polymorphisms of the Human Beta$_1$-Adrenergic Receptor Affect Agonist-Promoted Trafficking," *J Cardiovasc Pharmacol*, 2002, 39(2):155-60.

Sofowora GG, Dishy V, Muszkat M, et al, "A Common Beta$_1$-Adrenergic Receptor Polymorphism (Arg389Gly) Affect Blood Pressure Response to Beta-Blockade," *Clin Pharmacol Ther*, 2003, 73(4):366-71.

Terra SG, Hamilton KK, Pauly DF, et al, "Beta$_1$-Adrenergic Receptor Polymorphisms and Left Ventricular Remodeling Changes in Response to Beta-Blocker Therapy," *Pharmacogenet Genomics*, 2005, 15(4):227-34.

Terra SG, Pauly DF, Lee CR, et al, "Beta-Adrenergic Receptor Polymorphisms and Responses During Titration of Metoprolol Controlled Release/Extended Release in Heart Failure," *Clin Pharmacol Ther*, 2005, 77(3):127-37.

♦ **BETA1AR** *see* Beta$_1$-Adrenergic Receptor *on page 230*

Beta$_2$-Adrenergic Receptor

Synonyms ADRB2; B2AR

Chromosome Location 5q31-32

Clinically-Important Polymorphisms

Four nonsynonymous, coding polymorphisms have been identified: Arg16Gly, Gln27Glu, Val34Met, and Thr164Ile. The two most common mutations (with frequencies identified in African-Americans/ Caucasians/Asians) are the glycine at position 16 (51%/54%/41%) and the glutamate at position 27 (20%/35%/7%).

Multiple SNPs have also been identified in the promoter region including a Cys-19Arg transversion in the 5′ cistron promoter region, with Arg-19 allele frequencies of approximately 20% in African-Americans, 35% in Caucasians, and 8% in Asians.

Discussion The β_2-adrenergic receptor is a membrane bound, G-protein linked receptor. This receptor subtype plays a role in smooth muscle contraction and lipolysis. It is involved in the regulation of vascular tone, bronchial constriction, and uterine contraction. Variant forms of the β_2-adrenergic receptor gene display functional differences which may be clinically important. The codon 16, 27, and -19 SNPs appear to be in linkage disequilibrium.

The Val34Met polymorphism does not appear to have any functional effects. The codon 16 and 27 receptor polymorphisms influence receptor function *in vitro*, although evidence regarding exact relationships is conflicting.

The Gln27Glu genotype has been associated with fat mass, body mass index, and obesity in females. Lipolysis and fat oxidation promoted by acute submaximal exercise has been observed to be blunted in females with the 27Gln/Gln genotype (Macho-Azcarate, 2002).

The frequency of the Thr164Ile polymorphism is approximately 4%. It has been associated with decreased receptor signaling and, blunted cardiac response in transgenic mice. In addition, this polymorphism has been associated with decreases in exercise capacity and the composite of death or cardiovascular transplant in patients with congestive heart failure (Liggett, 1998; Wagoner, 2000).

Polymorphism of the β_2-adrenergic receptor may be related to variation in airway hyper-reactivity as well as responsiveness to β_2-agonist drugs. Although early studies suggested a relationship between *B2AR* genotype and airway hyper-responsiveness and asthma severity, the correlations have been inconsistent, and in some cases contradictory.

Since multiple polymorphisms may occur in both the sequences which encode the receptor as well as its regulatory sequences, the evaluation of haplotypes may yield more appropriate correlations to phenotype and drug response. Combinations of alleles may be more (Continued)

Beta$_2$-Adrenergic Receptor *(Continued)*

important in determining the relationship to phenotype than individual SNPs, and may explain why earlier investigations have yielded contrasting results.

β_2-adrenergic agonists:

The relationship of receptor polymorphisms to β-adrenergic receptor agonists appears to be complicated by discrepancies between observations made *in vitro* versus *in vivo* clinical trials. The *Gly16* genotype demonstrates enhanced down-regulation after exposure to stimulation *in vitro* (Green, 1994). However, *in vivo* responses generally indicate that the *Gly16* genotype may be less likely to demonstrate tachyphylaxis. A potential explanation may be that the receptor populations in *Gly16* individuals have been previously down-regulated by exposure to endogenous catecholamines (Liggett, 2000).

Cells transfected with the Gly16 genotype exhibit nearly 20% greater down-regulation after prolonged agonist exposure *in vitro* relative to Arg16 cells (Green, 1994; 1995). However, *in vivo* responses generally indicate that the Gly16 genotype may be less likely to demonstrate tachyphylaxis, which is consistent with *in vitro* observations of agonist-induced responses in human lung mast cells (Chong, 2000).

Israel and colleagues previously reported diminished morning peak expiratory flow rates (PEFR)s in patients homozygous for the Arg16 allele following regular use of albuterol (Israel, 2000). These results were extended in the BARGE study, a prospective, randomized clinical trial, which evaluated morning peak expiratory flow rates in patients with mild asthma after 16 weeks each of albuterol and placebo treatment (Israel, 2004). In this cross-over design, patients homozygous for the Arg/Arg or Gly/Gly genotype were enrolled and matched in pairs (opposite genotype, similar FEV1s) and assessed for PEFR at the start and end of the 16 week treatment period, consisting of regularly scheduled daily albuterol (or placebo) treatments (four times daily via metered dose inhaler), with rescue ipratropium. Change in morning PEFR while on treatment ($PEFR_{albuterol}$ minus $PEFR_{placebo}$) was -10 L/min for the Arg homozygotes compared to +14 L/min for the Gly homozygotes, for an overall genotype/treatment difference of -24 L/min (Arg response minus Gly response; p=0.0003). The improvement in lung function observed in the Gly/Gly patients in this study strongly refutes the notion of increased β receptor down-regulation or desensitization as a Gly predominant phenotype.

Dishy et al observed greater receptor desensitization with the Arg16 and Gln27 forms following isoproterenol infusion in healthy volunteers.

A potential explanation for the discrepancies between the *in vitro* and *in vivo* observations may be that in humans the Gly16 receptor has been previously down-regulated by exposure to endogenous catecholamines. This dynamic model of receptor kinetics, proposed by

Liggett et al, suggests that Gly16 expressed β receptors are preferentially down-regulated by endogenous catecholamines prior to exposure to pharmacologic agents. Under this model, tachyphylaxis and "apparent" loss of response to the effects of β_2-agonists would be more apparent in patients with the Arg16 genotype.

However, analysis of the Arg16Gly SNP alone may not be adequate. The BARGE trial did not enroll patients of a heterozygous status, so there was no opportunity to observe a "gene-dose response", which may have more convincingly suggested the effects were attributable to the Arg16Gly polymorphism. As such, there remains the issue of what other co-transmitted SNPs may contribute to this phenomenon. Drysdale et al, reported on 13 SNPs within the promoter and coding regions of the β_2 receptor which resolved into 5 common haplotypes. Analysis of β_2 agonist-induced bronchodilation in asthmatic patients revealed little association of response with individual SNPs, but significantly discriminated *in vivo* responses based on haplotype pairing. Given the degree of linkage disequilibrium observed with β_2 receptor polymorphisms, these authors concluded that analysis of individual SNPs in this setting provides less insight and inferior predictive power relative to the more robust haplotype analyses.

Although acute responses and extent of tachyphylaxis differ in patients with the *Gly16* genotype, use of a long-acting β_2-agonist (formoterol) maintained asthma control in a group of 24 patients with this genotype (Lipworth, 2000).

Carvedilol:

The β_2 receptor genotype has been correlated to improvements in left ventricular function following carvedilol therapy. Compared to homozygotes for Glu27, a smaller percentage of individuals who were homozygous for the *Gln27* allele demonstrated significant improvements in left ventricular function (Kaye, 2003).

May Alter Pharmacodynamics of β_2-adrenergic agonists

May Affect Disease Predisposition of Asthma, obesity, congestive heart failure

References

Dishy V, Sofowora GG, Xie HG, et al, "The Effect of Common Polymorphisms of the Beta$_2$-Adrenergic Receptor on Agonist-Mediated Vascular Desensitization," *N Engl J Med*, 2001, 345(14):1030-5.

Drysdale CM, McGraw DW, Stack CB, et al, "Complex Promoter and Coding Region Beta$_2$-Adrenergic Receptor Haplotypes Alter Receptor Expression and Predict *in vivo* Responsiveness," *Proc Natl Acad Sci U S A*, 2000, 97(19):10483-8.

Green S, Turki J, Innis M, et al, "Amino-Terminal Polymorphisms of the Human Beta$_2$-Adrenergic Receptor Impart Distinct Agonist-Promoted Regulatory Properties," *Biochemistry*, 1994, 33(32):9414-9.

Green SA, Turki J, Bejarano P, et al, "Influence of Beta$_2$-Adrenergic Receptor Genotypes on Signal Transduction in Human Airway Smooth Muscle Cells," *Am J Respir Cell Mol Biol*, 1995, 13(1):25-33.

Israel E, Drazen JM, Liggett SB, et al, "The Effect of Polymorphisms of the Beta$_2$-Adrenergic Receptor on the Response to Regular Use of Albuterol in Asthma," *Am J Respir Crit Care Med*, 2000, 162(1):75-80.

Johnson JA and Terra SG, "Beta-Adrenergic Receptor Polymorphisms: Cardiovascular Disease Associations and Pharmacogenetics," *Pharm Res*, 2002, 19(12):1779-87.

(Continued)

Beta$_2$-Adrenergic Receptor *(Continued)*

Kaye DM, Smirk B, Williams C, et al, "Beta-Adrenergic Genotype Influences the Response to Carvedilol in Patients With Congestive Heart Failure," *Pharmacogenetics*, 2003, 13(7):379-82.

Liggett SB, "Pharmacogenetics of Beta$_1$- and Beta$_2$-Adrenergic Receptors," *Pharmacology*, 2000, 61(3):167-73.

Liggett SB, "Polymorphisms of the Beta$_2$-Adrenergic Receptor," *N Engl J Med*, 2002, 346(7):536-8

Liggett SB, Wagoner LE, Craft LL, et al, "The Ile164 Beta$_2$-Adrenergic Receptor Polymorphism Adversely Affects the Outcome of Congestive Heart Failure," *J Clin Invest*, 1998, 102(8):1534-9.

Macho-Azcarate T, Marti A, Gonzalez A, et al, "Gln27Glu Polymorphism in the Beta$_2$-Adrenergic Receptor Gene and Lipid Metabolism During Exercise in Obese Women," *Int J Obes Relat Metab Disord*, 2002, 26(11):1434-41.

Taylor DR and Kennedy MA, "Beta-Adrenergic Receptor Polymorphisms and Drug Responses in Asthma," *Pharmacogenomics*, 2002, 3(2):173-84.

Taylor DR and Kennedy MA, "Genetic Variation of the Beta$_2$-Adrenoceptor: Its Functional and Clinical Importance in Bronchial Asthma," *Am J Pharmacogenomics*, 2001, 1(3):165-74.

Wagoner LE, Craft LL, Singh B, et al, "Polymorphisms of the Beta$_2$-Adrenergic Receptor Determine Exercise Capacity in Patients With Heart Failure," *Circ Res*, 2000, 86(8):834-40.

Beta$_3$-Adrenergic Receptor

Synonyms ADRB3; B3AR

Chromosome Location 8p12-11.2

Clinically-Important Polymorphisms Thr64Arg

Discussion A polymorphism in the β_3-adrenergic receptor gene (*Thr64Arg*) has been associated with insulin resistance (Widen, 1995), the time of onset of type 2 diabetes mellitus (Walston, 1995), and an increased capacity for obese individuals to gain weight (Clement, 1995).

Clozapine:

The *Thr64Arg* polymorphism was associated with a higher mean change in weight during treatment with clozapine (Basile, 2001).

May Alter Pharmacodynamics of Clozapine

References

Basile VS, Masellis M, McIntyre RS, et al, "Genetic Dissection of Atypical Antipsychotic-Induced Weight Gain: Novel Preliminary Data on the Pharmacogenetic Puzzle," *J Clin Psychiatry*, 2001, 62(Suppl 23):45-66.

Clement K, Vaisse C, Manning BS, et al, "Genetic Variation in the Beta$_3$-Adrenergic Receptor and an Increased Capacity to Gain Weight in Patients With Morbid Obesity," *N Engl J Med*, 1995, 333(6):352-4.

Walston J, Silver K, Bogardus C, et al, "Time of Onset of Noninsulin-Dependent Diabetes Mellitus and Genetic Variation in the Beta$_3$-Adrenergic-Receptor Gene," *N Engl J Med*, 1995, 333(6):343-7.

Widen E, Lehto M, Kanninen T, et al, "Association of a Polymorphism in the Beta$_3$-Adrenergic Receptor Gene With Features of the Insulin Resistance Syndrome in Finns," *N Engl J Med*, 1995, 333(6):348-51.

Beta-Fibrinogen

Synonyms FGB

Chromosome Location 4q28

Clinically-Important Polymorphisms Synonymous SNP in the promoter region *G-455A*

Discussion Elevated fibrinogen levels have been linked to an increased risk for thrombosis (myocardial infarction, deep venous thrombosis, stroke). However, it is not clear whether fibrinogen is a cause of thrombosis or simply a marker for other risk factors. The *G-455A* polymorphism in the gene that encodes for the β-chain is associated with elevated fibrinogen levels. The *-455AA* genotype was associated with higher plasma fibrinogen levels and greater progression of atherosclerotic disease than other β-fibrinogen genotypes (de Maat, 1998).

HMG CoA reductase inhibitors:

Treatment with pravastatin in patients with coronary heart disease offset the greater progression of coronary atherosclerosis observed with the *455AA* genotype in the placebo group (de Maat, 1998).

May Alter Pharmacokinetics of β-fibrinogen is not known to alter the metabolism of any drugs.

May Alter Pharmacodynamics of HMG CoA reductase inhibitors

May Affect Disease Predisposition of Thrombosis, deep venous thrombosis

Clinical Recommendations Data suggest that the β-fibrinogen genotype may be useful in predicting clinical outcomes with HMG CoA reductase inhibitor therapy in patients with coronary heart disease. The β-fibrinogen genotype may interact with the apolipoprotein E, stromelysin-1, ACE, and cholesterol ester transfer protein genes in predicting HMG CoA reductase inhibitor response.

Counseling Points Carrier status for the *-455AA* genotype has been associated with greater disease progression in individuals with coronary heart disease. Individuals with coronary heart disease who carry this allele should be encouraged to discuss the implications of their carrier status with their clinician or another healthcare professional.

References

de Maat MP, Kastelein JJ, Jukema JW, et al, "-455G/A Polymorphism of the Beta-Fibrinogen Gene Is Associated With the Progression of Coronary Atherosclerosis in Symptomatic Men: Proposed Role For an Acute-Phase Reaction Pattern of Fibrinogen. REGRESS Group," *Arterioscler Thromb Vasc Biol*, 1998, 18(2):265-71.

♦ **BKB2R** *see* Bradykinin B_2-Receptor *on page 237*

Bradykinin B_2-Receptor

Synonyms B2BKR; BDKRB2; BKB2R

Chromosome Location 14q32.1-32.2

Clinically-Important Polymorphisms Synonymous SNP in promoter region *(C-58T)*; +9/-9 exon 1 polymorphism

Discussion In animal models, stimulation of bradykinin B_2-receptors has been implicated in the pathogenesis of inflammation, pain, and tissue injury. In addition, stimulation of the bradykinin 2B receptor mediates a number of cardioprotective effects, resulting from the synthesis of endothelial mediators such as nitric oxide, prostaglandins, and tissue-type plasminogen activator. These mediators result in vasodilation, protection from hypertrophic stimuli, and antiatherosclerotic effects. Bradykinin stimulation also leads to ischemic preconditioning and an increase in insulin sensitivity.

(Continued)

Bradykinin B_2-Receptor *(Continued)*

With respect to the regulation of vascular tone, the BKB2R and angiotensin II type 1 receptor are antagonistic. Stimulation of bradykinin receptors leads to vasodilatation and enhanced sodium excretion. In addition to their effects on the formation of angiotensin II, ACE inhibitors increase bradykinin concentrations. Increased bradykinin concentrations may play a role in the development of ACE inhibitor-induced cough.

In addition to cardiovascular effects, the BKB2R exon 1 polymorphism may be a marker for susceptibility for progression of nephropathy in diabetic patients (Maltais, 2002). This polymorphism has also been associated with efficiency of skeletal muscle contraction and significantly associated with endurance among Olympic-level athletes.

ACE inhibitors:

Although data are inconsistent, the BKB2R has been associated with the ACE inhibitor-induced cough. Among hypertensives treated with an ACE inhibitor, the frequency of the *-58T* allele was significantly higher in those who developed a cough compared to cough-free individuals (Mukae, 2000). Other investigators reported no association between the BKB2R gene and a cough during ACE inhibitor therapy (Zee, 1998).

Angiotensin receptor antagonists and β-blockers:

In normotensive males, the +9/-9 exon 1 polymorphism of the gene encoding the bradykinin B_2-receptor has been associated with left ventricular growth in response to exercise. In a 48-week trial of antihypertensive therapy with either irbesartan or atenolol, individuals with the +9/+9 exon 1 polymorphism showed a lower reduction in left ventricular mass index relative to other genotypes which was independent of any changes in blood pressure (Hallberg, 2003).

May Alter Pharmacokinetics of Bradykinin B_2 receptor is not known to alter the metabolism of any drugs.

May Alter Pharmacodynamics of ACE inhibitors, angiotensin receptor antagonists, β-blockers

May Affect Disease Predisposition of CHF, left ventricular hypertrophy, diabetic nephropathy, Alzheimer's disease

Clinical Recommendations Because of the benefits of ACE inhibitor therapy, the inconsistencies in the data, and the fact that some study subjects with the *-58T* allele did not develop a cough with ACE inhibitors, the association between the BKB2R gene and an ACE inhibitor-induced cough is unlikely to influence prescribing practices.

References

Hallberg P, Lind L, Michaelsson K, et al, "B_2 Bradykinin (B2BKR) Polymorphism and Change in Left Ventricular Mass in Response to Antihypertensive Treatment: Results From the Swedish Irbesartan Left Ventricular Hypertrophy Investigation Versus Atenolol (SILVHIA) Trial," *J Hypertens*, 2003, 21(3):621-4.

Heitsch H, "The Therapeutic Potential of Bradykinin B_2-Receptor Agonists in the Treatment of Cardiovascular Disease," *Expert Opin Investig Drugs*, 2003, 12(5):759-70.

Maltais I, Bachvarova M, Malheux P, et al, "Bradykinin B_2-Receptor Gene Polymorphism Is Associated With Altered Urinary Albumin/Creatinine Values in Diabetic Patients," *Can J Physiol Pharmacol*, 2002, 80(4):323-7.

Mukae S, Aoki S, Itoh S, et al, "Bradykinin B_2-Receptor Gene Polymorphism Is Associated With Angiotensin-Converting Enzyme Inhibitor-Related Cough," *Hypertension*, 2000, 36(1):127-31.

Mukae S, Itoh S, Aoki S, et al, "Association of Polymorphisms of the Renin-Angiotensin System and Bradykinin B_2-Receptor With ACE-Inhibitor-Related Cough," *J Hum Hypertens*, 2002, 16(12):857-63.

Zee RY, Rao VS, Paster RZ, et al, "Three Candidate Genes and Angiotensin-Converting Enzyme Inhibitor-Related Cough: A Pharmacogenetic Analysis," *Hypertension*, 1998, 31(4):925-8.

Brain-Derived Neurotropic-Factor

Synonyms BDNF

Chromosome Location 11p13

Clinically-Important Polymorphisms Val66Met, -270C/T

Discussion BDNF is a member of the nerve growth factor family of trophic factors. In the brain BDNF has a trophic action on retinal, cholinergic, and dopaminergic neurons, and in the peripheral nervous system it acts on both motor and sensory neurons. It is the most widely distributed trophic factor in the brain and participates in neuronal growth, maintenance, and use-dependent plasticity mechanisms such as long-term potentiation and learning. The receptors for BDNF include a low affinity receptor, p75 and a receptor with specificity, a glycoprotein tyrosine kinase, TrkB.

Clozapine:

Statistical analysis was used to test the association between the BDNF-gene Val66Met polymorphism in 93 patients with schizophrenia with therapeutic response to clozapine. No significant difference in therapeutic response to clozapine was demonstrated comparing the three Val66Met - genotype subgroups (Hong, 2003).

Fluoxetine:

One hundred and ten patients with major depression who received four weeks of fluoxetine treatment were studied to determine the association between the BDNF Val66Met polymorphism and therapeutic response to fluoxetine. A trend for improved 4-week fluoxetine response was seen in the heterozygous patients compared to those who were homozygous (Tsai, 2003).

Lithium:

Eighty-eight patients with bipolar disorder were studied to determine the association between lithium prophylaxis and two polymorphism of the BDNF gene. The Val/Met genotype occurred more frequently and there was a trend for a higher incidence of the Met allele in those patients classified as excellent responders compared to nonresponders. In addition, a trend for *C/T* genotype and T allele occurred more frequently in the excellent responder compared to the nonresponders (Rybakowski, 2005).

May Alter Pharmacodynamics of Fluoxetine and lithium

(Continued)

Brain-Derived Neurotropic-Factor *(Continued)*

References

Hong CJ, Yu YW, Lin CH, et al, "An Association Study of a Brain-Derived Neurotrophic Factor Val66Met Polymorphism and Clozapine Response of Schizophrenic Patients," *Neurosci Lett*, 2003, 349(3):206-8.

Rybakowski JK, Suwalska A, Skibinska M, et al, "Prophylactic Lithium Response and Polymorphism of the Brain-Derived Neurotrophic Factor Gene," *Pharmacopsychiatry*, 2005, 38(4):166-70.

Tsai SJ, Cheng CY, Yu YW, et al, "Association Study of a Brain-Derived Neurotrophic-Factor Genetic Polymorphism and Major Depressive Disorders, Symptomatology, and Antidepressant Response," *Am J Med Genet B Neuropsychiatr Genet*, 2003, 123(1):19-22.

♦ **BRCA-1** *see* BRCA Genes *on page 240*

♦ **BRCA-2** *see* BRCA Genes *on page 240*

BRCA Genes

Synonyms BRCA-1; BRCA-2

Chromosome Location 17q21; 13q12.3

Clinically-Important Polymorphisms Three "founder" BRCA mutations include the 185delAG mutation, the 5382insC mutation, and the 6174 delT mutation. A large number of other mutations have also been described.

Discussion BRCA-1 and BRCA-2 are believed to be tumor suppression genes. They are located on the long arms of chromosomes 17 and 13, respectively. Both are large genes, distributed over approximately 100,000 base pairs of genomic DNA, and each encodes a large, negatively-charged protein. Inactivating mutations identified to date are distributed throughout both genes, with an increased frequency of two distinct BRCA-1 mutations and one BRCA-2 mutation in individuals of Ashkenazi Jewish descent.

Women carriers of germline BRCA-1 mutations have a lifetime risk of breast cancer exceeding 80% and of ovarian cancer approaching 60%. BRCA-2 mutations are associated with a similar increase in breast cancer, although the risk of ovarian cancer is elevated, it is not as high as the BRCA-1 mutants. Approximately 0.5% of women carry one of these mutations; however, the frequency may be as high as 2% in certain ethnic groups. In the case of BRCA-1 carriers, the risk of developing breast cancer prior to menopause is particularly increased. Their risk of contralateral breast cancer is also significantly higher as compared to the general population (4.2% to 53% vs 2%), and the grade of contralateral tumors is more aggressive. The hereditary breast cancer associated with BRCA-2 appears to be more heterogeneous than the BRCA-1 phenotype. It should be noted that 20% to 30% of BRCA carriers never develop breast or ovarian cancer, therefore, other factors must modify or offset this risk.

In general, women have a 10% lifetime risk of developing breast cancer and a 2% to 3% chance of ovarian cancer. Women with the BRCA-1/BRCA-2 mutations have an 80% chance of breast cancer and 60% chance of ovarian cancer. Patients and their families with these mutations are frequently referred for genetic testing counseling.

Oral contraceptives:

Among carriers of BRCA-1, women who use oral contraceptives for 5 years or more have a 33% increase in the risk of early onset breast cancer as compared to BRCA-1 carriers who never used this form of contraception (Narod, 2002).

May Alter Pharmacodynamics of Oral contraceptives

May Affect Disease Predisposition of Breast cancer, ovarian cancer

Laboratory Evaluation Commercial testing available

Clinical Recommendations Category 2 ASCO genetic test; consult ASCO Guidelines

References

Narod SA, Dube MP, Klijn J, et al, "Oral Contraceptives and the Risk of Breast Cancer in BRCA1 and BRCA2 Mutation Carriers," *J Natl Cancer Inst*, 2002, 94(23):1773-9.

Cardiac Potassium Ion Channel

Synonyms k-channel

Chromosome Location 11-KVLQT1; 7-HERG; 21-KCNE1, KCNE2

Clinically-Important Polymorphisms

Missense mutations in the KCNE2 leading to Gln9Glu and Met54Thr form of the MinK-related peptide-1

Nonsynonymous SNP in the KCNE2 gene leading to the Thr8Ala form of the MinK-related peptide-1

Arg583Cys in the C-terminal of the KVLQT1 protein

Arg784Trp in the C-terminal of the HERG protein

Discussion KCNE1 and KvLQT1 encode subunits of the IKs channel, while KCNE2 and HERG encode subunits of the IKr channel. Variations in these genes have been identified as a cause of the most common form of congenital long QT syndrome. It has been proposed that predisposition to arrhythmias with QT-prolonging agents may be related to the presence of mutations in the genes which encode potassium channel proteins. Some cases of drug-induced QT prolongation have been related to genetic causes.

QT-prolonging agents:

Phenotypic expression of a heterozygous mutation has been described in a patient who developed drug-induced cardiac arrest with cisapride, clarithromycin, and quinidine (Abbott, 1999) and a prolonged QT interval with procainamide and sulfamethoxazole (Sesti, 2000).

May Alter Pharmacokinetics of The cardiac potassium channel is not known to affect the metabolism of any drugs.

May Alter Pharmacodynamics of QT-prolonging agents, Class I and III antiarrhythmics, selected fluoroquinolones, some antipsychotics, TCAs

May Affect Disease Predisposition of Arrhythmia

Clinical Recommendations It remains to be seen whether molecular screening for mutations of candidate genes may allow identification of individuals at risk of drug-induced arrhythmias.

(Continued)

Cardiac Potassium Ion Channel *(Continued)*

Counseling Points Genetic variants in the cardiac potassium channel may influence a patient's risk for congenital long QT syndrome. Patients who have a genetic variant in this location should discuss the implications of the variant on their risk for arrhythmia with their clinician or another healthcare professional.

References

Abbott GW, Sesti F, Splawski I, et al, "MiRP1 Forms IKr Potassium Channels With HERG and Is Associated With Cardiac Arrhythmia," *Cell*, 1999, 97(2):175-87.

Bianchi L, Priori SG, Napolitano C, et al, "Mechanisms of I(Ks) Suppression in LQT1 Mutants," *Am J Physiol Heart Circ Physiol*, 2000, 279(6):H3003-11

Napolitano C, Schwartz PJ, Brown AM, et al, "Evidence for a Cardiac Ion Channel Mutation Underlying Drug-Induced QT Prolongation and Life-Threatening Arrhythmias," *J Cardiovasc Electrophysiol*, 2000, 11(6):691-6.

Sesti F, Abbott GW, Wei J, et al, "A Common Polymorphism Associated With Antibiotic-Induced Cardiac Arrhythmia," *Proc Natl Acad Sci U S A*, 2000, 97(19):10613-8.

Cardiac Sodium Channel

Synonyms SCN5A

Chromosome Location 3p21

Clinically-Important Polymorphisms Gly615Glu, Leu618Phe, Phe1250Leu in the intracellular domain of the alpha subunit region; Leu1825Pro in the C-terminus region

Discussion Subclinical mutations in SCN5A increase activity of the sodium channel and have been associated with congenital long QT syndromes and may increase the risk for drug-induced arrhythmias (Sesti, 2000).

QT-prolonging agents:

A novel missense mutation (Leu1825Pro) was identified in an elderly Japanese woman who developed torsade de pointes during treatment with cisapride (Makita, 2002). The Gly615Glu, Leu618Phe, and Phe1250Leu mutations of the SNC5A gene were identified in patients who developed torsade de pointes during treatment with quinidine and sotalol (Sesti, 2000).

May Alter Pharmacokinetics of The SNC5A gene is not known to affect the metabolism of any drugs.

May Alter Pharmacodynamics of QT-prolonging agents, Class I and III antiarrhythmics, selected fluoroquinolones, some antipsychotics, TCAs

May Affect Disease Predisposition of Arrhythmia

Clinical Recommendations It remains to be seen whether molecular screening for mutations of candidate genes may allow identification of individuals at risk of drug-induced arrhythmias.

Counseling Points Genetic variants in the cardiac sodium channel may influence a patient's risk for congenital long QT syndrome. Patients who have a genetic variant in this location should discuss the implications of the variant on their risk for arrhythmia with their clinician or another healthcare professional.

References

Makita NM, Horie T, Nakamura T, et al, "Drug-Induced Long QT Syndrome Associated With a Subclinical SCN5A Mutation," *Circulation*, 2002, 106(10):1269-74.

Sesti F, Abbott GW, Wei J, et al, "A Common Polymorphism Associated With Antibiotic-Induced Cardiac Arrhythmia," *Proc Natl Acad Sci U S A*, 2000, 97(19):10613-8.

- **CD243** *see* ATP-Binding Cassette, Sub-Family B, Member 1 *on page 224*
- **CETP** *see* Cholesteryl Ester Transfer Protein *on page 243*

Cholesteryl Ester Transfer Protein

Synonyms CETP

Chromosome Location 16q21

Clinically-Important Polymorphisms Presence *(B1)* or absence *(B2)* of a restriction site for the TaqI enzyme in intron 1 *(B1/B2)*.

Discussion The CETP is involved in the metabolism of high-density lipoprotein (HDL). The *B1B1* genotype has been associated with higher CETP concentrations, increased triglycerides and reduced high-density lipoprotein (HDL)-levels, and increased progression of coronary atherosclerosis (Kuivenhoven, 1998).

HMG CoA reductase inhibitors:

Among men with atherosclerosis, treatment with pravastatin slowed atherosclerosis progression in *B1B1* carriers, but not in those with the *B2B2* genotype. There was no association between the *B1/B2* genotype and changes in lipoprotein lipid levels with pravastatin (Kuivenhoven, 1998).

There was no association between the *B1/B2* genotype and the ability of pravastatin to reduce the risk of coronary events in a large study of men with hypercholesterolemia and no history and myocardial infarction.

Fibrates:

Among men with coronary heart disease, the *B1B1* genotype was associated with greater reductions in triglyceride levels with gemfibrozil compared to the *B1B2* and *B2B2* genotypes (Brousseau, 2002).

May Alter Pharmacokinetics of CETP is not known to alter the metabolism of any drugs.

May Alter Pharmacodynamics of HMG CoA reductase inhibitors, fibrates

May Affect Disease Predisposition of Atherosclerosis

Clinical Recommendations It is unclear whether the *CETP* gene will be useful in predicting response to HMG CoA-reductase inhibitors. The *CETP* genotype may interact with the apolipoprotein E, fibrinogen, stromelysin-1, and ACE genes in predicting HMG CoA-reductase inhibitor response.

Counseling Points Carrier status for the *B1B1* genotype has been associated with greater disease progression in individuals with coronary heart disease. Individuals with coronary heart disease who carry this allele should be encouraged to discuss the implications of their carrier status with their clinician or another healthcare professional.

References

Brousseau ME, O'Connor JJ Jr, Ordovas JM, et al, "Cholesteryl Ester Transfer Protein TaqI B2B2 Genotype is Associated With Higher HDL Cholesterol Levels and Lower Risk of Coronary Heart Disease End Points in Men With HDL Deficiency: Veterans

(Continued)

Cholesteryl Ester Transfer Protein *(Continued)*

Affairs HDL Cholesterol Intervention Trial," *Arterioscler Thromb Vasc Biol*, 2002, 22(7):1148-54.

Kuivenhoven JA, Jukema JW, Zwinderman AH, et al, "The Role of a Common Variant of the Cholesteryl Ester Transfer Protein Gene in the Progression of Coronary Atherosclerosis. The Regression Growth Evaluation Statin Study Group," *N Engl J Med*, 1998, 338(2):86-93.

♦ **CLCS** *see* ATP-Binding Cassette, Sub-Family B, Member 1 *on page 224*

COMT

Synonyms COMT-L; val-COMT

Chromosome Location 22q11

Clinically-Important Polymorphisms Val(158)Met (also known as Val(108)Met when in soluble form)

Discussion Catechol-O-methyltransferase catalyzes a methyl group transfer from S-adenosylmethionine to catecholamines, including the neurotransmitters dopamine, epinephrine, and norepinephrine. Catechol-O-methyltransferase mediates metabolism of catecholamines, and is an important regulator of both dopaminergic and noradrenergic neurotransmission. This is also one of the major degradative pathways of drugs used in the treatment of hypertension, asthma, and Parkinson disease.

COMT is found in two forms in tissues, a soluble form (S-COMT) and a membrane-bound form (MB-COMT). A methionine substitution for valine at codon 158 results in a gene product which is three to four times less active than the high-activity allele. The genes exhibit codominant expression, with heterozygotes demonstrating intermediate activity. Polymorphism of the COMT gene is common in the human population, with up to 25% of Caucasians being homozygous for the low-activity allele (COMT-L, COMT-met). This genotype appears to be less common in Asians than in Caucasians.

The *Val15Met* genotype has been linked to the expression of a variety of complex disease states, and may be a contributing factor in their development. The role of a single polymorphism in these diseases is likely to be limited, given the complex pathogenesis of these disorders. Associations include Parkinson's disease (Goudreau, 2002), schizophrenia (Bilder, 2002; Harrison, 2003), Alzheimer's disease (Qu, 2001), atherosclerosis (Mehrabian, 2002), ADHD (Kirley, 2002; Qian, 2003), panic disorder (Woo, 2002), and breast cancer incidence in a limited population (Kocabas, 2002).

Antipsychotics:

Having both low activity of the catechol-O-methyltransferase enzyme and high activity of the ACE genotypes has been associated with poor response to conventional antipsychotics (Illi, 2003). The daily antipsychotic dosage that patients received during their maintenance treatment was significantly ($p<0.05$) higher in patients with the L/L(met/met) genotype than in the other patients (Inada, 2003).

Twenty inpatients with schizophrenia or schizoaffective disorder were administered cognitive tests after 4 weeks of antipsychotic treatment or placebo in a double-blind within subject study. Patients homozygous for the COMT Met allele displayed significant improvement on the working memory task after antipsychotic treatment. Patients homozygous for the COMT Val allele did not show working memory improvement with treatment. Other COMT polymorphisms were not associated with significant differences between treatment and placebo (Weickert, 2004).

Thirty patients with acute untreated schizophrenia underwent COMT Val/Met genotyping and entered an 8-week prospective study of olanzapine treatment. Met allele load predicted improvement in working memory performance and negative symptom improvement after 8 weeks of treatment (Bertolino, 2004).

Lithium:

In a group of approximately 200 patients with bipolar disorder or depression, no association between lithium efficacy and polymorphisms at the COMT loci was found (Serretti, 2001).

Opiates:

Individuals who are homozygous for the MET allele demonstrated diminished μ-opioid responses, correlating with higher sensory and affective ratings of pain. In contrast, individuals who were homozygous for the Val allele withstood significantly greater saline doses than other volunteers and rated the resulting pain as less bothersome. Some of the variability in pain tolerance and opiate requirements may be linked to these observations.

Tardive dyskinesia:

Tardive dyskinesia was not associated with the polymorphisms of 5HT2A receptor gene, serotonin transporter gene, and catechol-O-methyltransferase gene (Herken, 2003).

May Alter Pharmacodynamics of Opiates/narcotic analgesics and olanzapine

May Affect Disease Predisposition of Alzheimer's disease, anxiety disorder, atherosclerosis, attention-deficit disorder, breast cancer, panic disorder, Parkinson's disease, schizophrenia

References

Bertolino A, Caforio G, Blasi G, et al, "Interaction of COMT (Val(108/158)Met) Genotype and Olanzapine Treatment on Prefrontal Cortical Function in Patients With Schizophrenia," *Am J Psychiatry*, 2004, 161(10):1798-805.

Bilder RM, Volavka J, Czobor P, et al, "Neurocognitive Correlates of the COMT Val(158)Met Polymorphism in Chronic Schizophrenia," *Biol Psychiatry*, 2002, 52(7):701-7.

Enoch MA, Schuckit MA, Johnson BA, et al, "Genetics of Alcoholism Using Intermediate Phenotypes," *Alcohol Clin Exp Res*, 2003, 27(2):169-76.

Goudreau JL, Maraganore DM, Farrer MJ, et al, "Case-Control Study of Dopamine Transporter-1, Monoamine Oxidase-B, and Catechol-O-methyl Transferase Polymorphisms in Parkinson's Disease," *Mov Disord*, 2002, 17(6):1305-11.

Harrison PJ and Owen MJ, "Genes for Schizophrenia? Recent Findings and Their Pathophysiological Implications," *Lancet*, 2003, 361(9355):417-9.

Herken H, Erdal ME, Boke O, et al, "Tardive Dyskinesia Is Not Associated With the Polymorphisms of 5-HT2A Receptor Gene, Serotonin Transporter, Gene, and Catechol-O-methyltransferase Gene," *Eur Psychiatry*, 2003, 18(2):77-81.

Illi A, Kampman O, Anttila S, et al, "Interaction Between Angiotensin-converting Enzyme and Catechol-O-methyltransferase Genotypes in Schizophrenics With Poor Response to Conventional Neuroleptics," *Eur Neuropsychopharmacol*, 2003, 13(3):147-51.

(Continued)

COMT *(Continued)*

Inada T, Nakamura A, and Iijima Y, "Relationship Between Catechol-O-Methyltransferase Polymorphism and Treatment-Resistant Schizophrenia," *Am J Med Genet B Neuropsychiatr Genet*, 2003, 120(1):35-9.

Kirley A, Hawi Z, Daly G, et al, "Dopaminergic System Genes in ADHD: Toward a Biological Hypothesis," *Neuropsychopharmacology*, 2002, 27(4):607-19.

Kocabas NA, Sardas S, Cholerton S, et al, "Cytochrome P450 CYP1B1 and Catechol O-methyltransferase (COMT) Genetic Polymorphisms and Breast Cancer Susceptibility in a Turkish Population," *Arch Toxicol*, 2002, 76(11):643-9.

Qian Q, Wang Y, Zhou R, et al, "Family-Based and Case-Control Association Studies of Catechol-O-methyltransferase in Attention-Deficit Hyperactivity Disorder Suggest Genetic Sexual Dimorphism," *Am J Med Genet*, 2003, 118B(1):103-9.

Qu T, Manev R, and Manev H, "5-Lipoxygenase (5-LOX) Promoter Polymorphism in Patients With Early-Onset and Late-Onset Alzheimer's Disease," *J Neuropsychiatry Clin Neurosci*, 2001, 13(2):304-5.

Serretti A, Lilli R, Mandelli L, et al, "Serotonin Transporter Gene Association With Lithium Prophylaxis in Mood Disorders," *Pharmacogenomics J*, 2001, 1:71-7.

Weickert TW, Goldberg TE, Mishara A, et al, "Catechol-O-Methyltransferase Val108/158Met Genotype Predicts Working Memory Response to Antipsychotic Medications," *Biol Psychiatry*, 2004, 56(9):677-82.

Zubieta JK, Heitzeg MM, Smith YR, et al, "COMT val158met Genotype Affects µ-Opioid Neurotransmitter Responses to a Pain Stressor," *Science*, 2003, 299(5610):1240-3.

♦ **COMT-L** *see* COMT *on page 244*

♦ **CPC8** *see* CYP2C8 *on page 248*

CYP1A2

Related Information

Cytochrome P450 Enzymes: Substrates, Inhibitors, and Inducers *on page 29*

Synonyms Cytochrome P450 Isoenzyme 1A2

Chromosome Location 15q22-qter

Clinically-Important Polymorphisms

C-A in first intron at position 734 (*C-C* genotype) has low potential for induction.

G-A in 5′ flanking region at -2964 associated with a significant decrease in CYP1A2 activity (identified in Japanese smokers).

Discussion CYP1A2 is an important drug-metabolizing enzyme. Decreases in activity may lead to significant changes in serum concentrations of individual drugs, which may lead to toxicity. Only a small number of substrates have been specifically studied; however, these results may generalize to other drugs which share this pathway, particularly when this pathway serves as the primary route of drug metabolism.

Clozapine:

Polymorphisms of 1A2 have been linked to clinically-relevant pharmacokinetic data with the antipsychotics. The levels of 1A2 have been found to be elevated in clozapine nonresponders (Bender and Eap 1998). Recently a C to A transversion in the first intron of CYP1A2 was found. This SNP is associated with variation in 1A2 inducibility due to cigarette smoke. The *A/A* genotype is more inducible than the *C/A* or *C/C* genotype (Sachse, 1999). This may have clinical implications for patients with schizophrenia who smoke. A G to A transversion in the 5′ flanking region of 1A2 at position -2964 has also been associated with decreased 1A2 activity in Japanese subjects (Nakajima, 1999). Other authors have examined these polymorphisms in relation to clozapine pharmacokinetics and unable to find a relationship (Masellis, 1998; van der Weide, 2003).

The role of the *C-A* polymorphism of CYP1A2 in interindividual variations in clozapine-induced weight gain was evaluated. Patients with the *C/C* genotype exhibited higher mean weight gain, but no strong association was observed (Basile, 2001).

Haloperidol:

No relationship between polymorphism and haloperidol or reduced haloperidol concentrations have been identified.

Polymorphisms of 1A2 at position 784 in the first intron has been associated with tardive dyskinesia. AIMS scores in subjects with a *C/C* genotype was 2.7- to 3.4-fold higher than those with a *C/A* or *A/A* genotype (Basile, 2000). In smokers, the AIMS scores were 5.4-fold to 4.7-fold greater with a *C/C* genotype compared to the other groups. However, others have failed to replicate these results (Schulze, 2001). Basile also examined the interaction between dopamine 3 receptors and CYP1A2 and the risk for tardive dyskinesia. Patients with both the *G/G* genotype at the dopamine 3 receptor and the *C/C* genotype at the CYP1A2 had the most severe tardive dyskinesia.

Olanzapine:

Other authors found no relationship between 1A2 and 2D6 phenotypes and olanzapine pharmacokinetics (Hagg, 2001).

Trazodone:

No association between phenotype and steady-state concentrations of trazodone and mCPP in both smokers and nonsmokers.

May Alter Pharmacokinetics of Caffeine, clomipramine, clozapine, cyclobenzaprine, doxepin, fluvoxamine, mirtazapine, pimozide, propranolol, ropinirole, tacrine, thiothixene, trifluoperazine, verapamil, other CYP1A substrates

Counseling Points CYP1A2 is involved in the metabolism of many psychiatric medications. Polymorphisms within 1A2 may result in lower plasma concentrations of these medications which may predispose patients to disease relapse. Patients who smoke may be at a higher risk for these changes in metabolism.

References

Basile VS, Masellis M, McIntyre RS, et al, "Genetic Dissection of Atypical Antipsychotic-Induced Weight Gain: Novel Preliminary Data on the Pharmacogenetic Puzzle," *J Clin Psychiatry*, 2001, 62(Suppl 23):45-66.

Basile VS, Ozdemir V, Masellis M, et al, "A Functional Polymorphism of the Cytochrome P450 1A2 (CYP1A2) Gene: Association With Tardive Dyskinesia in Schizophrenia," *Mol Psychiatry*, 2000, 5(4):410-7.

Bender S and Eap CB, "Very High Cytochrome P4501A2 Activity and Nonresponse to Clozapine," *Arch Gen Psychiatry*, 1998, 55(11):1048-50.

Hagg S, Spigset O, Lakso HA, et al, "Olanzapine Disposition in Humans Is Unrelated to CYP1A2 and CYP2D6 Phenotypes," *Eur J Clin Pharmacol*, 2001, 57(6-7):493-7.

Masellis M, Basile VS, Macciardi FM, et al, "Genetic Prediction of Antipsychotic Response Following Switch From Typical Antipsychotics to Clozapine," *XXIst*

(Continued)

CYP1A2 *(Continued)*

Collegium Internationale Neuro Psychopharmacologicum (CINP) Congress, Glasgow, Scotland, 1998.

Nakajima M, Yokoi T, Mizutani M, et al, "Genetic Polymorphism of the 5′-Flanking Region of the Human CYP1A2 Gene: Effect on the CYP1A2 Inducibility in Humans," *J Biochem (Tokyo)*, 1999, 125(4):803-8.

Sachse C, Brockmoller J, Bauer S, et al, "Functional Significance of a C-->A Polymorphism in Intron 1 of the Cytochrome P450 CYP1A2 Gene Tested With Caffeine," *Br J Clin Pharmacol*, 1999, 47(4):445-9.

Schulze TG, Schumacher J, Muller DJ, et al, "Lack of Association Between a Functional Polymorphism of the Cytochrome P450 1A2 (CYP1A2) Gene and Tardive Dyskinesia in Schizophrenia," *Am J Med Genet*, 2001, 105:498-501.

van der Weide J, Steijns LS, and van Weelden MJ, "The Effect of Smoking and Cytochrome P450 CYP1A2 Genetic Polymorphism on Clozapine Clearance and Dose Requirement," *Pharmacogenetics*, 2003, 13(3):169-72.

CYP2C8

Related Information

Cytochrome P450 Enzymes: Substrates, Inhibitors, and Inducers *on page 29*

Synonyms CPC8; P450 MP-12/MP-20

Chromosome Location 10q24.1

Clinically-Important Polymorphisms CYP2C8*3

Discussion CYP2C8 is an important drug-metabolizing enzyme. Decreases in activity may lead to significant changes in serum concentrations of individual drugs, which may lead to toxicity. Only a small number of substrates have been specifically studied; however, these results may generalize to other drugs which share this pathway, particularly when this pathway serves as the primary route of drug metabolism. A lower activity has been associated with the CYP2C8*3 variant of this enzyme.

Repaglinide:

The CYP2C8*3 allele (139Lys, 399Arg polymorphism) has been associated with reduced plasma concentrations of repaglinide. The authors note that this was not an expected result, since the CYP2C8 variant has been associated with reduced metabolism of other substrates. No significant differences in glucose response to repaglinide were associated with CYP2C8 genotype.

May Alter Pharmacodynamics of Repaglinide, other CYP2C8 substrates

References

Niemi M, Leathart JB, Neuvonen M, et al, "Polymorphisms in CYP2C8 Is Associated With Reduced Plasma Concentrations of Repaglinide," *Clin Pharmacol Ther*, 2003, 74(4):380-7.

CYP2C9

Related Information

Cytochrome P450 Enzymes: Substrates, Inhibitors, and Inducers *on page 29*

Synonyms Cytochrome P450 Isoenzyme 2C9

Chromosome Location 10q24

Clinically-Important Polymorphisms The three common allelic variants identified for the CYP2C9 gene are CYP2C9*1 (wild-type),

CYP2C9*2 and CYP2C9*3. The *2 allele is reported to occur with a frequency of 4% to 11% in African-Americans and Caucasians, respectively, while the *3 allele frequency is 2% to 7% respectively. These variants are associated with moderate to significant reductions in catabolic activity.

Discussion CYP2C9 is an important drug-metabolizing enzyme. Decreases in activity may lead to significant changes in serum concentrations of individual drugs, which may lead to toxicity. Only a small number of substrates have been specifically studied; however, these results may generalize to other drugs which share this pathway, particularly when this pathway serves as the primary route of drug metabolism.

Warfarin:

The S-isomer of warfarin, which has 5-fold greater anticoagulant activity than the R-isomer, is metabolized by the CYP2C9 enzyme (Hirsh, 2001). Several investigators have reported significantly lower warfarin clearance rates, lower warfarin dose requirements, more difficulty with warfarin initiation, and greater bleeding risk among CYP2C9*2 and CYP2C9*3 allele carriers compared to CYP2D9*1 homozygotes (Aithal, 1999; Steward, 1997; Higashi, 2002).

A retrospective study of 125 Italian patients evaluated the influence of CYP2C9 genotype on dose requirements of warfarin during the induction phase (first 24 days) of therapy (Peyvandi, 2004). INR values were monitored every 3-4 days to assess therapeutic response. Allelic frequencies of the variant CYP enzymes were 13% (*2) and 9% (*3) and comparable to previous reports. Patients with the *2 variant required average daily doses that were 17% lower than patients with the wild-type allele ($p<0.0001$) and exhibited a significantly higher frequency of exceeding an upper INR limit of 3 ($p=0.006$). Similarly, the *3 variant patients required significantly lower daily doses (40% on average, $p<0.0001$) and exceeded the INR limited twice as often as wild-type patients ($p=0.012$).

Angiotensin II type 1 receptor blockers:

Losartan is metabolized to its active metabolite E-3174 by CYP2C9. In healthy volunteers, plasma concentrations of E-3174 were significantly lower in those with the CYP2C9*1/*3 and *2/*3 genotypes compared to those with the CYP2C9*1/*1 and *1/*2 genotypes (Yasar, 2002).

CYP2C9 catalyzes the oxidation of irbesartan. In hypertensive subjects, treatment with irbesartan resulted in significantly greater reductions in diastolic blood pressure in patients with the CYP2C9*1/CYP2C9*2 genotype compared to patients with the CYP2C9*1/CYP2C9*1 genotype (Hallberg, 2002). One patient had the *1/*3 genotype and experienced excessive blood pressure reduction.

CYP2C9 catalyzes the metabolism of candesartan. A case report of an elderly Japanese man noted an increased AUC of candesartan relative to population averages in a patient with the CYP2C9*1/*3

(Continued)

CYP2C9 *(Continued)*

genotype. The patient developed sustained symptomatic hypotension following the initiation of candesartan therapy.

Phenytoin:

Phenytoin is a substrate for CYP2C9. The mean dose of phenytoin required to achieve therapeutic serum concentrations has been correlated to CYP2C9 genotype. Individuals carrying at least one variant CYP2C9 allele required a mean phenytoin dose, which was approximately 37% lower than the mean dose required in individuals with the wild-type allele. A maintenance dose <200 mg/day was required in 47% of variant carriers, while 58% of wild-type patients required a dose >300 mg/day (van der Weide, 2001).

Case reports of toxicity have been attributed to the CYP2C9 genotype, including a patient who was homozygous for the CYP2C9*3 allele (Brandolese, 2001). In addition, rare alleles may be responsible for idiosyncratic toxicity, as noted in a female African-American who presented with phenytoin toxicity and was later determined to carry a null allele (*6) of the CYP2C9 isoenzyme (Kidd, 2001).

In a regression analysis which included CYP2C9, 2C19 and MDR1 variant alleles, the number of variant CYP2C9 alleles was a major determinant of phenytoin plasma levels, and the number of variant MDR1 alleles further contributed to the prediction of phenytoin plasma levels. CYP2C19*2 did not appear to contribute to individual variability. In the regression equation, the number of variant CYP2C9 and MDR1 allels explained 15.4% of the variability of phenytoin plasma levels (Kerb, 2001).

Glyburide and glimepiride:

Glyburide and glimepiride are substrates for CYP2C9. Significant pharmacokinetic differences have been noted to be associated with CYP2C9 genotype. In subjects determined to be homozygous for the CYP2C9*3 allele, the median AUC of glyburide was 280% while that of glimepiride was 267% as compared to subjects with the CYP2C9*1/*1 genotype. However, responses to glyburide and glimepiride, as determined from blood glucose values, were not significantly affected by the CYP2C9 genotype (Niemi, 2002).

May Alter Pharmacokinetics of Angiotensin receptor antagonists, fluoxetine, fosphenytoin, phenytoin, warfarin, and other CYP2C9 substrates

Counseling Points Some patients with a polymorphism of CYP2C9 may require less drug for substrates of CYP2C9 to reach steady-state concentrations and may experience more side effects.

References

Aithal GP, Day CP, Kesteven PJ, et al, "Association of Polymorphisms in the Cytochrome P450 CYP2C9 With Warfarin Dose Requirement and Risk of Bleeding Complications," 1999, 353(9154):717-9.

Brandolese R, Scordo MG, Spina E, et al, "Severe Phenytoin Intoxication in a Subject Homozygous for CYP2C9*3," *Clin Pharmacol Ther*, 2001, 70(4):391-4.

Hallberg P, Karlsson J, Kurland L, et al, "The CYP2C9 Genotype Predicts the Blood Pressure Response to Irbesartan: Results From the Swedish Irbesartan Left Ventricular Hypertrophy Investigation vs Atenolol (SILVHIA) Trial," *J Hypertens*, 2002, 20(10):2089-93.

Higashi MK, Veenstra DL, Kondo LM, et al, "Association Between CYP2C9 Genetic Variants and Anticoagulation-Related Outcomes During Warfarin Therapy," *JAMA*, 2002, 287(13):1690-8.

Hirsh J, Dalen J, Anderson DR, et al, "Oral Anticoagulants: Mechanism of Action, Clinical Effectiveness, and Optimal Therapeutic Range," *Chest*, 2001, 119(1 Suppl):8S-21S.

Kerb R, Aynacioglu AS, Brockmoller J, et al, "The Predictive Value of MDR1, CYP2C9, and CYP2C19 Polymorphisms for Phenytoin Plasma Levels," *Pharmacogenomics J*, 2001, 1(3):204-10.

Kidd RS, Curry TB, Gallagher S, et al, "Identification of a Null Allele of CYP2C9 in an African-American Exhibiting Toxicity to Phenytoin," *Pharmacogenetics*, 2001, 11(9):803-8.

Kirchheiner J and Brockmoller J, "Clinical Consequences of Cytochrome P450 2C9 Polymorphisms," *Clin Pharmacol Ther*, 2005, 77(1):1-16.

Lee CR, Goldstein JA, and Pieper JA, "Cytochrome P450 2C9 Polymorphisms: A Comprehensive Review of the *in vitro* and Human Data," *Pharmacogenetics*, 2002, 12(3):251-63.

Niemi M, Cascorbi I, Timm R, et al, "Glyburide and Glimepiride Pharmacokinetics in Subjects With Different CYP2C9 Genotypes," *Clin Pharmacol Ther*, 2002, 72(3):326-32.

Peyvandi F, Spreafico M, Siboni SM, et al, "CYP2C9 Genotypes and Dose Requirements During the Induction Phase of Oral Anticoagulant Therapy," *Clin Pharmacol Ther*, 2004, 75(3):198-203.

Steward DJ, Haining RL, Henne KR, et al, "Genetic Association Between Sensitivity to Warfarin and Expression of CYP2C9*3," *Pharmacogenetics*, 1997, 7(5):361-7.

Uchida S, Watanabe H, Nishio S, et al, "Altered Pharmacokinetics and Excessive Hypotensive Effect of Candesartan in a Patient With the CYP2C9*1/*3 Genotype," *Clin Pharmacol Ther*, 2003, 74(5):505-8.

van der Weide J, Steijns LS, van Weelden MJ, et al, "The Effect of Genetic Polymorphism of Cytochrome P450 CYP2C9 on Phenytoin Dose Requirement," *Pharmacogenetics*, 2001, 11(4):287-91.

Yasar U, Forslund-Bergengren C, Tybring G, et al, "Pharmacokinetics of Losartan and Its Metabolite E-3174 in Relation to the CYP2C9 Genotype," *Clin Pharmacol Ther*, 2002, 71(1):89-98.

CYP2C19

Related Information

Cytochrome P450 Enzymes: Substrates, Inhibitors, and Inducers *on page 29*

Synonyms Cytochrome P450 Isoenzyme 2C19

Chromosome Location 10q24.1-q24.3

Clinically-Important Polymorphisms *2 through *8: inactive (in up to 20% of Asians [*2 and *3], 3% of Caucasians, 19% of African Americans, 8% of Africans, up to 71% of Pacific islanders)

Discussion CYP2C19 is an important drug-metabolizing enzyme. CYP2C19 genotypes correspond to the extensive metabolizer (2 wild-type alleles), intermediate metabolizer (1 wild-type and 1 variant allele), and poor metabolizer (2 variant alleles) phenotypes. Decreases in activity with the intermediate and poor metabolizer phenotypes may lead to significant changes in serum concentrations of individual drugs, which may lead to increased drug response and toxicity. Only a small number of substrates have been specifically studied; however, these results may generalize to other drugs which share this pathway,

(Continued)

CYP2C19 *(Continued)*

particularly when this pathway serves as the primary route of drug metabolism.

Lansoprazole:

Metabolism of proton pump inhibitors may influence their kinetics and efficacy. In a clinical evaluation, gastroesophageal reflux disease cure with lansoprazole was correlated to both the grade of disease prior to treatment and CYP2C19 genotype status. The cure rate in the homozygous extensive metabolizer phenotype was 46%, while the cure rate in patients with the poor metabolizer phenotype was 85% (Furuta, 2002).

Schwab et al, prospectively evaluated a cohort of 131 German patients treated for *H. pylori* using quadruple therapy (lansoprazole + amoxicillin + clarithromycin + metronidazole). Eradication rate was analyzed in comparison with lansoprazole steady-state serum levels and CYP2C19 genotype. Genotype distribution was as follows: *CYP2C19*1/*1* (65.6%), *CYP2C19*1/*2* (32.1%), and *CYP2C19*2/*2* (2.3%). There was a significant gene-dose response relationship with increasing eradication rate as a function of reduced CYP enzyme function. Patients homozygous for the variant gene experienced 100% eradication as compared to heterozygous (97.8%) and wild-type patients (80.2%) ($p < 0.01$). Serum lansoprazole levels also followed a similar rank order, with significantly higher median levels seen in the homozygous variant patients (753 ng/mL) compared to heterozygous (59 ng/mL) and wild-type patients (21 ng/mL) ($p < 0.001$).

These data are consistent with previous studies showing that pharmacogenetic variation of CYP metabolism influences clinical response (Furuta, 2002; Furuta, 2001; Sapone, 2003). This would be expected given that reduced metabolism of proton pump inhibitors would increase the AUC of these agents, and in agreement with the observation that enhanced acid suppression improves antibiotic efficacy and aids in ulcer healing (Klotz, 2000). However, it should be noted that there were potentially confounding variables not adequately addressed in this study. Though not analyzed statistically, a marked difference was observed in the percentage of wild-type patients compared to carriers of the variant gene exhibiting resistance to metronidazole (38.5% vs 20%) and clarithromycin (7.7% vs 0%). As there were no differences in the serum levels of these agents, the impact of antimicrobial resistance should be considered as a factor in the outcome.

Omeprazole:

Cure rates for *H. pylori* infection with dual (omeprazole/amoxicillin) and triple (omeprazole/amoxicillin/clarithromycin) therapy were dependent on CYP2C19 genotype (and also bacterial sensitivity to clarithromycin with triple therapy). Greater eradication rates occurred with the poor and intermediate metabolizer phenotypes compared to the extensive metabolizer phenotype. (Furuta, 1998; Furata, 2001).

The development of low vitamin B_{12} serum concentrations in association with long-term omeprazole may be dependent on CYP2C19 genotype. Patients with mutations in the *CYP2C19* gene were noted to have lower serum concentrations as compared to individuals with the wild-type genotype. These differences were only apparent after long-term treatment (Sagar, 1999).

CYP2C19 genotype has been correlated to markers of adverse effects with long-term omeprazole therapy. Levels of chromogranin A, which is a marker for hyperplasia of enterochromaffin-like cells, increased significantly in intermediate metabolizers, but not extensive metabolizers following omeprazole treatment for 1 year. Serum pepsinogen I, which is a marker of gastric atrophy, decreased significantly in intermediate, compared to extensive metabolizers after omeprazole therapy for 1 year (Sagar, 2000).

Rabeprazole:

Cure rates for *H. pylori* infection by dual therapy (rabeprazole/amoxicillin) were dependent on CYP2C19 genotype. Dual therapy was apparently effective for heterozygous extensive metabolizer and poor metabolizer genotypes. However, efficacy could be improved for patients with homozygous extensive metabolizer genotypes through the use of high-dose dual therapy. The authors proposed that genotyping could be a useful tool to aid in the optimal dual treatment with these agents (Furuta, 2001).

Phenytoin:

In a regression analysis which included CYP2C9, 2C19, and MDR1 gene polymorphisms, the number of variant CYP2C9 alleles was a major determinant, and the number of MDR1*T alleles further contributed to the prediction of phenytoin plasma levels. CYP2C19*2 did not appear to contribute to individual variability. The regression equation explained 15.4% of the variability of phenytoin data (Kerb, 2001).

SSRI:

A case of serotonin syndrome associated with tramadol and citalopram highlights the clinical importance of combined heterozygous genotypes of CYP2D6 and CYP2C19 (Mahlberg, 2004).

Tacrolimus:

The pharmacokinetics of tacrolimus was altered when lansoprazole was added to therapy in patients with either the *CYP2C19*1/*2* or *CYP2C19*2/*3* genotype. The lower activity of CYP2C19 associated with these mutations resulted in a greater dependence on CYP3A4 metabolism, indirectly leading to increased inhibition of tacrolimus metabolism. This unusual 'chain-reaction' effect serves as an example of the complexity of evaluating drug interaction mechanisms, as well as the genetic influences on drug metabolism/interactions (Itagaki, 2003; Takahashi, 2004).

May Alter Pharmacokinetics of Proton pump inhibitors, citalopram, clomipramine, diazepam, escitalopram, fosphenytoin, imipramine, mephenytoin, mephobarbital, methsuximide, moclobemide, phenobarbital, phenytoin, propranolol, sertraline, trimipramine, other CYP2C19 substrates

(Continued)

CYP2C19 *(Continued)*

Laboratory Evaluation Commercial testing available

Clinical Recommendations Genotyping for common CYP2C19 polymorphisms may be useful to optimize therapy with proton pump inhibitors for reflux disease and *H. pylori* infection.

References

Furuta T, Ohashi K, Kamata T, et al, "Effect of Genetic Differences in Omeprazole Metabolism on Cure Rates for *Helicobacter pylori* Infection and Peptic Ulcer," *Ann Intern Med*, 1998, 129(12):1027-30.

Furuta T, Shirai N, Takashima M, et al, "Effect of Genotypic Differences in CYP2C19 on Cure Rates for *Helicobacter pylori* Infection by Triple Therapy With a Proton Pump Inhibitor, Amoxicillin, and Clarithromycin," *Clin Pharmacol Ther*, 2001, 69(3):158-68.

Furuta T, Shirai N, Takashima M, et al, "Effects of Genotypic Differences in CYP2C19 Status on Cure Rates for *Helicobacter pylori* Infection by Dual Therapy With Rabeprazole Plus Amoxicillin," *Pharmacogenetics*, 2001, 11(4):341-8.

Furuta T, Shirai N, Watanabe F, et al, "Effect of Cytochrome P4502C19 Genotypic Differences on Cure Rates for Gastroesophageal Reflux Disease by Lansoprazole," *Clin Pharmacol Ther*, 2002, 72(4):453-60.

Itagaki F, Homma M, Yuzawa K, et al, "Drug Interaction of Tacrolimus and Proton Pump Inhibitors in Renal Transplant Recipients With CYP2C19 Gene Mutation," *Transplant Proc*, 2003, 34(7):2777-8.

Kerb R, Aynacioglu AS, Brockmoller J, et al, "The Predictive Value of MDR1, CYP2C9, and CYP2C19 Polymorphisms for Phenytoin Plasma Levels," *Pharmacogenomics J*, 2001, 1(3):204-10.

Klotz U, "Pharmacokinetic Considerations in the Eradication of *Helicobacter pylori*," *Clin Pharmacokinet*, 2000, 38(3):243-70.

Mahlberg R, Kunz D, Sasse J, et al, "Serotonin Syndrome With Tramadol and Citalopram," *Am J Psychiatry*, 2004, 161(6):1129.

Sagar M, Bertilsson L, Stridsberg M, et al, "Omeprazole and CYP2C19 Polymorphism: Effects of Long-Term Treatment on Gastrin, Pepsinogen I, and Chromogranin A in Patients With Acid Related Disorders," *Aliment Pharmacol Ther*, 2000, 14(11):1495-502.

Sagar M, Janczewska I, Ljungdahl A, et al, "Effect of CYP2C19 Polymorphism on Serum Levels of Vitamin B12 in Patients on Long-Term Omeprazole Treatment," *Aliment Pharmacol Ther*, 1999, 13(4):453-8.

Sapone A, Vaira D, Trespidi S, et al, "The Clinical Role of Cytochrome P450 Genotypes in *Helicobacter pylori* Management," *Am J Gastroenterol*, 2003, 98(5):1010-5.

Takahashi K, Motohashi H, Yonezawa A, et al, "Lansoprazole-Tacrolimus Interaction in Japanese Transplant Recipient With CYP2C19 Polymorphism," *Ann Pharmacother*, 2004, 38(5):791-4.

CYP2D6

Related Information

Cytochrome P450 Enzymes: Substrates, Inhibitors, and Inducers *on page 29*

Synonyms Cytochrome P450 Isoenzyme 2D6

Chromosome Location 22q13.1

Clinically-Important Polymorphisms

Increased activity: CYP2D6*2

Diminished activity: CYP2D6*10, CYP2D6*17

Diminished/absent activity: CYP2D6*3, CYP2D6*4, CYP2D6*5

Absent activity: CYP2D6*6, CYP2D6*7, CYP2D6*8

Discussion CYP2D6 is an important drug-metabolizing enzyme. Decreases in or loss of activity may lead to significant changes in serum concentrations of individual drugs, which may lead to toxicity. Only a small number of substrates have been specifically studied;

however, these results may generalize to other drugs which share this pathway, particularly when this pathway serves as the primary route of drug metabolism.

Significant variation in CYP2D6 activity has been associated with key polymorphisms, and these variations occur with different frequencies among populations. In Americans and Europeans, between 1% and 5% of individuals carry two or more copies of the variant *CYP2D6*2* allele which confers the ultrarapid metabolizer phenotype for CYP2D6 substrates (Agundez, 1995; Dahl, 1995).

Several genotypes are associated with diminished or absent CYP2D6 activity. The variant *CYP2D6*10* allele, with a frequency of about 50% in Asians (Ingelman-Sundberg, 1999), and the variant *CYP2D6*17* allele, with a frequency of about 34% in black Africans (Masimirembwa, 1996), are associated with reduced CYP2D6 activity. *CYP2D6* alleles associated with an absence of CYP2D6 activity include *CYP2D6*3*, *CYP2D6*4*, *CYP2D6*5*, *CYP2D6*6*, *CYP2D6*7*, and *CYP2D6*8*. Two alleles associated with an absence of activity are found in approximately 7% of Caucasians, but fewer than 3% of black Africans and 1% of Asians. Low activity may lead to a reduced formation of an active metabolite (and a loss of drug effect), or reduced capacity for metabolism/detoxification leading to toxicity (Chou, 2000) from normal dosages of a drug metabolized by this pathway.

Antidepressants:

The CYP2D6 genotype was associated with adverse effects and clinical nonresponse in patients treated with CYP2D6 dependent tricyclic antidepressants (Rau, 2004). In poor metabolizers, the mean half-life of desipramine was 125 hours, while the mean half-life in extensive metabolizers was 22 hours.

Antipsychotics:

The poor metabolizer genotype may be a predisposing factor for antipsychotic-induced extrapyramidal side effects. This may be useful to know prior to initiating antipsychotic treatment (Scordo, 2000).

Atomoxetine:

Disposition and metabolism was characterized in a small group of patients based on CYP2D6 metabolizer status (Sauer, 2003). Patients were evaluated for the poor metabolizer (PM) genotype (homozygosity for alleles *3, *4, *5, *6, *7, or *8) or the extensive metabolizer (EM) genotype under a condition of steady-state dosing. Although the range of metabolites was similar between the two groups, patients of PM status exhibited a nearly 3- and 4-fold increased mean half-life for atomoxetine and it's primary glucuronide metabolite compared to EM status. Similarly, the AUC for all radiolabeled-equivalent metabolites was over 4-fold higher in the PM group.

Clozapine:

CYP2D6 has been implicated in the metabolism of clozapine, but no relationship has been found (Arranz, 1995).

(Continued)

CYP2D6 *(Continued)*

Codeine:

Conversion to morphine is mediated by CYP2D6. Deficient activity of this isoenzyme may be associated with decreased effectiveness of codeine. Conversely, the ultrarapid metabolizer status conferred by gene duplication may result in extensive conversion to morphine and thus increased opioid-mediated effects.

A study by Williams et al, sought to evaluate the analgesic response and plasma morphine level relative to genotype following codeine or morphine administration in pediatric patients undergoing routine adenotonsillectomy. Patients were genotyped into four phenotypic categories based on metabolic status: poor, intermediate/poor, intermediate, or extensive. Patients received either IM codeine (1.5 mg/kg, n=48) or morphine (0.15 mg/kg, n=48) during anesthesia, followed by discretionary IV/PO morphine postoperatively. Time to postoperative pain medication supplementation and morphine blood levels were evaluated relative to metabolizer status. In children receiving codeine who exhibited reduced enzyme activity (poor/intermediate metabolizer status), morphine levels were significantly lower compared to extensive metabolizers ($p<0.02$). Although the codeine-receiving group experienced a significantly greater demand for supplemental analgesia postoperatively, this effect was not associated with any phenotype, and did not correlate with plasma morphine levels.

Another report describes a patient who developed acute opioid intoxication following a relatively low dosing regimen of oral codeine (Gasche, 2004). The elderly patient presented with bilateral pneumonia and was initiated on codeine 25 mg three times daily for cough suppression, as well as clarithromycin and voriconazole. Within days of treatment, the patient became unresponsive (Glasgow score = 6) and exhibited hypoxia associated with respiratory depression, but subsequently recovered with naloxone treatment. At the time of coma, the patient's plasma codeine and morphine levels were 114 mcg/L and 80 mcg/L, respectively, with significant elevation of glucuronide conjugates. Evaluation of CYP3A4 via standard dextromethorphan metabolism assay showed a reduction in activity as evidenced by a lower presence of the N-demethylated metabolite. Further, CYP2D6 isozyme activity analysis revealed a dextromethorphan/dextrorphan ratio of 0.0005, consistent with the ultrarapid metabolizer status. This finding was supported by genotyping analysis which showed the presence of 3 or more functional alleles of CYP2D6. Clearly, the patient's adverse response was due to acute opioid toxicity given that the blood morphine level was 20- to 80-fold higher than that expected in healthy individuals of normal metabolic activity. Taken together, these data suggest that significant codeine toxicity can be elicited in patients with increased 2D6 activity, particularly in the presence of reduced 3A4 activity.

Haloperidol:

CYP2D6 has been shown to have a relationship with the development of tardive dyskinesia (Ellingrod, 2002) and pseudoparkinsonism (Brockmoller, 2002), although other investigators have not found a relationship between 2D6 poor metabolizers and the occurrence of tardive dyskinesia (Arthur, 1995; Armstrong, 1997; Andreasen, 1997; Basile, 2000; Ohmori, 1999). Patients heterozygous for the CYP2D6*3 or *4 alleles who smoke cigarettes may have the highest risk for the development of abnormal movements and tardive dyskinesia compared to those homozygous for the *1 allele or nonsmokers (20% vs 78%) (Ellingrod, 2002). These subjects may shunt antipsychotic metabolism through other pathways induced by cigarette smoke. This induction may result in formation of neurotoxic metabolites leading to increased AIMS scores and a higher incidence of tardive dyskinesia, compared to subjects without these alleles.

Metoprolol:

In Chinese subjects, the *CYP2D6*10A* allele was associated with higher metoprolol plasma concentrations and lower urinary metoprolol metabolite levels compared to the *CYP2D6*1* allele (Huang, 1999). Similarly, *CYP2D6* genotype correlated with metoprolol AUC, oral clearance, and S-/R-enantiomeric ratios in patients with hypertension and heart failure. However, *CYP2D6* genotype did not correlate with metoprolol-induced adverse effects, antihypertensive activity, or cardiac decompensation in heart failure (Zineh, 2004; Terra, 2005).

Olanzapine:

No relationship between *CYP1A2* and *CYP2D6* phenotypes and olanzapine pharmacokinetics has been found (Hagg, 2001).

A relationship between polymorphism of *2D6* and weight gain from olanzapine has been found. Subjects with a heterozygous **1/*3, *4 2D6* genotype experienced a statistically significantly larger percentage change in BMI than the homozygous **1/*1* group (128% vs 112%) (Ellingrod, 2002). Thus, polymorphisms of CYP isoenzymes may be the trigger needed for excessive weight gain and other morbidity associated with olanzapine and other AAPs.

Risperidone:

The poor metabolizer phenotype for 2D6 may be clinically important for patients treated with risperidone (Kohnke, 2002). Poor metabolizers may not tolerate risperidone well (Bork, 1999). The CYP2D6 poor metabolizer phenotype was associated with risperidone related adverse drug reactions (odds ratio (OR) corrected for clinical variables 3.4 (1.5-8.0)) and discontinuation due to adverse drug reactions (corrected OR 6.0 (1.4-25.4)) (de Leon, 2005).

Serotonin 5-HT$_3$ receptor antagonists:

Genotypic variation may influence the efficacy of serotonin antagonists in the treatment of chemotherapy-induced nausea and vomiting. Variation in 2D6 metabolism has been previously correlated to a lack of response to tropisetron and ondansetron. In a prospective study of 270 cancer patients receiving moderately to

(Continued)

CYP2D6 *(Continued)*

highly emetogenic chemotherapy, patients were stratified by the extent of CYP2D6-mediated metabolism (Kaiser, 2002). In this study, 7.8% of patients were categorized as "poor" metabolizers (PM), 33% were intermediate metabolizers (IM), 58% were extensive metabolizers (EM), and 1.5% were considered "ultraextensive" metabolizers (UM). Patients exhibiting the PM phenotype showed significantly higher plasma concentrations of tropisetron 6 hours postdosing compared to all other phenotypes. Up to 24 hours postchemotherapy, UM patients suffered significantly more episodes of vomiting compared to PM, IM, or EM patients. Given that patients of an "intermediate" status (ie, IM or EM) showed a significantly lower blood level of the 5-HT_3 antagonist (compared to PM), one could have predicted a correspondingly increased number of vomiting episodes. This did not appear to be the case; although, these intergroup comparisons were not statistically evaluated. One can conclude that direct comparisons between PM and UM patients revealed a significant phenotype-response effect. Results with ondansetron trended in a similar fashion, but were not statistically significant.

A study by Candiotti et al, evaluated genotype vs response in 250 women receiving prophylactic ondansetron (4 mg) 30 minutes prior to extubation. Ultrarapid metabolizers were defined as those patients with ≥3 copies of functional CYP2D6 alleles. Five of eleven of these patients (45%) experienced vomiting compared to 1 or 12 patients (8%) of the poor metabolizer status (p<0.01). There was no difference between the groups in terms of incidence of nausea.

SSRIs:

Case reports of toxicity and death have been attributed to CYP2D6 mutations (Sallee, 2000). Case reports of diminished response were retrospectively attributed to a duplication of the gene encoding 2D6. Most SSRIs are inhibitors of CYP2D6 and may cause toxic concentrations of tricyclic antidepressants when used in combination. No effect on medication-related adverse reactions were found in 122 geriatric patients with major depression treated with paroxetine (Murphy, 2003). However, CYP2D6 poor metabolizers treated with paroxetine had a significantly higher incidence of sexual dysfunction compared to those who were not poor metabolizers (Zourkova, 2002). A case of serotonin syndrome associated with tramadol and citalopram highlights the clinical importance of combined heterozygeous genotypes of CYP2D6 and CYP2C19 (Mahlberg, 2004).

May Alter Pharmacokinetics of CYP2D6 substrates

Atomoxetine, carvedilol, codeine, desipramine, flecainide, haloperidol, metoprolol, mexiletine, ondansetron, propafenone, propranolol, risperidone, timolol, tricyclic antidepressants

May Alter Pharmacodynamics of Codeine, haloperidol, olanzapine, risperidone, SSRIs

Laboratory Evaluation Commercial testing available

References

Agundez JA, Ledesma MC, Ladero JM, et al, "Prevalence of CYP2D6 Gene Duplication and Its Repercussion on the Oxidative Phenotype in a White Population," *Clin Pharmacol Ther*, 1995, 57(3):265-9.

Andreassen OA, MacEwan T, Gulbandsen AK, et al, "Nonfunctional CYP2D6 Alleles and Risk for Neuroleptic-Induced Movement Disorders in Schizophrenic Patients," *Psychopharmacology (Berl)*, 1997, 131(2):174-9.

Armstrong M, Daly AK, Blennerhassett R, et al, "Antipsychotic Drug-Induced Movement Disorders in Schizophrenics in Relation to CYP2D6 Genotype," *Br J Psychiatry*, 1997, 170:23-6.

Arranz MJ, Dawson E, Shaikh S, et al, "Cytochrome P4502D6 Genotype Does Not Determine Response to Clozapine," *Br J Clin Pharmacol*, 1995, 39(4):417-20.

Arthur H, Dahl ML, Siwers B, et al, "Polymorphic Drug Metabolism in Schizophrenic Patients With Tardive Dyskinesia," *J Clin Psychopharmacol*, 1995, 15(3):211-6.

Basile VS, Ozdemir V, Masellis M, et al, "A Functional Polymorphism of the Cytochrome P450 1A2 (CYP1A2) Gene: Association With Tardive Dyskinesia in Schizophrenia," *Mol Psychiatry*, 2000, 5(4):410-7.

Bork JA, Rogers T, Wedlund PJ, et al, "A Pilot Study on Risperidone Metabolism: The Role of Cytochromes P450 2D6 and 3A," *J Clin Psychiatry*, 1999, 60(7):469-76.

Brockmoller J, Kirchheiner J, Schmider J, et al, "The Impact of the CYP2D6 Polymorphism on Haloperidol Pharmacokinetics and on the Outcome of Haloperidol Treatment," *Clin Pharmacol Ther*, 2002, 72(4):438-52.

Candiotti KA, Birnbach DJ, Lubarsky DA, et al, "The Impact of Pharmacogenomics on Postoperative Nausea and Vomiting: Do CYP2D6 Allele Copy Number and Polymorphisms Affect the Success or Failure of Ondansetron Prophylaxis?" *Anesthesiology*, 2005, 102(3):543-9.

Chou WH, Yan FX, de Leon J, et al, "Extension of a Pilot Study: Impact From the Cytochrome P450 2D6 Polymorphism on Outcome and Costs Associated With Severe Mental Illness," *J Clin Psychopharmacol*, 2000, 20(2):246-51.

Dahl ML, Johansson I, Bertilsson L, et al, "Ultrarapid Hydroxylation of Debrisoquine in a Swedish Population. Analysis of the Molecular Genetic Basis," *J Pharmacol Exp Ther*, 1995, 274(1):516-20.

de Leon J, Susce MT, Pan RM, et al, "The CYP2D6 Poor Metabolizer Phenotype May Be Associated With Risperidone Adverse Drug Reactions and Discontinuation," *J Clin Psychiatry*, 2005, 66(1):15-27.

Ellingrod VL, Miller D, Schultz SK, et al, "CYP2D6 Polymorphisms and Atypical Antipsychotic Weight Gain," *Psychiatr Genet*, 2002, 12(1):55-8.

Ellingrod VL, Schultz SK, and Arndt S, "Abnormal Movements and Tardive Dyskinesia in Smokers and Nonsmokers With Schizophrenia Genotyped for Cytochrome P450 2D6," *Pharmacotherapy*, 2002, 22(11):1416-9.

Gasche Y, Daali Y, Fathi M et al, "Codeine Intoxication Associated With Ultrarapid CYP2D6 Metabolism," *New Engl J Med*, 2004, 351(27):2827-31.

Hagg S, Spigset O, Lakso HA, et al, "Olanzapine Disposition in Humans in Unrelated to CYP1A2 and CYP2D6 Phenotypes," *Eur J Clin Pharmacol*, 2001, 57(6-7):493-7.

Huang J, Chuang SK, Cheng CL, et al, "Pharmacokinetics of Metoprolol Enantiomers in Chinese Subjects of Major CYP2D6 Genotypes," *Clin Pharmacol Ther*, 1999, 65(4):402-7.

Ingelman-Sundberg M, Oscarson M, and McLellan RA, "Polymorphic Human Cytochrome P450 Enzymes: An Opportunity for Individualized Drug Treatment," *Trends Pharmacol Sci*, 1999, 20(8):342-9.

Kaiser R, Sezer O, Papies A, et al, "Patient-Tailored Antiemetic Treatment With 5-Hydroxytryptamine Type-3 Receptor Antagonists According to Cytochrome P-450 2D6 Genotypes," *J Clin Oncol*, 2002, 20(12):2805-11.

Kohnke MD, Griese EU, Stosser D, et al, "Cytochrome P450 2D6 Deficiency and Its Clinical Relevance in a Patient Treated With Risperidone," *Pharmacopsychiatry*, 2002, 35(3):116-8.

Mahlberg R, Kunz D, Sasse J, et al, "Serotonin Syndrome With Tramadol and Citalopram," *Am J Psychiatry*, 2004, 161(6):1129.

Masimirembwa C, Persson I, Bertilsson L, et al, "A Novel Mutant Variant of the CYP2D6 Gene (CYP2D6*17) Common in a Black African Population: Association With Diminished Debrisoquine Hydroxylase Activity," *Br J Clin Pharmacol*, 1996, 42(6):713-9.

(Continued)

CYP2D6 *(Continued)*

Murphy GM, Kremer C, Rodrigues HE, et al, "Pharmacogenetics of Antidepressant Medication Intolerance," *Am J Psychiatry*, 2003, 160(10):1830-5.

Ohmori O, Kojima H, Shinkai T, et al, "Genetic Association Analysis Between CYP2D6*2 Allele and Tardive Dyskinesia in Schizophrenic Patients," *Psychiatry Res*, 1999, 87(2-3):239-44.

Rau T, Wohlleben G, Wuttke H, et al, "CYP2D6 Genotype: Impact on Adverse Effects and Nonresponse During Treatment With Antidepressants-A Pilot Study," *Clin Pharmacol Ther*, 2004, 75(5):386-93.

Sallee FR, DeVane CL, Ferrell RE, et al, "Fluoxetine-Related Death in a Child With Cytochrome P450 2D6 Genetic Deficiency," *J Child Adolesc Psychopharmacol*, 2000, 10(1):27-34.

Sauer JM, Ponsler GD, Mattiuz EL, et al, "Disposition and Metabolic Fate of Atomoxetine Hydrochloride: The Role of CYP2D6 in Human Disposition and Metabolism," *Drug Metab Dispos*, 2003, 31(1):98-107.

Scordo MG, Spina E, Romeo P, et al, "CYP2D6 Genotype and Antipsychotic-Induced Extrapyramidal Side Effects in Schizophrenic Patients," *Eur J Clin Pharmacol*, 2000, 56(9-10):679-83.

Terra SG, Pauly DF, Lee CR, et al, "β-Adrenergic Receptor Polymorphisms and Responses During Titration of Metoprolol Controlled Release/Extended Release in Heart Failure," *Clin Pharmacol Ther*, 2005, 77(3):127-37.

Williams DG, Patel A, and Howard RF, "Pharmacogenetics of Codeine Metabolism in an Urban Population of Children and its Implications for Analgesic Reliability," *Br J Anaesth*, 2002, 89(6):839-45.

Zineh I, Beitelshees AL, Gaedigk A, et al, "Pharmacokinetics and CYP2D6 Genotypes do not Predict Metoprolol Adverse Events or Efficacy in Hypertension," *Clin Pharmacol Ther*, 2004, 76(6):536-44.

Zourkova A and Hadasova E, "Relationship Between CYP 2D6 Metabolic Status and Sexual Dysfunction in Paroxetine Treatment," *J Sex Marital Ther*, 2002, 28(5):451-61.

CYP3A4

Related Information

Cytochrome P450 Enzymes: Substrates, Inhibitors, and Inducers *on page 29*

Chromosome Location 7q21.1

Clinically-Important Polymorphisms A number of polymorphisms have been identified. CYP3A4*1 represents the wild type. CYP3A4*3 has been referred to as CYP3A4-V (variant).

A number of other SNPs which produce coding changes have been identified. *In vitro*, CYP3A4*17 demonstrates a lower turnover for probe substrates, while CYP3A4*18 demonstrates a higher turnover rate. Other SNPs which produce coding changes include CYP3A4*3, CYP3A4*15, and CYP3A4*19. A large number of other variants have been described, including CYP3A4*1B, CYP3A4*2, CYP3A4*4, CYP3A4*5, CYP3A4*6, CYP3A4*8, CYP3A4*11, CYP3A4*12, and CYP3A4*13, CYP3A5*3.

Racial variability in the frequency of individual SNPs has been identified. In one series, CYP3A*15 was identified only in Black populations with an allelic frequency of 4%. CYP3A4*17 and CYP3A4*3 were identified in Caucasians with allelic frequencies 2% and 4%, respectively. CYP3A4*18 and CYP3A4*19 were only observed in Asians at allelic frequencies of 2% (Dai, 2001).

Discussion The expression of CYP3A4 varies 40-fold in individual human livers, and metabolism of CYP3A4 substrates varies at least 10-fold *in vivo*. The CYP3A family is encoded by 4 separate genes and

2 pseudogenes. Many studies have not been able to establish a predictive value to a known genotype. Conclusive correlations between individual polymorphisms have not been limited to date.

Although the genetic component of the interindividual variability of CYP3A4 enzyme activity seems to be high, a key role for the variant alleles has not been able to be identified in patients low CYP3A4 activity. Unknown mutations that affect CYP3A4 or other functionally-related genes may be associated with low CYP3A4 activity (Garcia-Martin, 2002).

Cyclophosphamide:

Cyclophosphamide requires activation by CYP3A3/4 to its active form. A variant allele has been described which occurs in 45% of African Americans and only 9% of Caucasians. This variant has been associated with a decrease in the activation of cyclophosphamide, potentially resulting in diminished efficacy. In addition, variability in metabolism of substrates may lead to enhanced toxicity. Decreased survival has been associated with the variant allele (Petros, 2002).

Midazolam:

The variability in intestinal and hepatic CYP3A activity using midazolam as an *in vivo* probe is modest, and common polymorphisms in CYP3A4 and CYP3A5 do not appear to have important functional significance (Floyd, 2003).

May Alter Pharmacokinetics of Cyclophosphamide, other CYP3A4 substrates

May Alter Pharmacodynamics of Cyclophosphamide, other CYP3A4 substrates

Laboratory Evaluation Commercial testing available

References

Dai D, Tang J, Rose R, et al, "Identification of Variants of CYP3A4 and Characterization of Their Abilities to Metabolize Testosterone and Chlorpyrifos," *J Pharmacol Exp Ther*, 2001, 299(3):825-31.

Floyd MD, Gervasini G, Masica AL, et al, "Genotype-Phenotype Associations for Common CYP3A4 and CYP3A5 Variants in the Basal and Induced Metabolism of Midazolam in European- and African-American Men and Women," *Pharmacogenetics*, 2003, 13(10):595-606.

Garcia-Martin E, Martinez C, Pizarro RM, et al, "CYP3A4 Variant Alleles in White Individuals With Low CYP3A4 Enzyme Activity," *Clin Pharmacol Ther*, 2002, 71(3):196-204.

Petros W, Hopkins P, Vredenburgh J, et al, "Associations Between Variants in Several Drug Metabolism Genes and Chemotherapy Pharmacokinetics or Clinical Response," Proc Am Assoc Cancer Res, 2001, 42:1435.

CYP3A5

Related Information

Cytochrome P450 Enzymes: Substrates, Inhibitors, and Inducers *on page 29*

Chromosome Location 7q21.1

Clinically-Important Polymorphisms A common polymorphism exists in the noncoding region intron 3 (A6986G) leading to a truncated splice variant and nonfunctional protein. Of the population expressing the 3A5 isozyme, the variant CYP3A5*3 allele has been reported to (Continued)

CYP3A5 *(Continued)*

exist in 27-50% of African Americans, 85-95% of white Caucasians, and 60-73% of Asians (Hustert, 2001).

Discussion The importance of the CYP3A superfamily of metabolic enzymes is apparent given they account for nearly 50% of the hepatic cytochrome P-450 content. To date, most of the interest has focused on the most abundant and well-characterized member, CYP3A4. However, some reports suggest that a lesser known isoform, CYP3A5 may account for nearly 50% of the hepatic CYP3A enzymes in Caucasians and African-Americans who express the 3A5 isoform (Williams, 2002). Studies to date have often not distinguished between substrate affinities for the 3A4 vs 3A5 enzymes, frequently grouping them together as a CYP3A4/5 designation. However, the recognition of certain individuals possessing significantly higher 3A5 content suggests a potentially larger metabolic role for this enzyme.

Cyclosporine:

Haufroid et al, showed a 1.6-fold increase in cyclosporine dose-adjusted trough levels in renal transplant patients exhibiting the **3/*3* variant compared to wild-type carriers. These data are supported by Min et al, who showed that mean AUC values (ng*h/mL) for cyclosporine-receiving healthy volunteers were significantly different between the homozygous wild-type group (4962 ± 1074, n=6) and the homozygous variant group (6677 ± 1153, n =6; *p*=0.04). However, Hesselink found no association between cyclosporine dose-adjust trough levels and CYP3A5 genotype dosing in 50 stable renal transplant patients receiving cyclosporine.

Tacrolimus:

Several studies have been conducted to evaluate the influence of *CYP3A5* genotype and tacrolimus dosing. Haufroid et al studied 50 stable renal transplant patients. Dose-adjusted trough levels were 3- and nearly 6-fold higher in patients homozygous for the *CYP3A5*3/*3* variant relative to heterozygotes and homozygous wild-type, respectively. Regression analysis indicated that presence of the variant allele accounted for approximately 45% of the interindividual dosing variability.

A similar study by Tsuchiya et al, evaluated 30 renal transplant patients 28 days post-transplantation. Compared to wild-type carriers, *CYP3A5*3/*3* patients exhibited statistically significant lower dose per body weight requirements and increased dose-adjusted trough levels and AUC.

In a study of 83 adult lung transplant recipients, the 12 hour post-dose ratio of tacrolimus trough blood level normalized to daily dose was compared with genotype at 1, 3, 6, 9 and 12 months post-transplant. Compared to wild-type carriers (ie, **1/*1* and **1/*3* combined), homozygous variant patients demonstrated statistically significantly elevated ratios at each time point, ranging from 2-fold at 1 month to over 8-fold at 1 year (Zheng, 2004).

In a study of 110 renal transplant patients, Hesselink et al determined that dose-adjusted tacrolimus trough levels were significantly higher in *CYP3A5*3/*3* patients (94 ng/mL, n=45) versus wild-type carriers (61 ng/mL, n=17) ($p<0.0001$).

Of the studies discussed above, only Hesselink et al evaluated *CYP3A4* genotype in parallel, finding a lower tacrolimus dose requirement associated with the wild-type 3A4 allele. Interestingly, they observed a significant co-association of the wild-type *3A4*1* and *3A5*3/*3* alleles (80% of study population were homozygous for both alleles), both genotypes associated with lower tacrolimus dose requirements. However, the study did not normalize dose as a function of enzyme content or maximal activity. Thus, the significance of relative contributions of each enzyme to the overall metabolism of tacrolimus remains unclear.

May Alter Pharmacokinetics of Tacrolimus, cyclosporine, other CYP3A5 substrates

May Alter Pharmacodynamics of Tacrolimus, cyclosporine, other CYP3A5 substrates

References

Haufroid V, Mourad M, Van Kerckhove V, et al, "The Effect of CYP3A5 and MDR1 (ABCB1) Polymorphisms on Cyclosporine and Tacrolimus Dose Requirements and Trough Blood Levels in Stable Renal Transplant Patients," *Pharmacogenetics*, 2004, 14(3):147-54.

Hesselink DA, van Schaik RH, van der Heiden IP, et al, "Genetic Polymorphisms of the CYP3A4, CYP3A5, and MDR-1 Genes and Pharmacokinetics of the Calcineurin Inhibitors Cyclosporine and Tacrolimus," *Clin Pharmacol Ther*, 2003, 74(3):245-54.

Hustert E, Haberl M, Burk O, et al, "The Genetic Determinants of the CYP3A5 Polymorphism," *Pharmacogenetics*, 2001, 11(9):773-9.

Min DI, Ellingrod VL, Marsh S, et al, "CYP3A5 Polymorphism and the Ethnic Differences in Cyclosporine Pharmacokinetics in Healthy Subjects," *Ther Drug Monit*, 2004, 26(5):524-8.

Williams JA, Ring BJ, Cantrell VE, et al, "Comparative Metabolic Capabilities of CYP3A4, CYP3A5, and CYP3A7," *Drug Metab Dispos*, 2002, 30(8):883-91.

Zheng H, Zeevi A, Schuetz E, et al, "Tacrolimus Dosing in Adult Lung Transplant Patients is Related to Cytochrome P4503A5 Gene Polymorphism," *J Clin Pharmacol*, 2004, 44(2):135-40.

- **CYP11B2** *see* Aldosterone Synthase *on page 208*
- **Cytochrome P450 Isoenzyme 1A2** *see* CYP1A2 *on page 246*
- **Cytochrome P450 Isoenzyme 2C9** *see* CYP2C9 *on page 248*
- **Cytochrome P450 Isoenzyme 2C19** *see* CYP2C19 *on page 251*
- **Cytochrome P450 Isoenzyme 2D6** *see* CYP2D6 *on page 254*
- **D_2** *see* D_2 Receptor *on page 263*
- **D_{2L}** *see* D_2 Receptor *on page 263*

D_2 Receptor

Synonyms D_2; D_{2L}; D_{2S}; DRD2

Chromosome Location 11q23

Clinically-Important Polymorphisms -141 C Ins/Del, TaqI A, TaqI B, rs1125394

Discussion Dopamine-2 receptors are of paramount importance in mental health, especially in regard to antipsychotics. Estimates of clinical potency of antipsychotic agents correlates with their potency *in*

(Continued)

D_2 Receptor *(Continued)*

vitro to inhibit binding of ligands to D_2 dopamine receptors. Almost all antipsychotics have high affinity for D_2 receptors. Atypical antipsychotics also have affinity for the D_2 receptors, but some (clozapine, quetiapine) have lower affinities than others. It appears that blockade of dopamine at the D_2 receptor is required for a drug to possess antipsychotic activity.

Antipsychotics:

One hundred and forty-four patients with schizophrenia were assessed to determine the role the A1 allele of Taq 1A polymorphism of the D_2 dopamine receptor gene on prolactin levels in patients treated with antipsychotic agents. Patients with the A1 allele had prolactin levels 40% higher than patients without this allele (Young, 2004).

Clozapine:

The "141 C Ins/Del polymorphism has been associated with short-term antipsychotic response (Malhotra, 1999) but not long-term response (Arranz, 1998).

One hundred and eighty-three Caucasian and 49 African-American patients with schizophrenia refractory or intolerant to conventional antipsychotics were genotyped to investigate the effect of 12 single nucleotide polymorphisms spanning the entire dopamine D2 gene on clozapine response. The TaqIA, TaqIB, and rs1125394 polymorphisms were predictive of clozapine response in the African-American sample. No significant associations were found in the Caucasian sample. In addition, no association between the "141 C Ins/Del polymorphism and clozapine response was found in either sample (Hwang, 2005).

Haloperidol:

Heterozygous patients showed a greater improvement in positive but not negative symptoms compared to patients homozygous for allele 2 (Schafer, 2001).

Thirty-two untreated schizophrenic inpatients (16 males, 16 females) were treated with bromperidol for a two week period. Female patients with the TaqA1 allele had the highest prolactin response to bromperidol and represent a group who may be at an increased risk for adverse effects associated with antipsychotic induced hyperprolactinemia (Mihara, 2001).

Lithium:

No association between lithium's efficacy and polymorphisms of the D_2 receptor was seen in a group of 125 patients with depression or bipolar disorder treated with lithium prophylaxis (Serretti, 1999).

NMS:

Preliminary work has suggested that the TaqI A polymorphism is associated with the predisposition to NMS (Suzuki, 2001). However, others show that the Taq-I A polymorphism does not appear to be associated with the development of NMS in schizophrenic patients treated with antipsychotics (Kishida, 2003).

Polydipsia:

Patients with polydipsia (n=64) and those without polydipsia (n=91) were tested for an association between polydipsia in schizophrenia and three functional polymorphisms (-141C Ins/Del, Ser311Cys, TaqIA) of the dopamine D_2 receptor gene. Of the three polymorphisms, TaqIA was significantly associated with polydipsia. Haplotype analysis of the three markers found an increased significance of the association ($p<0.01$). Individual comparison of the common haplotypes showed that haplotype Ins-Cys-A1 was significantly less ($p<0.01$) frequent in patients with polydipsia (Matsumoto, 2005).

Risperidone:

A relationship between the Taq 1 A2/A2 genotype and failure to respond to risperidone has been reported (Mata, 2002).

SSRI:

No association between D_2 and D_4 receptor polymorphisms and response to paroxetine or fluvoxamine has been demonstrated (Serretti, 2001).

Tardive dyskinesia:

Increased frequency of the *A2* allele in patients with tardive dyskinesia (Chen, 1997)

May Alter Pharmacodynamics of Antipsychotic agents and potentially other D2 receptor antagonists

May Affect Disease Predisposition of Alzheimer's disease, anxiety disorder, affective disorder, schizophrenia, alcoholism, substance abuse, Parkinson's disease

References

Arranz MJ, Li T, Munro J, et al, "Lack of Association Between a Polymorphism in the Promoter Region of the Dopamine$_2$-Receptor Gene and Clozapine Response," *Pharmacogenetics*, 1998, 8(6):481-4.

Chen CH, Wei FC, Koong FJ, et al, "Association of the Taq-I A Polymorphism of Dopamine D_2 Receptor Gene and Tardive Dyskinesia in Schizophrenia," *Biol Psychiatry*, 1997, 41(7):827-9.

Hwang R, Shinkai T, De Luca V, et al, "Association Study of 12 Polymorphisms Spanning the Dopamine D_2 Receptor Gene and Clozapine Treatment Response in Two Treatment Refractory/Intolerant Populations," *Psychopharmacology (Berl)*, 2005, Apr 14; [Epub ahead of print].

Kishida I, Kawanishi C, Furuno T, et al, "Lack of Association in Japanese Patients Between Neuroleptic Malignant Syndrome and the Taq-I A Polymorphism of the Dopamine D_2 Receptor Gene," *Psychiatr Genet*, 2003, 13(1):55-7.

Malhotra AK, Buchanan RW, Kim S, et al, "Allelic Variation in the Promoter Region of the Dopamine D2 Receptor Gene and Clozapine Response," *Schizophr Res*, 1999, 36:92-3.

Mata I, Arranz MJ, Lai T, et al, "The Serotonergic System Influences Individual's Response to Risperidone," *Am J Med Genet*, 2002, 114:728.

Matsumoto C, Shinkai T, De Luca V, et al, "Association Between Three Functional Polymorphisms of the Dopamine D_2 Receptor Gene and Polydipsia in Schizophrenia," *Int J Neuropsychopharmacol*, 2005, 8(2):245-53.

Mihara K, Suzuki A, Kondo T, et al, "Relationship Between Taq1 A Dopamine D2 Receptor (DRD2) Polymorphism and Prolactin Response to Bromperidol," *Am J Med Genet*, 2001, 105(3):271-4.

Schafer M, Rujescu D, Giegling I, et al, "Association of Short-Term Response to Haloperidol Treatment With a Polymorphism in the Dopamine D_2 Receptor Gene," *Am J Psychiatry*, 2001, 158(5):802-4.

(Continued)

D_2 Receptor *(Continued)*

Serretti A, Lilli R, Lorenzi C, et al, "Dopamine Receptor D_2 and D_4 Genes, GABA(A) $Alpha_1$ Subunit Genes and Response to Lithium Prophylaxis in Mood Disorders," *Psychiatry Res*, 1999, 87(1):7-19.

Serretti A, Zanardi R, Cusin C, et al, "No Association Between Dopamine D_2 and D_4 Receptor Gene Variants and Antidepressant Activity of Two Selective Serotonin Reuptake Inhibitors," *Psychiatry Res*, 2001, 104(3):195-203.

Suzuki A, Kondo T, Otani K, et al, "Association the Taq-I A Polymorphism of the Dopamine D_2 Receptor Gene With Predisposition to Neuroleptic Malignant Syndrome," *Am J Psychiatry*, 2001, 158(10):1714-6.

Young RM, Lawford BR, Barnes M, et al, "Prolactin Levels in Antipsychotic Treatment of Patients With Schizophrenia Carrying the DRD2*A1 Allele," *Br J Psychiatry*, 2004, 185:147-51.

♦ **D_{2S}** *see* D_2 Receptor *on page 263*

♦ **D_3** *see* D_3 Receptor *on page 266*

D_3 Receptor

Synonyms D_3; DRD3

Chromosome Location 3q13.3

Clinically-Important Polymorphisms Serine to Glycine (Ser9Gly), a novel polymorphism in the promoter region of the gene (*-205 A/G*) (Ishiguro, 2000), polymorphism associated with the development of tardive dyskinesias. It is also predictive of the occurrence of tardive dyskinesia.

Discussion There are two major categories of dopamine receptors, namely the D_1-like and D_2-like. The D_1-like receptors include D_1 and D_5 receptors. The D_2-like receptors include two isoforms of the D_2 receptor, the D_3 receptor, and the D_4 receptor. The D_1 and D_5 receptors activate adenylyl cyclase. The D_2 receptors possess several actions, including the inhibition of adenylyl cyclase activity, suppression of calcium currents, and activation of potassium currents. The effector system to which the D_3 and D_4 receptors couple has not been defined with certainty.

Atypical Antipsychotics:

Seventy-five patients with schizophrenia were evaluated to investigate the relationship between polymorphism of the dopamine D_3 receptor and dopamine transporter. The results suggested that the ser/ser genotype of the dopamine D_3 receptor is associated with more severe executive dysfunction and poorer therapeutic response in patients with schizophrenia (Szekeres, 2004).

Clozapine:

No significant association with response (Shaikh, 1996; Malhotra, 1998). However, in a sample of 32 patients with schizophrenia, an association was found between treatment response and the allele *9Gly* (p=0.006) and with genotypes consisting of *9Gly* (p=0.033). Combined analysis of two previous studies (Shaikh, 1996; Malhotra, 1998) support these findings (p=0.004) (Scharfetter, 1999).

Lithium:

No association between lithium's efficacy and polymorphisms of the D3 receptor was seen in a group of 125 patients with depression or bipolar disorder treated with lithium prophylaxis (Serretti, 1998).

Olanzapine:

A cohort of 50 individuals of Basque origin who received olanzapine for at least 3 months were assessed using the PANSS scale. The average improvement in positive symptoms was higher in those individuals with the *9Gly* and *-205G* alleles (Staddon, 2002).

Tardive dyskinesia:

Polymorphism of the D_3 receptor has been related to the development of tardive dyskinesia. Excess of the *Gly/Gly* genotype has been found in patients with tardive dyskinesia (Steen, 1997; Segman, 1999; Basile, 1999; Lovlie, 2000; Liao, 2001), although this was not replicated by others (Rietschel, 2000; Gaitonde, 1996; Inada, 1997; Garcia-Barcelo, 2001). Basile examined the interaction between dopamine 3 receptors and CYP1A2 and the risk for tardive dyskinesia. Patients with both the *G/G* genotype at the dopamine 3 receptor and the *C/C* genotype at the CYP1A2 had the most severe tardive dyskinesia (Basile, 2000).

Fifty-five patients with schizophrenia and tardive dyskinesia were compared with 58 who did not have tardive dyskinesia. Patients carrying the cytochrome P450 17alpha-hyrdroxylase A2-A2 genotype and the dopamine D_3gly allele had the highest orofacial, distal, and incapacitation scores suggesting an increased risk in those chronically exposed to conventional antipsychotic agents (Segman, 2002).

May Alter Pharmacodynamics of Haloperidol, olanzapine, risperidone, and potentially other antipsychotics

May Affect Disease Predisposition of Alzheimer's disease, anxiety disorder, affective disorder, schizophrenia, alcoholism, substance abuse, Parkinson's disease

References

Basile VS, Masellis M, Badri F, et al, "Association of the Mscl Polymorphism of the Dopamine D_3 Receptor Gene With Tardive Dyskinesia in Schizophrenia," *Neuropsychopharmacology*, 1999, 21(1):17-27.

Basile VS, Ozdemir V, Masellis M, et al, "A Functional Polymorphism of the Cytochrome P450 1A2 (CYP1A2) Gene: Association With Tardive Dyskinesia in Schizophrenia," *Mol Psychiatry*, 2000, 5(4):410-7.

Gaitonde EJ, Morris A, Sivagnanasundaram S, et al, "Assessment of Association of D_3 Dopamine Receptor Mscl Polymorphism With Schizophrenia: Analysis of Symptom Ratings, Family History, Age at Onset, and Movement Disorders," *Am J Med Genet*, 1996, 67(5):455-8.

Garcia-Barcelo MM, Lam LC, Ungvari GS, et al, "Dopamine D_3 Receptor Gene and Tardive Dyskinesia in Chinese Schizophrenic Patients," *J Neural Transm*, 2001, 108(6):671-7.

Inada T, Dobashi I, Sugita T, et al, "Search for a Susceptibility Locus for Tardive Dyskinesia," *Hum Psychopharmacol*, 1997, 12:35-9.

Ishiguro H, Okuyama Y, Toru M, et al, "Mutation and Association Analysis of the 5′ Region of the Dopamine D3 Receptor Gene in Schizophrenia Patients: Identification of the Ala38Thr Polymorphism and Suggested Association Between DRD3 Haplotypes and Schizophrenia," *Mol Psychiatry*, 2000, 5(4):433-8.

Lerer B, Segman RH, Fangerau H, et al, "Pharmacogenetics of Tardive Dyskinesia. Combined Analysis of 780 Patients Supports Association With Dopamine D3

(Continued)

D_3 Receptor *(Continued)*

Receptor Gene Ser9Gly Polymorphism," *Neuropsychopharmacology*, 2002, 27:105-19.

Liao DL, Yeh YC, Chen HM, et al, "Association Between the Ser9Gly Polymorphism of the Dopamine D3 Receptor Gene and Tardive Dyskinesia in Chinese Schizophrenic Patients," *Neuropsychobiology*, 2001, 44(2):95-8.

Lovlie R, Daly AK, Blennerhassett R, et al, "Homozygosity for Gly-9 Variant of the Dopamine D3 Receptor and Risk for Tardive Dyskinesia in Schizophrenic Patients," *Int J Neuropsychopharmacol*, 2000, 3(1):61-6.

Lundstrom K and Turpin MP, "Proposed Schizophrenia-Related Gene Polymorphism. Expression of the Ser9Gly Mutant Human Dopamine D3 Receptor With the Semliki-Forest Virus System," *Biochem Biophys Commun*, 1996, 225:1068-72.

Malhotra AK, Goldman D, Buchanan RW, et al, "The Dopamine D3 Receptor (DRD3) Ser9Gly Polymorphism and Schizophrenia: A Haplotypes Relative Risk Study and Association With Clozapine Response," *Mol Psychiary*, 1998, 3(1):72-5.

Potkin SG, Kennedy JL, and Basile VS, "Combining Brain Imaging and Pharmacogenetics in Understanding Clinical Response in Alzheimer's Disease and Schizophrenia," *Pharmacogenetics of Psychotropic Drugs*, Lerer B (ed), New York, NY: Cambridge University Press, 2002, 391-400.

Rietschel M, Krauss H, Muller DJ, et al, "Dopamine D3 Receptor Variant and Tardive Dyskinesia," *Eur Arch Psychiatry Clin Neurosci*, 2000, 250(1):31-5.

Scharfetter J, Chaudhry HR, Hornik K, et al, "Dopamine D3 Receptor Gene Polymorphism and Response to Clozapine in Schizophrenic Pakastani Patients," *Eur Neuropsychopharmacol*, 1999, 10(1):17-20.

Segman R, Neeman T, Heresco-Levy U, et al, "Genotypic Association Between the Dopamine D3 Receptor Gene and Tardive Dyskinesia in Chronic Schizophrenia," *Mol Psychiatry*, 1999, 4(3):247-53.

Segman RH, Heresco-Levy U, Yakir A, et al, "Interactive Effect Of Cytochrome P450 17Alpha-Hydroxylase and Dopamine D_3 Receptor Gene Polymorphisms on Abnormal Involuntary Movements in Chronic Schizophrenia," *Biol Psychiatry*, 2002, 51(3):261-3.

Serretti A, Lilli R, Lorenzi C, et al, "Dopamine Receptor D3 Gene and Response to Lithium Prophylaxis in Mood Disorders," *Int J Neuropsychopharmacol*, 1998, 1:125-9.

Shaikh S, Collier DA, Sham P, et al, "Allelic Association Between a Ser-9-Gly Polymorphism of the D3 Receptor Gene and Schizophrenia," *Hum Genet*, 1996, 97(6):714-9.

Staddon S, Arranz MJ, Mancama D, et al, "Clinical Applications of Pharmacogenetics in Psychiatry," *Psychopharmacology (Berl)*, 2002, 162(1):18-23.

Steen VM, Lovlie R, MacEwan T, et al, "Dopamine D3 Receptor Gene Variant and Susceptibility to Tardive Dyskinesia in Schizophrenic Patients," *Mol Psychiatry*, 1997, 2(2):139-45.

Szekeres G, Keri S, Juhasz A, et al, "Role of Dopamine D_3 Receptor (DRD3) and Dopamine Transporter (DAT) Polymorphism in Cognitive Dysfunctions and Therapeutic Response to Atypical Antipsychotics in Patients With Schizophrenia," *Am J Med Genet B Neuropsychiatr Genet*, 2004, 124(1):1-5.

♦ **D_4** *see* D_4 Receptor *on page 268*

D_4 Receptor

Synonyms D_4; DRD4

Chromosome Location 11p15.5

Clinically-Important Polymorphisms Exon III 48bp vntr; Exon I 12 bp repeat, Exon I 13 bp deletion; Gly11Arg; repeat within first intron

Discussion There are two major categories of dopamine receptors, namely the D_1-like and D_2-like. The D_1-like receptors include D_1 and D_5 receptors. The D_2-like receptors include two isoforms of the D_2 receptor, the D_3 receptor, and the D_4 receptor. The D_1 and D_5 receptors activate adenylyl cyclase. The D_2 receptors possess several actions, including the inhibition of adenylyl cyclase activity, suppression of calcium currents, and activation of potassium currents. The effector system to which the D_3 and D_4 receptors couple has not been defined with certainty.

Antipsychotics:

Eighty patients with schizophrenia were studied to investigate whether polymorphisms of the 48-bp tandem repeats in the exon 3 of the dopamine D_4 receptor are related to antipsychotic response. The presence of the homozygous four 48-bp repeats in both alleles in exon 3 of the dopamine D_4 gene was associated with a lower prevalence of negative symptoms in remission and antipsychotic response in acute treatment. This was particularly true in male schizophrenic patients (Hwu, 1998).

Dopamine D_4 polymorphisms in the third intron were characterized in 28 patients receiving conventional antipsychotics, 32 patients receiving clozapine and 57 healthy controls. Patients responding to conventional antipsychotics carried the allele for the long form of the D_4 receptor less frequently than patients responding to clozapine or the healthy controls (Cohen, 1999).

Clozapine:

No significant association established between polymorphisms of the D_4 receptor and therapeutic effect (Rao, 1994; Shaikh, 1995; Rietschel, 1996; Kohn, 1997). However, Ozdemir reported an association between a repeat polymorphism within the first intron of the D_4 receptor (Ozdemir, 1999).

Lithium:

No association between lithium's efficacy and polymorphisms of the D_4 receptor was seen in a group of 125 patients with depression or bipolar disorder treated with lithium prophylaxis (Serretti, 1999).

Risperidone:

No significant association was found between the D_4 genotype and clinical response, but carriers of less than 7 repeat alleles demonstrated a higher response rate (Zalsman, 2003).

SSRI:

No association between D_2 and D_4 receptor polymorphism and response to paroxetine or fluvoxamine was demonstrated (Serretti, 2001).

May Alter Pharmacodynamics of Haloperidol, risperidone, and potentially other antipsychotic agents

May Affect Disease Predisposition of Schizophrenia

References

Cohen BM, Ennulat DJ, Centorrino F, et al, "Polymorphisms of the Dopamine D4 Receptor and Response to Antipsychotic Drugs," *Psychopharmacology (Berl)*, 1999, 141(1):6-10.

Hwu HG, Hong CJ, Lee YL, et al, "Dopamine D4 Receptor Gene Polymorphisms and Neuroleptic Response in Schizophrenia," *Biol Psychiatry*, 1998, 44(6):483-7.

Kohn Y, Ebstein RP, Heresco-Levy U, et al, "Dopamine D_4 Receptor Gene Polymorphisms: Relation to Ethnicity, No Association With Schizophrenia and Response to Clozapine in Israeli Subjects," *Eur J Neuropsychopharmacol*, 1997, 7(1):39-43.

Ozdemir V, Masellis M, Basile VS, et al, "Variability in Response to Clozapine: Potential Role of Cytochrome P450 1A2 and the Dopamine D_4 Receptor Gene," *CNS Spectrums*, 1999, 4:30-56.

(Continued)

D_4 Receptor *(Continued)*

Rao PA, Picckar D, Gejman PV, et al, "Allelic Variation in the D_3 Dopamine Receptor (DRD4) Gene Does Not Predict Response to Clozapine," *Arch Gen Psychiatry*, 1994, 51(11):912-7.

Rietschel M, Naber D, Oberlander H, et al, "Efficacy and Side Effects of Clozapine: Testing for Association With Allelic Variation in the Dopamine D_4 Receptor Gene," *Neuropsychopharmacology*, 1996, 15(5):491-6.

Serretti A, Lilli R, Lorenzi C, et al, "Dopamine Receptor D_2 and D_4 Genes, GABA(A) $Alpha_1$ Subunit Genes and Response to Lithium Prophylaxis in Mood Disorders," *Psychiatry Res*, 1999, 87:7-19.

Serretti A, Zanardi R, Cusin C, et al, "No Association Between Dopamine D_2 and D_4 Receptor Gene Variants and Antidepressant Activity of Two Selective Serotonin Reuptake Inhibitors," *Psychiatry Res*, 2001, 104:195-203.

Shaikh S, Collier DA, Sham P, et al, "Analysis of Clozapine Response and Polymorphism of the Dopamine D_4 Receptor Gene (DRD4) in Schizophrenic Patients," *Am J Med Genet*, 1995, 60(6):541-5.

Zalsman G, Frisch A, Lev-Ran S, et al, "DRD4 Exon III Polymorphism and Response to Risperidone in Israeli Adolescents With Schizophrenia: A Pilot Pharmacogenetic Study," *Eur Neuropsychopharmacol*, 2003, 13(3):183-5.

♦ **DA** *see* Dopamine Transporter *on page 270*

♦ **DAT** *see* Dopamine Transporter *on page 270*

♦ **DAT1** *see* Dopamine Transporter *on page 270*

♦ **Deafness, X-Linked 7** *see* Glutathione-S-Transferase Pi *on page 283*

♦ **DFN7** *see* Glutathione-S-Transferase Pi *on page 283*

♦ **Diaphorase-4** *see* NAD(P)H Quinone Oxidoreductase *on page 309*

Dihydropyrimidine Dehydrogenase

Synonyms DPD; DPYD

Chromosome Location 1p22

Discussion A deficiency in dihydropyrimidine dehydrogenase (DPD) is inherited as an autosomal recessive trait. It has been estimated that up to 3% of the Caucasian population are deficient in DPD activity. Enzyme deficiencies are related in up to 17 different reported mutations which are associated with an 8- to 21-fold variability in enzymatic activity. Of note, cimetidine (and possibly all H-2s) have been identified as inhibitors of DPD.

Fluorouracil:

Approximately 80% of a dose of fluorouracil is metabolized by DPD. Deficiency has been correlated to a prolongation of fluorouracil's half-life and increased neurological and hematological toxicity (Collie-Duguid, 2000).

May Alter Pharmacokinetics of Fluorouracil, capecitabine

References

Collie-Duguid ES, Etienne MC, Milano G, et al, "Known Variant DPYD Alleles Do Not Explain DPD Deficiency in Cancer Patients," *Pharmacogenetics*, 2000, 10(3):217-23.

Dopamine Transporter

Synonyms DA; DAT1; DAT

Clinically-Important Polymorphisms 10-repeat allele

Discussion The dopamine transporter is selective for dopamine and is in part responsible for the termination of its action at the postsynaptic receptors.

Methylphenidate:

The 10-repeat allele at the dopamine transporter gene may be associated with a poor response to methylphenidate in children with attention-deficit/hyperactivity disorder (Roman, 2002; Rohde, 2003).

Conversely, one hundred and nineteen Irish children with ADHD were studied to determine the impact of the dopamine transporter gene. An association between the 10-repeat VNTR dopamine transporter gene polymorphism and methylphenidate response was found (Kirley, 2003).

May Alter Pharmacodynamics of Methylphenidate

May Affect Disease Predisposition of Attention-deficit/hyperactivity disorder

References

Kirley A, Lowe N, Hawi Z, et al, "Association of the 480 bp DAT1 Allele With Methylphenidate Response in a Sample of Irish Children With ADHD," *Am J Med Genet B Neuropsychiatr Genet*, 2003, 121(1):50-4.

Rohde LA, Roman T, Szobot C, et al, "Dopamine Transporter Gene, Response to Methylphenidate and Cerebral Blood Flow in Attention-Deficit/Hyperactivity Disorder: A Pilot Study," *Synapse*, 2003, 48(2):87-9.

Roman T, Szobot C, Martins S, et al, "Dopamine Transporter Gene and Response to Methylphenidate in Attention-Deficit/Hyperactivity Disorder," *Pharmacogenetics*, 2002, 12(6):497-9.

♦ **DPD** *see* Dihydropyrimidine Dehydrogenase *on page 270*
♦ **DPYD** *see* Dihydropyrimidine Dehydrogenase *on page 270*
♦ **DRD2** *see* D_2 Receptor *on page 263*
♦ **DRD3** *see* D_3 Receptor *on page 266*
♦ **DRD4** *see* D_4 Receptor *on page 268*
♦ **DT-Diaphorase** *see* NAD(P)H Quinone Oxidoreductase *on page 309*
♦ **EC 1.6.99.2** *see* NAD(P)H Quinone Oxidoreductase *on page 309*
♦ **EGFR** *see* Epidermal Growth Factor Receptor *on page 271*
♦ **ENaC-Beta** *see* Epithelial Sodium Channel Beta-Subunit *on page 273*

Epidermal Growth Factor Receptor

Synonyms EGFR

Chromosome Location 7p12

Clinically-Important Polymorphisms A variety of somatic mutations in exons 18 through 21 corresponding to the tyrosine kinase domain of this receptor, specifically localized to the the P-loop, the activation loop (A-loop), and the α C helix have been correlated to clinical response.

Discussion Epithelial cell survival appears to be partly mediated by both the epidermal growth factor receptor (EGFR) and extracellular cell adhesion receptors. These receptor share a signal transduction pathway which controls expression and activation of one family of apoptosis regulators (Bcl-2). Activation of EGFR is frequently observed in neoplastic tumors of epithelial origin. Differences in

(Continued)

Epidermal Growth Factor Receptor *(Continued)*

susceptibility to EGFR blockade may be influenced by the relative need for EGFR stimulation as a survival signal in epithelial cells. According to this hypothesis, physiologic cell-cell contacts in normal epithelial cells provide adequate survival signaling, while neoplastic cell survival is dependent to a much higher degree on signals mediated by EGFR. Therefore, these cells may be more susceptible to the induction of apoptosis by EGFR blockade.

EGFR mutations in unselected NSCLC patients are infrequent, occurring in only one of 61 samples tested by Paez and colleagues; however, EGFR mutations are correlated with patient characteristics. Mutations are more frequent in adenocarcinomas (15/70 or 21%) than in other NSCLCs (1/49 or 2%), more frequent in women (9/45 or 20%) than in men (7/74 or 9%), and more frequent in the patients from Japan (15/58 or 26%, and 14/41 adenocarcinomas or 32%) than in those from the United States (1/61 or 2%, and 1/29 adenocarcinomas or 3%).

Gefitinib:

Gefitinib is an EGFR inhibitor that produces responses in a subgroup of patients (approximately 10% to 19%) with treatment-refractory advanced nonsmall-cell lung cancer. The basis for a differential sensitivity is not clear, since these effects do not appear to correlate with the level of EGFR expression.

In a retrospective analysis, a variety of mutations in exons 19 and 21 corresponding to the ATP cleft of the tyrosine kinase domain of this receptor have been correlated to clinical response (Lynch, 2004). At least two mutations were evaluated *in vitro* and were associated with increased levels of activation and longer duration of activation following stimulation by EGF. In addition, these receptors appeared to be more susceptible to inhibition by gefitinib as compared to the wild-type receptor. Potentially, evaluation for mutations of this receptor domain may be useful in the identification of patients who are most likely to benefit from gefitinib therapy.

Additionally, Paez and colleagues sequenced the kinase domain (exons 18 through 24) in tumors from the four patients who progressed on gefitinib finding no mutations, while five tumors from gefitinib-responsive patients all contained EGFR kinase domain mutations. The chi-square test revealed the difference in EGFR mutation frequency between gefitinib responders (5/5) and nonresponders (0/4) to be statistically significant with p=0.0027; whereas, the difference between the gefitinib responders and unselected U.S. NSCLC patients (5/5 versus 1/61) was also significant with $P < 10^{-12}$ (20) Consistent with this finding, Lynch et al, noted that 8 of 9 patients with the kinase domain mutations responded to gefitinib compared to 0 of 7 patients without the mutation (p<0.001).

A number of EGFR inhibitors (ie, erlotinib/Tarceva®) are in clinical development for treating cancer. Ongoing studies are evaluating the role of EGFR mutations in response to these agents.

May Alter Pharmacodynamics of Gefitinib, erlotinib (Tarceva®)

May Affect Disease Predisposition of NSCLC

Clinical Recommendations There is currently no clinically available test for EGFR mutations and EGFR mutations as predictors of clinical response to gefitinib have not been prospectively validated. While analysis of EGFR mutations shows promise, analysis is not currently recommended for routine use.

References

Kari C, Chan TO, Rocha de Quadros M, et al, "Targeting the Epidermal Growth Factor Receptor in Cancer: Apoptosis Takes Center Stage," *Cancer Res*, 2003, 63(1):1-5.

Lynch TJ, Bell DW, Sordella R, et al, "Activating Mutations in the Epidermal Growth Factor Receptor Underlying Responsiveness of Nonsmall-cell Lung Cancer to Gefitinib," *N Engl J Med*, 2004, 350:(21):2129-39.

Paez JG, Janne PA, Lee JC, et al, "EGFR Mutations in Lung Cancer: Correlation With Clinical Response to Gefitinib Therapy," *Science*, 2004, 304(5676):1497-500.

Epithelial Sodium Channel Beta-Subunit

Synonyms ENaC-Beta

Chromosome Location 16p12

Clinically-Important Polymorphisms Nonsynonymous SNP in exon 12 *(Thr594Met)*

Discussion The ENaC is an important regulator of epithelial cell sodium exchange. Sodium reabsorption through ENaC within the distal nephron regulates sodium balance, and contributes to regulation of circulating blood volume and blood pressure. Expression of ENaC is regulated by aldosterone. Rare genetic disorders of sodium channel activity (Liddle's syndrome and pseudohypoaldosteronism type 1) have been described. Liddle's syndrome is an autosomal dominant trait resulting in pseudoaldosteronism and salt-sensitive hypertension. Systemic pseudohypoaldosteronism type I is an autosomal recessive disorder that arises from loss of function mutations. These result in a severe salt-wasting syndrome in neonates, which is resistant to mineralocorticoid supplementation. In addition to genetic syndromes, additional polymorphisms of the epithelial cell sodium channel have been described. The *Thr594Met* polymorphism occurs in approximately 5% of persons of African descent and has been associated with hypertension (Baker, 1998).

Amiloride:

Monotherapy with amiloride 10 mg twice a day was shown to control blood pressure as effectively as two antihypertensive medications in hypertensive individuals of African descent with the *Thr594Met* polymorphism (Baker, 2002).

May Alter Pharmacokinetics of The ENaC gene is not known to affect the metabolism of any drugs.

May Alter Pharmacodynamics of Amiloride

May Affect Disease Predisposition of Hypertension

Clinical Recommendations Genotyping for the *Thr594Met* polymorphism may have a role in the management of individuals of African descent with drug-resistant hypertension.

(Continued)

Epithelial Sodium Channel Beta-Subunit *(Continued)*

Counseling Points Carrier status of the *Thr594Met* polymorphism may influence sodium sensitivity and risk for hypertension. Individuals should discuss the implications of having this variant with their clinician or another healthcare professional.

References

Baker EH, Dong YB, Sagnella GA, et al, "Association of Hypertension With T594M Mutation in Beta Subunit of Epithelial Sodium Channels in Black People Resident in London," *Lancet*, 1998, 351(9113):1388-92.

Baker EH, Duggal A, Dong Y, et al, "Amiloride, A Specific Drug for Hypertension in Black People With T594M Variant?" *Hypertension*, 2002, 40(1):13-7.

♦ **ERCC1** *see* Excision Repair Cross-Complementing Rodent Repair Deficiency, Complementation Group 1 *on page 274*

♦ **ERCC2** *see* Excision Repair Cross-Complementing Rodent Repair Deficiency, Complementation Group 2 *on page 277*

Excision Repair Cross-Complementing Rodent Repair Deficiency, Complementation Group 1

Synonyms ERCC1; UV20

Chromosome Location 19q13.2-q13.3

Clinically-Important Polymorphisms Two functionally synonymous polymorphisms have been described: A C to T transversion at codon 118 and a C to A transversion at position 8092 in the 3′ untranslated region. In a small US study of 128 NSCLC patients of mixed ethnicity, the reported genotype frequencies of the codon 118 polymorphism was 40% (T/T), 39% (C/T), and 21% (C/C), and the C8092A polymorphism was 53% (C/C), 41% (C/A), and 6% (A/A) (Zhou, 2004).

Discussion Cells are capable of activating DNA repair pathways in response to genotoxic exposures. The nucleotide excision repair pathway regulates removal of damaged DNA segments followed by resynthesis. A group of enzymes, including XPC and TFIIH, recognize the damaged structure and initiate a process which opens the helix several base pairs surrounding the damage. ERCC1 is an endonuclease which removes the targeted DNA segment.

Literature reports have established a link between enhanced ERCC1 mRNA levels and clinical resistance to platinum-based treatment. This resistance has been demonstrated in several tumor types, which is consistent with the crucial role ERCC1 plays in the nucleotide excision repair mechanism (Zhou, 2004). Limited evidence suggests that the codon 118 mutation increases ERCC1 mRNA levels, which was associated with reduced survival in platinum-treated colorectal cancer patients (Park, 2003) and non-small cell lung cancer patients (Rosell, 2004). The C8092A mutation has been suggested to increase ERCC1 mRNA stability, and comparatively, the wild-type genotype has been linked to risk of adult-onset glioma (Chen, 2000).

DNA repair mechanisms are quite complex. ERCC1 functions as a complex in concert with xeroderma pigmentosum complement F (XPF). In addition, ERCC1 mRNA levels have been closely correlated with 8-oxoguanine DNA glycosylase, a component of the base excision repair pathway (Rosell, 2003). Therefore, correlation of genetic variants of ERCC1 with clinical response must be interpreted carefully, as the role of several other repair mechanisms (and their respective genetic expression patterns) protein systems may be significant.

Platinum-based chemotherapy:

In a retrospective analysis of 128 patients treated for advanced non-small cell lung cancer, overall survival was evaluated as a function of ERCC1 genotype (Zhou, 2004). Stage III and IV patients presented with adenocarcinoma (51%), squamous cell carcinoma (20%), or large cell carcinoma (18%), and were treated with platinum compounds (eg, carboplatin or cisplatin) with a majority of stage III patients receiving adjunctive radiotherapy. No significant differences in median survival times were noted for stage III or IV patients who were carriers of the codon 118 variant (C/T or T/T). However, a composite of stage III patients exhibiting the 8092 C/A or A/A genotype showed a 60% reduction in survival time (15.4 months) compared to homozygous wild-types (38.7 months, $p = 0.004$). No difference was observed in stage IV patients.

A study conducted by Ryu et al analyzed the survival rate of 109 non-small cell lung cancer patients receiving cisplatin combination chemotherapy in conjunction with ERCC1 and XPD genotype. Median survival or response to chemotherapy was not significantly different among patients exhibiting either of the two XPD polymorphisms (Lys751Gln and Asp312Asn). However, it should be noted that the sample size of patients carrying the variant alleles was quite small, and there were no homozygous variants of either polymorphism. In contrast, patients carrying the variant allele for codon 118 of ERCC1 did show a significantly shorter survival time (281 days) as compared to wild-type (486 days, $p = 0.0058$). Also of note, a significantly larger proportion of non-responder patients (48%) carried the heterozygous genotype compared to patients categorized as responders (35%, $p = 0.0443$ for adjusted OR).

The effects of ERCC1 polymorphisms on the occurrence of toxicity was evaluated in a retrospective analysis of 214 stage III or IV non-small cell lung cancer patients treated with platinum-based chemotherapy (Suk, 2005). Using a logistic regression model that adjusted for covariates, polymorphisms of C8092A or codon 118 did not correlate with the incidence of either overall or hematologic grade 3/4 toxicity. However, carriers of the C8092A allele did show a significantly increased risk of grade 3 or 4 gastrointestinal toxicity (adjusted odds ratio of 2.33, 95% CI; 1.07-5.05, $p = 0.03$). As variants of this nucleotide excision repair pathway are not known to

(Continued)

Excision Repair Cross-Complementing Rodent Repair Deficiency, Complementation Group 1 *(Continued)*

influence the kinetics of platinum-based compounds, the mechanism of this observation is unclear.

Stoehlmacher et al conducted a retrospective review of several polymorphic metabolic and DNA repair pathway enzymes and their association with survival and disease progression in 106 patients with refractory stage IV colorectal cancer. Patients received standard combination therapy of 5-FU and oxaliplatin. The relative risk of death in patients carrying the variant codon 118 allele was significantly increased (p = 0.021, log rank test). Homozygous variant patients experienced a 1.86-fold increased risk, while heterozygotes were at 2.29-fold increased risk of death. Risk of disease progression did not differ based on genotype. In a multivariate combined analysis of polymorphisms in ERCC1(118), ERCC2(751), GSTP1(105), and TS, presence of two or more "favorable" genotypes (determined by the univariate risk analysis) was significantly predictive of survival.

May Alter Pharmacodynamics of Cisplatin and other platinum derivatives such as carboplatin, oxaliplatin

May Affect Disease Predisposition of Colorectal cancer, lung cancer, oligoastrocytoma

Clinical Recommendations There is currently no clinically available test for ERCC1 polymorphisms as a predictor of clinical response to platinum compounds. Analysis is not currently recommended for routine use.

References

Chen P, Wiencke J, Aldape K, et al, "Association of an ERCC1 Polymorphism With Adult-Onset Glioma," *Cancer Epidemiol Biomarkers Prev*, 2000, 9(8):843-7.

Park DJ, Zhang W, Stoehlmacher J, et al, "ERCC1 Gene Polymorphism as a Predictor for Clinical Outcome in Advanced Colorectal Cancer Patients Treated with Platinum-Based Chemotherapy," *Clin Adv Hematol Oncol*, 2003, 1:162-6.

Rosell R, Danenberg KD, Alberola V, et al, "Ribonucleotide Reductase Messenger RNA Expression and Survival in Gemcitabine/Cisplatin-treated Advanced Nonsmall-cell Lung Cancer Patients," *Clin Cancer Res*, 2004, 10(4):1318-25.

Rosell R, Taron M, Barnadas A, et al, "Nucleotide Excision Repair Pathways Involved in Cisplatin Resistance in Non-Small-Cell Lung Cancer," *Cancer Control*, 2003, 10(4):297-305.

Ryu JS, Hong YC, Han HS, et al, "Association Between Polymorphisms of ERCC1 and XPD and Survival in Non-Small Cell Lung Cancer Patients Treated With Cisplatin Combination Chemotherapy," *Lung Cancer*, 2004, 44(3):311-6.

Stoehlmacher J, Park DJ, Zhang W, et al, "A Multivariate Analysis of Genomic Polymorphisms: Prediction of Clinical Outcome to 5-FU/Oxaliplatin Combination Chemotherapy in Refractory Colorectal Cancer," *Br J Cancer*, 2004, 91(2):344-54.

Suk R, Gurubhagavatula S, Park S, et al, "Polymorphisms in ERCC1 and Grade 3 or 4 Toxicity in Non-Small Cell Lung Cancer Patients," *Clin Cancer Res*, 2005, 11(4):1534-8.

Zhou W, Gurubhagavatula S, Liu G, et al, "Excision Repair Cross-Complementation Group 1 Polymorphism Predicts Overall Survival in Advanced Non-Small Cell Lung Cancer Patients Treated With Platinum-Based Chemotherapy," *Clin Cancer Res*, 2004, 10(15):4939-43.

Excision Repair Cross-Complementing Rodent Repair Deficiency, Complementation Group 2

Synonyms ERCC2; XPD; xeroderma pigmentosum group D

Chromosome Location 19q13.2-3

Clinically-Important Polymorphisms Asp312Asn and Lys751Gln

Discussion A rare inherited disorder, xeroderma pigmentosum, is associated with a high risk of malignancy. Through the investigation of this syndrome, a number of genes which encode proteins for DNA repair have been identified. Collectively, these are known as the ERCC2 (formerly XPD) genes. The ERCC2 gene product is involved in the DNA repair process. ERCC2 is one of nine polypeptide subunits of the general transcription factor TFIIH. It appears to participate through the coordination of TFIIH assembly. Mutations of the ERCC2 gene have been correlated to a lower capacity to facilitate DNA repair. The clinical impact of this genetic variation is complex. On the one hand, a reduced capacity for DNA repair may facilitate the growth of aggressive tumors, and thus may hasten clinical decline. Conversely, impaired DNA repair mechanisms have been suggested as a condition favoring the efficacy of DNA damage-inducing chemotherapeutic agents, such as the platinum compounds.

The polymorphism is common, with a variant frequency of approximately 32% in patients with NSCLC and 41% in normal Caucasian volunteers (Vodicka, 2004).

Cisplatin:

A study conducted by Ryu et al analyzed the survival rate of 109 non-small cell lung cancer patients receiving cisplatin combination chemotherapy in conjunction with ERCC1 and XPD(ERCC2) genotype. Median survival was not different among patients exhibiting either of the two XPD polymorphisms (Lys751Gln and Asp312Asn). However, it should be noted that the sample size of patients carrying the variant alleles was quite small and there were no homozygous variants of either polymorphism.

However, in an evaluation of more than 1000 subjects with NSCLC treated with cisplatin, Gurubhagavatula and colleagues showed that the ERCC2 *Asn* polymorphism predicted poorer overall survival. Individuals who were wild-type or heterozygous had a median survival of 15.2-16.3 months compared to individuals homozygous for the *Asn* allele with a median survival of 6.6 months.

Breast cancer patients with at least one *Asn* allele at position 312 or the *Gln* allele at position 751 were observed to have a higher number of PAH-DNA adducts following treatment (Tang, 2002).

Oxaliplatin:

In 73 patients with metastatic colorectal cancer treated with oxaliplatin/5FU, response rate for the wild type XPD (ie, Lys/Lys at 751) was 24% (5/21). Heterozygous (Lys/Gln) and homozygous (Gln/Gln) genotypes showed significantly lower response rates of

(Continued)

Excision Repair Cross-Complementing Rodent Repair Deficiency, Complementation Group 2 *(Continued)*

10% (4/39) and 10% (1/10), respectively (*p*=0.015) (Park, 2001). Likewise, median survival times followed the same pattern as a function of genotype and were (in months): 17.4 (Lys/Lys), 12.8 (Lys/Gln), and 3.3 (Gln/Gln) (*p*=0.002).

Stoehlmacher et al conducted a retrospective review of several polymorphic metabolic and DNA repair pathway enzymes and their association with survival and disease progression in 106 patients with refractory stage IV colorectal cancer. Patients received standard combination therapy of 5-FU and oxaliplatin. The relative risk of death in patients carrying the variant Lys751Gln allele was significantly increased (*p*=0.049, log rank test). Homozygous variant patients experienced a 2.44-fold increased risk, while heterozygotes were at 1.87-fold increased risk of death. Risk of disease progression did not differ based on genotype. In a multivariate combined analysis of polymorphisms in ERCC1(118), ERCC2(751), GSTP1(105) and TS, presence of two or more "favorable" genotypes (determined by the univariate risk analysis) was significantly predictive of survival.

The studies discussed above suggest that patients possessing a genotype associated with reduced DNA repair capabilities may deteriorate more rapidly than patients with higher functioning repair pathways. If this is subsequently proven to be true, this would seem to indicate a more pronounced genomic effect on disease progression rather than impact on pharmacotherapeutic outcome. However, large-scale, prospective studies are needed, particularly comparing platinum vs nonplatinum therapies in the context of genotype, to better understand the relationship between DNA repair mechanisms and drug response.

May Alter Pharmacodynamics of Cisplatin and other platinum derivatives such as carboplatin, oxaliplatin

May Affect Disease Predisposition of Lung cancer, prostate cancer

Clinical Recommendations There is currently no clinically available test for XPD polymorphisms and XPD polymorphisms as predictors of clinical response to cisplatin have not been prospectively validated. Analysis is not currently recommended for routine use.

References

Camps C, Sarries C, Roig B, et al, "Assessment of Nucleotide Excision Repair XPD Polymorphisms in the Peripheral Blood of Gemcitabine/Cisplatin-treated Advanced Nonsmall-cell Lung Cancer Patients," *Clin Lung Cancer*, 2003, 4(4):237-41.

Gao WM, Romkes M, Day RD, et al, "Association of the DNA Repair Gene XPD Asp312Asn Polymorphism With p53 Gene Mutations in Tobacco-related Nonsmall Cell Lung Cancer," *Carcinogenesis*, 2003, 24(10):1671-6.

Gurubhagavatula S, Lin G, Park S, et al, "XPD and XRCC1 Genetic Polymorphisms Are Prognostic Indicators in Advanced Nonsmall-cell Lung Cancer Patients Treated With Platinum Chemotherapy," *J Clin Oncol*, 2004, 22(13):2594-601.

Park DJ, Stoehlmacher J, Zhang W, et al, "A Xeroderma Pigmentosum Group D Gene Polymorphism Predicts Clinical Outcome to Platinum-Based Chemotherapy in Patients With Advanced Colorectal Cancer," *Cancer Res*, 2001, 61(24):8654-8.

Rybicki BA, Conti DV, Moreira A, et al, "DNA Repair Gene XRCC1 and XPD Polymorphisms and Risk of Prostate Cancer," *Cancer Epidemiol Biomarkers Prev*, 2004, 13(1):23-9.

Ryu JS, Hong YC, Han HS, et al, "Association Between Polymorphisms of ERCC1 and XPD and Survival in Non-Small Cell Lung Cancer Patients Treated With Cisplatin Combination Chemotherapy," *Lung Cancer*, 2004, 44(3):311-6.

Stoehlmacher J, Park DJ, Zhang W, et al, "A Multivariate Analysis of Genomic Polymorphisms: Prediction of Clinical Outcome to 5-FU/Oxaliplatin Combination Chemotherapy in Refractory Colorectal Cancer," *Br J Cancer*, 2004, 91(2):344-54.

Tang D, Cho S, Rundle A, et al, "Polymorphisms in the DNA Repair Enzyme XPD Are Associated With Increased Levels of PAH-DNA Adducts in a Case-control Study of Breast Cancer," *Breast Cancer Res Treat*, 2002, 75(2):159-66.

Vodicka P, Kumar R, Stetina R, et al, "Genetic Polymorphisms in DNA Repair Genes and Possible Links With DNA Repair Rates, Chromosomal Aberrations and Single-strand Breaks in DNA," *Carcinogenesis*, 2004, 25(5)6:757-63.

Vogel U, Laros I, Jacobsen NR, et al, "Two Regions in Chromosome 19q13.2-3 are Associated With Risk of Lung Cancer," *Mutat Res*, 2004, 546(1-2):65-74.

♦ **F5** *see* Factor V *on page 279*

Factor V

Synonyms F5

Chromosome Location 1q23

Clinically-Important Polymorphisms Factor V Leiden results from a nonsynonymous SNP at nucleotide 1691 (G/A) resulting in the *506Gln* polymorphism.

Discussion The 506Gln mutation in the factor V gene (factor V Leiden) is an established risk factor for venous thrombosis. This mutation confers resistance to activated protein C.

Oral contraceptives:

The factor V Leiden mutation occurs in about 5% of the Caucasian population and has been correlated with an increased risk of venous thrombosis, and may predispose to thrombosis in patients receiving estrogens, including oral contraceptives (Vandenbroucke, 1994). Differences in the potential for venous thrombosis have been observed in some, but not all studies evaluating second and third generation oral contraceptives. Estrogen-induced changes in factor V attenuated by a second-generation progestin, but not by a third generation progestin, have been proposed as a basis for greater risk of thrombosis associated with third generation agents (Kemmeren, 2002).

May Alter Pharmacokinetics of The factor V Leiden gene is not known to alter the pharmacokinetics of any drugs

May Alter Pharmacodynamics of Oral contraceptives, estrogen

May Affect Disease Predisposition of Thrombosis, deep venous thrombosis

Laboratory Evaluation Screening for the *506Gln* polymorphism should be considered in potential oral contraceptive users with a positive family history of thrombosis.

Clinical Recommendations Individuals with the *506Gln* allele who used oral contraceptive are at markedly increased risk for venous (Continued)

Factor V *(Continued)*

thromboembolism. Clinicians should consider alternative contraceptive methods in *506Gln* carriers, especially if other genetic mutations in the coagulation cascade are also present.

References

Kemmeren JM, Algra A, Meijers JC, et al, "Effect of Second- and Third-Generation Oral Contraceptives on Fibrinolysis in the Absence or Presence of the Factor V Leiden Mutation," *Blood Coagul Fibrinolysis*, 2002, 13(5):373-81.

Vandenbroucke JP, Koster T, Briet E, et al, "Increased Risk of Venous Thrombosis in Oral-Contraceptive Users Who Are Carriers of Factor V Leiden Mutation," *Lancet*, 1994, 344(8935):1453-7.

♦ **FAEES3** *see* Glutathione-S-Transferase Pi *on page 283*

♦ **Fatty Acid Ethyl Ester Synthase III** *see* Glutathione-S-Transferase Pi *on page 283*

♦ **Fc Gamma RIIa** *see* Platelet Fc Gamma Receptor *on page 312*

♦ **FCG R2A** *see* Platelet Fc Gamma Receptor *on page 312*

♦ **FGB** *see* Beta-Fibrinogen *on page 236*

♦ **G6PD** *see* Glucose-6-Phosphate Dehydrogenase *on page 281*

♦ **GABA-A** *see* Gamma-Aminobutyric Acid (GABA) Type A Receptor Alpha$_1$ Subunit *on page 280*

Gamma-Aminobutyric Acid (GABA) Type A Receptor Alpha$_1$ Subunit

Synonyms GABA-A; γ-Aminobutyric Acid (GABA) Type A Receptor Alpha$_1$ Subunit GABA

Discussion GABA is formed from the enzymatic breakdown of glutamate via the enzyme glutamic acid decarboxylase. Degradation of GABA occurs via GABA transaminase and the GABA transporter. Two forms of GABA exist: GABA-A and GABA-B. GABA-A is a ligand-gated ion channel which can be allosterically modulated by nearby receptors which may mediate a wide range of CNS effects. Namely, anxiolytic, sedative/hypnotic, anticonvulsant, and behavioral effects. Three molecular subunits for the GABA-A receptor exist: alpha, beta, and gamma. GABA binds to the alpha and beta subunits. The benzodiazepines bind to the gamma subunit. The GABA-B receptor is a G-protein receptor. It is not modulated by the benzodiazepines nor is its physiology well known. However, baclofen binds selectively.

Lithium:

No association between lithium's efficacy and polymorphisms at the γ-aminobutyric acid (GABA) type A receptor α_1 subunit was seen in a group of 125 patients with depression or bipolar disorder treated with lithium prophylaxis (Serretti, 1999).

May Alter Pharmacodynamics of Lithium

References

Serretti A, Lilli R, Lorenzi C, et al, "Dopamine Receptor D_2 and D_4 Genes, GABA(A) Alpha$_1$ Subunit Genes and Response to Lithium Prophylaxis in Mood Disorders," *Psychiatry Res*, 1999, 87:7-19.

♦ **GB3** *see* G-Protein Beta$_3$ Subunit *on page 286*

Glucose-6-Phosphate Dehydrogenase

Synonyms G6PD

Chromosome Location Xq28

Clinically-Important Polymorphisms Over 300 variants have been described that result in deficient enzymatic activity.

Discussion Glucose-6-phosphate dehydrogenase is an enzyme that catalyzes the oxidation of glucose-6-phosphate to 6-phosphogluconate, reducing NADP to NADPH. NADPH is involved in protecting erythrocytes from oxidative stress. Over 300 variants of the G6PD enzyme have been reported, resulting in a wide range of potential enzymatic activity and symptoms. Glucose-6-phosphate dehydrogenase deficiency is inherited as an X-linked genetic trait.

Over 200 million people are estimated to have a genetic deficiency of the G6PD enzyme. Individuals from the Mediterranean basin, Southeast Asia, Africa, and India have a higher prevalence of this trait. Variants in the extent of G6PD-deficiency have been noted. The reduction in enzyme activity is more pronounced in older red blood cells, resulting in hemolysis when the red cell is no longer able to maintain its integrity. Severity of the deficiency determines the point at which red cells are lysed. Severe deficiency leads to a dramatic reduction in RBC lifespan, and a chronic hemolytic anemia. Females may experience difficulty carrying a pregnancy to term.

In patients with less severe deficiency, exposure to certain chemicals or infections may trigger hemolysis. Some foods, including fava beans, have been associated with hemolytic reactions. Exposure to specific drugs and/or drug classes may lead to acute hemolysis. This has been described for primaquine, chloramphenicol, acetanilide, phenacetin, vitamin K, sulfonamides, and nitrofurans. Case reports have identified other drugs (ie, acetaminophen), which may not be directly related to hemolysis.

May Alter Pharmacodynamics of Quinine derivatives, sulfonamides, chloramphenicol, nitrofuran-containing drugs

Laboratory Evaluation Commercial testing for G6PD is available.

♦ **Glutathione S-Aryltransferase** *see* Glutathione-S-Transferase Alpha 1 *on page 282*

Glutathione-S-Transferase

Synonyms GST M1; GST T1; GST

Discussion Glutathione conjugation of tacrine-reactive metabolites depends in part on the activity of glutathione-S-transferases of which two isozymes (GST M1 and GST T1) are polymorphically expressed.

Tacrine:

The combined deficiency of the *M1* and *T1* alleles in glutathione-S-transferase genes increases the susceptibility to tacrine-induced hepatotoxicity (Simon, 2000).

May Alter Pharmacodynamics of Tacrine

(Continued)

Glutathione-S-Transferase *(Continued)*

References

Simon T, Becquemont L, Mary-Krause M, et al, "Combined Glutathione-S-Transferase M1 and T1 Genetic Polymorphism and Tacrine Hepatotoxicity," *Clin Pharmacol Ther*, 2000, 67(4):432-7.

Glutathione-S-Transferase Alpha 1

Synonyms GST; GSTA1; Glutathione S-Aryltransferase

Chromosome Location 6p12.1

Clinically-Important Polymorphisms Two polymorphisms have been described which influence the expression of this GST in liver: -52G>A and -69C>T. Frequency of occurrence for the heterozygous/homozygous allelic genotypes is similar within Caucasian (48%/57%) and African-American (17%/13%) populations (Sweeney, 2003).

Discussion Glutathione S-transferase (GST) refers to a family of enzymes known to detoxify many electrophilic compounds, including carcinogens, chemotherapeutic drugs, and environmental toxins. Distinct isozymes have been described resulting from polymorphisms in the promoter region leading to decreased expression of the enzymes and/or reduced catalytic activity. Altered metabolism (ie, reduced detoxification) of drugs such as cyclophosphamide may result in increased cytotoxic activity and therefore increased therapeutic efficacy.

In a retrospective evaluation of 245 women treated with cyclophosphamide (in combination with other chemotherapy and/or radiation) for breast cancer, patients that were homozygous for the mutant GSTA1 allele had a reduced hazard of death (hazard ratio = 0.3) within 5 years post-diagnosis compared to combined wild type/heterozygous patients. No survival benefit was realized beyond 5 years.

May Alter Pharmacodynamics of Cyclophosphamide

May Affect Disease Predisposition of Prostate cancer, colorectal cancer

Counseling Points Polymorphisms of the GST enzyme family may result in enhanced cytotoxity from cyclophosphamide and related chemical entities due to altered drug metabolism. However, the reduced detoxification may in turn lead to a higher incidence of adverse effects or toxicities. This phenomenon has not been prospectively studied.

References

Komiya Y, Tsukino H, Nakao H, et al, "Human Glutathione S-transferase A1, T1, M1, and P1 Polymorphisms and Susceptibility to Prostate Cancer in the Japanese Population," *J Cancer Res Clin Oncol*, 2005, 131(4):238-42.

Sweeney C, Ambrosone CB, Joseph L, et al, "Association Between a Glutathione S-Transferase A1 Promoter Polymorphism and Survival After Breast Cancer Treatment," *Int J Cancer*, 2003, 103(6):810-4.

van der Logt EM, Bergevoet SM, Roelofs HM, et al, "Genetic Polymorphisms in UDP-Glucuronosyltransferases and Glutathione S-Transferases and Colorectal Cancer Risk," *Carcinogenesis*, 2004, 25(12):2407-15.

Glutathione-S-Transferase Pi

Synonyms DFN7; Deafness, X-Linked 7; FAEES3; Fatty Acid Ethyl Ester Synthase III; GST3; GST; GSTP1; PI

Chromosome Location 11q13

Clinically-Important Polymorphisms Single nucleotide substitution 1578A>G giving rise to Isoleucine (Ile) conversion to Valine (Val) at position 105 within the substrate binding domain. Heterozygous (Ile/Val) and homozygous (Val/Val) frequency in Caucasians reported at 33% and 14%, respectively (Rollinson, 2000).

Discussion Glutathione-S-transferase (GST) refers to a family of enzymes known to detoxify many electrophilic compounds, including carcinogens, chemotherapeutic drugs, and environmental toxins. Distinct isozymes have been described resulting from polymorphisms in the promoter region leading to decreased expression of the enzymes and/or reduced catalytic activity. Watson et al had previously demonstrated that polymorphism of the GSTP1 gene resulted in reduced catalytic activity in a gene-dose dependent manner. Altered metabolism (ie, reduced detoxification) of drugs such as cyclophosphamide or platinum-containing compounds may result in increased cytotoxic activity and therefore increased therapeutic efficacy.

In a retrospective study comparing standard vs high-dose chemotherapy regimens in 222 multiple myeloma patients, those patients receiving standard dose regimens and possessing the variant GSTP1 (Val) genotype had a significant improvement in the progression-free survival as compared to the Ile/Ile genotype (adjusted hazard ratio: 0.55 for Val/Ile and 0.52 for Val/Val). However, these polymorphisms did not provide any benefit in the high-dose treatment arm (Dasgupta, 2003).

Similarly, Sweeney and colleagues evaluated survival as a function of genotype in 240 women treated for breast cancer. Of the 189 genotyped patients who received chemotherapy (most commonly cyclophosphamide, 5-flurouracil, and doxorubicin), those patients homozygous for reduced enzymatic function (Val/Val) had a 30% death hazard compared to the common allele (Ile/Ile). Heterozygous patients showed an 80% hazard risk relative to the common allele.

Oxaliplatin/5-Fluorouracil:

In a retrospective evaluation of 107 patients with metastatic colorectal cancer, overall survival was analyzed in comparison to genotyping for the Ile105Val polymorphism for GSTP1 (Stoehlmacher, 2002). Related glutathione synthase enzyme genes (*GSTM1* and *GSTT1*) were also evaluated. Patients participating in this study were of mixed gender and ethnicity. Treatment consisted of oxaliplatin infusion (130 mg/m2) every 3 weeks in combination with 5-FU (200 mg/m2/day) as a weekly infusion for 10 weeks. The majority of these patients (76%) were refractory to previous irinotecan therapy.

In the overall population, the probability of survival at the 18 month evaluation time point was significantly correlated with histology,

(Continued)

Glutathione-S-Transferase Pi *(Continued)*

site of tumor, and ECOG performance status. The relative risk of dying for patients was significantly associated with the lower activity phenotypes of polymorphic GSTP1. After adjustment for tumor site and performance scores, the Val/Val genotyped patients demonstrated greater than a 3-fold increase in mean survival (24.9 months) relative to the homozygous Ile/Ile genotype (7.9 months), with heterozygotes surviving a median of 13.3 months ($p < 0.001$ for log-rank test).

No significant association between survival and genotypes of *GSTT1* and *GSTM1* was observed. This observation is consistent with the finding that these proteins are expressed in low amounts in colorectal tumor tissue, while GSTP1 has been shown to be readily detectable in colon cancer (Stoehlmacher, 2002; Moscow, 1989).

A follow-up study by Stoehlmacher (2004) replicated these findings. In this study, a retrospective review evaluated several polymorphic metabolic and DNA repair pathway enzymes and their association with survival and disease progression in 106 patients with refractory stage IV colorectal cancer. Patients received standard combination therapy of 5-FU and oxaliplatin. Both the relative risk of dying and disease progression was significantly higher (via log rank test) in patients genotyped for the wild-type allele compared to the reduced catalytic activity Val105 variant. In a multivariate combined analysis of polymorphisms in ERCC1(118), ERCC2(751), GSTP1(105) and TS, presence of two or more "favorable" genotypes (determined by the univariate risk analysis) was significantly predictive of survival.

May Alter Pharmacodynamics of Busulphan, chlorambucil, cisplatin, cyclophosphamide, doxorubicin, etoposide, fluorouracil, melphalan, oxalaplatin, thiotepa, vincristine

May Affect Disease Predisposition of Asthma, cirrhosis/pancreatitis (alcohol-induced), lung adenocarcinoma

Counseling Points Polymorphisms of the GST enzyme family may result in enhanced cytotoxity from cyclophosphamide and related chemical entities due to altered drug metabolism. This pharmacogenetic effect may lead to the identification of patients likely to experience an improved clinical response and longer survival. However, the reduced detoxification may in turn lead to a higher incidence of adverse effects or toxicities. This phenomenon has not been prospectively studied.

References

Dasgupta RK, Adamson PJ, Davies FE, et al, "Polymorphic Variation in GSTP1 Modulates Outcome Following Therapy for Multiple Myeloma," *Blood*, 2003, 102(7):2345-50.

Moscow JA, Fairchild CR, Madden MJ, et al, "Expression of Anionic Glutathione-S-Transferase and P-Glycoprotein Genes in Human Tissues and Tumors," *Cancer Res*, 1989, 49(6):1422-8.

Rollinson S, Roddam P, Kane E, et al, "Polymorphic Variation Within the Glutathione S-Transferase Genes and Risk of Adult Acute Leukemia," *Carcinogenesis*, 2000, 21(1):43-7.

Stoehlmacher J, Park DJ, Zhang W, et al, "Association Between Glutathione S-Transferase P1, T1, and M1 Genetic Polymorphism and Survival of Patients With Metastatic Colorectal Cancer," *J Natl Cancer Inst*, 2002, 94(12):936-42.

Stoehlmacher J, Park DJ, Zhang W, et al, "A Multivariate Analysis of Genomic Polymorphisms: Prediction of Clinical Outcome to 5-FU/Oxaliplatin Combination Chemotherapy in Refractory Colorectal Cancer," *Br J Cancer*, 2004, 91(2):344-54.

Sweeney C, McClure GY, Fares MY, et al, "Association Between Survival After Treatment for Breast Cancer and Glutathione S-Transferase P1 Ile105Val Polymorphism," *Cancer Res*, 2000, 60(20):5621-4.

Watson MA, Stewart RK, Smith GB, et al, "Human Glutathione S-Transferase P1 Polymorphisms: Relationship to Lung Tissue Enzyme Activity and Population Frequency Distribution," *Carcinogenesis*, 1998, 19(2):275-80.

Glycoprotein IIIa Receptor

Synonyms GPIIIa

Chromosome Location 17q21.32

Clinically-Important Polymorphisms Nonsynonymous SNP resulting in substitution of Leu(Pl^{A1}) or Pro(Pl^{A2}) at codon 33 in exon 2

Discussion Fibrinogen binds to glycoprotein IIb/IIIa receptors expressed on the platelet surface to cross link adjacent platelets as the final common pathway of platelet aggregation. Although data are inconsistent, the GPIIIa $Pl^{A1/A2}$ polymorphism has been associated with platelet aggregation and the effects of aspirin on platelet aggregation in *in vitro* studies.

Antiplatelet therapy:

The GPIIIa Pl^{A2} allele was associated with greater restenosis and risk for subacute coronary thrombosis during combination therapy with aspirin and ticlopidine in patients who had undergone coronary artery stent implantation (Kastrati, 2000; Walter, 1997).

HMG CoA reductase inhibitors:

In myocardial infarction survivors, the greatest reductions in fatal coronary heart disease or nonfatal myocardial infarction with pravastatin occurred in those with the Pl^{A2} allele and either the ACE *ID* or ACE *DD* genotype (Bray, 2001).

May Alter Pharmacokinetics of GPIIIa is not known to alter the metabolism of any drugs.

May Alter Pharmacodynamics of Aspirin, ticlopidine, clopidogrel, glycoprotein IIb/IIIa antagonists, dipyridamole, HMG CoA reductase inhibitors

May Affect Disease Predisposition of Coronary thrombosis

Clinical Recommendations The data suggest that the GPIIIa may be a predictor of the effectiveness of antiplatelet therapy in preventing subacute thrombosis following coronary artery stent implantation.

References

Bray PF, Cannon CP, Goldschmidt-Clermont P, et al, "The Platelet Pl(A2) and Angiotensin-Converting Enzyme (ACE) D Allele Polymorphisms and the Risk of Recurrent Events After Acute Myocardial Infarction," *Am J Cardiol*, 2001, 88(4):347-52.

Kastrati A, Koch W, Gawaz M, et al, "PlA Polymorphism of Glycoprotein IIIa and Risk of Adverse Events After Coronary Stent Placement," *J Am Coll Cardiol*, 2000, 36(1):84-9.

Walter DH, Schachinger V, Elsner M, et al, "Platelet Glycoprotein IIIa Polymorphisms and Risk of Coronary Stent Thrombosis," *Lancet*, 1997, 350(9086):1217-9.

♦ **GNAS1** *see* Gs Protein Alpha-Subunit *on page 288*

- **GNB3** *see* G-Protein Beta$_3$ Subunit *on page 286*
- **GNT1** *see* UDP-Glucuronosyltransferase 1 Family, Polypeptide A1 *on page 322*
- **GP170** *see* ATP-Binding Cassette, Sub-Family B, Member 1 *on page 224*
- **GPIIIa** *see* Glycoprotein IIIa Receptor *on page 285*

G-Protein Beta$_3$ Subunit

Synonyms GB3; GNB3

Chromosome Location 12p13

Clinically-Important Polymorphisms Synonymous SNP in exon 10 *(C825T)*

Discussion The *825T* allele has been associated with enhanced intracellular signal transduction and sodium hydrogen exchange *in vitro*, and reduced plasma renin activity in hypertensive patients (Siffert, 1995; Schunkert, 1998). These genes are also major candidates in association studies on affective disorders and response to antidepressants. The *T* allele has also been linked to risk for hypertension in some populations.

Antidepressants:

An association between the *TT* genotype and response to antidepressant treatment after 4 weeks was identified (Zill, 2000). Depressed patients under the age of 25 with the *T* allele had a poorer response to nortriptyline. However, in those patients older than 25 years of age, antidepressant response was not predicted (Joyce, 2003). *T*-allele carriers showed a higher baseline HAM-D score and a significantly better response to antidepressants than those with the *CC* genotype (Lee, 2004). In a sample of bipolar and major depressives treated with fluvoxamine 300 mg/day or paroxetine 40 mg/day, subjects with the T/T genotype showed a better response to treatment independent of demographic and clinical variables (Serretti, 2003).

Hydrochlorothiazide:

Compared to the *CC* genotype, the *TT* genotype was associated with significantly greater blood pressure response to 4-week treatment with hydrochlorothiazide in hypertensive patients (Turner, 2001). After linear regression, the overall contribution of the *C825T* polymorphism to drug response was approximately 5%.

Lithium:

In a group of approximately 200 patients with bipolar disorder or depression, no association between lithium efficacy and polymorphisms at the G-protein beta-3 subunit loci was found (Serretti, 2001).

Sibutramine:

Sibutramine was more effective in producing weight loss in individuals with the *CC* genotype than in subjects with the *TT/TC* genotypes (Hauner, 2003).

Nitroglycerin:

Young, healthy subjects with the *T* allele were noted to have an increased vasodilatory response to nitroglycerin. It is not clear whether nitroglycerin activates G-protein linked receptors, or whether nitroglycerin mediates the release on an endogenous substance which acts upon these receptors. This may contribute to some of the variability in response to nitrate-derived vasodilators.

May Alter Pharmacodynamics of Antidepressants (tricyclics and SSRIs), loop diuretics, nitroglycerin, sibutramine, thiazide diuretics, and potentially other CYP2D6 substrates

May Affect Disease Predisposition of Hypertension, depression

Clinical Recommendations Future studies may show that the GNB3 gene interacts with other genes, such as the alpha-adducin gene, to determine response to diuretics in hypertension. The GNB3 gene alone appears to contribute minimally to thiazide diuretic response. However, the *C825T* polymorphism appears to be predictive for identifying obese individuals who will benefit from sibutramine treatment. For some antidepressants presence of the T allele or the TT genotype has been associated with increased response.

Counseling Points Since hypertension and depression are diseases with polygenic etiology, carrier status of the *GNB3* variant allele does not necessarily predispose a person to developing hypertension, its sequelae, or depression.

References

Hauner H, Meier M, Jockel KH, et al, "Prediction of a Successful Weight Reduction Under Sibutramine Therapy Through Genotyping of the G-Protein Beta$_3$ Subunit Gene (GNB3) C826T Polymorphism," *Pharmacogenetics*, 2003, 13(8):453-9.

Joyce PR, Mulder RT, Luty SE, et al, "Age-Dependent Antidepressant Pharmacogenomics: Polymorphisms of the Serotonin Transporter and G Protein Beta Subunit as Predictors of Response to Fluoxetine and Nortriptyline," *Int J Neuropsychopharmacol*, 2003, 6(4):339-46.

Kirchheiner J, Brosen K, Dahl ML, et al, "CYP2D6 and CYP2C19 Genotype-Based Dose Recommendations for Antidepressants: A First Step Towards Subpopulation-Specific Dosages," *Acta Psychiatr Scand*, 2001, 104(3):173-92.

Lee HJ, Cha JH, Ham BJ, et al, "Association Between a G-Protein Beta$_3$ Subunit Gene Polymorphism and the Symptomatology and Treatment Responses of Major Depressive Disorders," *Pharmacogenomics J*, 2004, 4(1):29-33.

Mitchell A, Buhrmann S, Seifert A, et al, "Venous response to Nitroglycerin Is Enhanced in Young, Healthy Carriers of the 825T Allele of the G Protein Beta$_3$ Subunit Gene (GNB3)," *Clin Pharmacol Ther*, 2003, 74(5):499-504.

Morita S, Shimoda K, Someya T, et al, "Steady-State Plasma Levels of Nortriptyline and Its Hydroxylated Metabolites in Japanese Patients: Impact of CYP2D6 Genotype on the Hydroxylation of Nortriptyline," *Clin Psychopharmacol*, 2000, 20(2):141-9.

Schunkert H, Hense HW, Doring A, et al, "Association Between a Polymorphism in the G Protein Beta$_3$ Subunit Gene and Lower Renin and Elevated Diastolic Blood Pressure Levels," *Hypertension*, 1998, 32(3):510-3.

Serretti A, Lilli R, Mandelli L, et al, "Serotonin Transporter Gene Association With Lithium Prophylaxis in Mood Disorders," *Pharmacogenomics J*, 2001, 1:71-7.

Serretti A, Lorenzi C, Cusin C, et al, "SSRIs Antidepressant Activity is Influenced By Gβ3 Variants," *Eur Neuropsychopharmacol*, 2003, 13(2):117-22.

Siffert W, Rosskopf D, Moritz A, et al, "Enhanced G Protein Activation in Immortalized Lymphoblasts From Patients With Essential Hypertension," *J Clin Invest*, 1995, 96(2):759-66.

Turner ST, Schwartz GL, Chapman AB, et al, "C825T Polymorphism of the G Protein Beta$_3$ Subunit and Antihypertensive Response to a Thiazide Diuretic," *Hypertension*, 2001, 37(2 Part 2):739-43.

(Continued)

G-Protein Beta$_3$ Subunit *(Continued)*

Zill P, Baghai TC, Zwanzger P, et al, "Evidence for an Association Between a G-Protein Beta3-Gene Variant With Depression and Response to Antidepressant Treatment," *Neuroreport*, 2000, 11(9):1893-7.

Gs Protein Alpha-Subunit

Synonyms GNAS1

Chromosome Location 20q13

Clinically-Important Polymorphisms Synonymous SNP at codon 131 creating a restriction site for the *Fok*I restriction enzyme; T/C point mutation in exon 5; ATT → ATC at codon 131

Discussion Gs is a ubiquitous protein that couples receptors to adenylyl cyclase, which is required to generate intracellular cAMP following receptor stimulation. Mutations of Gs(alpha) are present in endocrine tumors, fibrous dysplasia of bone, and McCune-Albright syndrome.

Reports of altered levels of the stimulatory G-proteins in depression have been presented. Investigations into whether a polymorphism in the stimulatory alpha subunit of G-proteins may be associated with major depression or response to antidepressant medications has been reported (Zill, 2002).

The Gs-proteins mediate activation of adenylyl cyclase by the β-adrenoceptor. Alteration of the GNAS1 has been associated with essential hypertension. A polymorphism has been identified which may be recognized by the presence (+) or absence (-) of a restriction site for the enzyme *Fok*I.

Antidepressants:

No evidence of an association between the alpha subunit of G-protein and major depression and response to antidepressant medication was reported (Zill, 2002).

β-blockers:

In a retrospective study, the frequency of the *Fok*I+ allele was higher in hypertensive individuals who had a good response (>15 mm Hg decline in mean arterial pressure) to β-blocker therapy compared to those with a poor response (<11 mm Hg decline in mean arterial pressure) (Jia, 1999). The *GNAS1* genotype was the only independent predictor of BP response identified in a multiple linear regression analysis.

May Alter Pharmacokinetics of The GNAS1 gene is not known to alter the metabolism of any drugs.

May Alter Pharmacodynamics of β-adrenergic receptor antagonists, antidepressants (cyclic and SSRIs)

May Affect Disease Predisposition of Depression, endocrine neoplasia

Clinical Recommendations The role of the GNAS1 in predicting β-blocker response must be confirmed in a prospectively designed study before its clinical utility will be realized.

Counseling Points Since hypertension is a disease with polygenic etiology, carrier status of the *GNAS1* variant allele does not necessarily predispose a person to developing hypertension or its sequelae.

References

Jia H, Hingorani AD, Sharma P, et al, "Association of the G(s)alpha Gene With Essential Hypertension and Response to Beta-Blockade," *Hypertension*, 1999, 34(1):8-14.

Zill P, Baghai TC, Zwanzger P, et al, "Association Analysis of a Polymorphism in the G-Protein Stimulatory Alpha Subunit in Patients With Major Depression," *Am J Med Genet*, 2002, 114(5):530-2.

♦ **GST** *see* Glutathione-S-Transferase *on page 281*

♦ **GST3** *see* Glutathione-S-Transferase Pi *on page 283*

♦ **GSTA1** *see* Glutathione-S-Transferase Alpha 1 *on page 282*

♦ **GST M1** *see* Glutathione-S-Transferase *on page 281*

♦ **GSTP1** *see* Glutathione-S-Transferase Pi *on page 283*

♦ **GST T1** *see* Glutathione-S-Transferase *on page 281*

Histamine 1 and 2 Receptors

Synonyms HR1; HR2

Chromosome Location 3p25; 5q35.3

Clinically-Important Polymorphisms -1018G/A, -1068A/G, Asp349Glu, Leu449Ser, Lys19Asn, Phe358D

Discussion Histaminic activity is believed to be involved in schizophrenia. Within the brain, histaminic receptors project from the tuberomammillary nucleus of the posterior hypothalamus, with both H_1 and H_2 receptors being present in the caudate, putamen, neocortex, and hippocampus. There are at least four types of histamine receptors (H_1, H_2, H_3, and H_4). The H_1 receptor has a role in sleep, wakefulness, feeding, and drinking, while the H_2 receptor is primarily involved in gastrointestinal functions.

No relationship between clozapine response and these polymorphisms have been found. Additionally, no relationship between these polymorphisms and weight gain from clozapine have been found (Basile, 2001). An association between the genotype at the H2-1018-G/A locus and clinical response to clozapine was found but when correction for multiple testing was performed, significance was lost (Mancama, 2002).

May Alter Pharmacodynamics of Clozapine, olanzapine, and other H_1 and H_2 receptor antagonists

May Affect Disease Predisposition of Schizophrenia, obesity

References

Basile VS, Masellis M, McIntyre RS, et al, "Genetic Dissection of Atypical Antipsychotic-Induced Weight Gain: Novel Preliminary Data on the Pharmacogenetic Puzzle," *J Clin Psychiatry*, 2001, 62(Suppl 23):45-66.

Mancama D, Arranz MJ, Munro J, et al, "Investigation of Promoter Variants of the Histamine 1 and 2 Receptors in Schizophrenia and Clozapine Response," *Neurosci Lett*, 2002, 333(3):207-11.

Mancama D, Arranz MJ, Munro J, et al, "The Histamine-1 and Histamine-2 Receptor Genes - Candidates for Schizophrenia and Clozapine Drug Response," *GeneScreen*, 2000, 1:29-34.

♦ **HLA** *see* Human Leukocyte Antigen *on page 301*

HLA-A1

Synonyms MMC-IA

Chromosome Location 6p21.3

(Continued)

HLA-A1 *(Continued)*

Discussion

Clozapine:

Clozapine responders vs nonresponders 76% predictive value (a combination of 6 polymorphisms were included in the analysis) (Arranz, 2000).

The ability to predict response may be linked at least in part to a genetic polymorphism of HLA-A1, an allele that has a higher distribution in the Scandinavian population than the incidence noted in granulocytopenic patients (Lahdelma, 2001).

May Alter Pharmacodynamics of Clozapine

May Affect Disease Predisposition of Schizophrenia, clozapine-induced agranulocytosis

References

Arranz MJ, Munro J, Birkett J, et al, "Pharmacogenetic Prediction of Clozapine Response," *Lancet*, 2000, 355(921):1615-6.

Lahdelma L, Ahokas A, Andersson LC, et al, "Mitchell B. Balter Award. Human Leukocyte Antigen-A1 Predicts a Good Therapeutic Response to Clozapine With a Low Risk of Agranulocytosis in Patients With Schizophrenia," *J Clin Psychopharmacol*, 2001, 21(1):4-7.

♦ **HLUGP4** *see* UDP-Glucuronosyltransferase 1 Family, Polypeptide A9 *on page 326*

HMG-CoA Reductase

Synonyms 3-hydroxy-3-methylglutaryl-Coenzyme A Reductase; HMGCR

Chromosome Location 5q13.3

Clinically-Important Polymorphisms Single nucleotide polymorphisms at positions 12 (intron 5) and 29 (intron 15)

Discussion HMG-CoA reductase catalyzes the conversion of HMG-CoA to mevalonate, and represents the rate-limiting step of cholesterol synthesis. In addition, this enzyme plays a role in a number of other synthetic pathways. The enzyme is inhibited by feedback inhibition from a variety of sterols derived from internalization and degradation of LDL particles. HMG-CoA reductase inhibitors, or "statins," occupy a portion of the enzyme's binding site, blocking interaction with its substrate. Inhibition of this enzyme results in increased expression of LDL receptors, which in turn increases the clearance of LDL particles from the plasma. Therapy with HMG-CoA reductase inhibitors has been demonstrated to result in important reductions in the development of atherosclerosis and coronary events.

HMG-CoA reductase inhibitors:

A total of 148 SNPs within 10 candidate genes related to lipid metabollism, synthesis, and distribution, and statin metabolism were genotyped in 1536 pravastatin-treated individuals. Two common and closely linked SNPs within the HMG-CoA reductase gene were significantly correlated with response. These were identified as SNP 12 and SNP 29. Neither polymorphism was associated with baseline cholesterol levels. However, these variants were found to influence the extent of response to statin therapy. Individuals with the variant genotype had a diminished response to pravastatin therapy (40 mg/day for 24 weeks). A 22% smaller reduction in total cholesterol, and a 19% smaller reduction in LDL cholesterol was associated with the variant genotype. The absolute difference in total and LDL cholesterol reduction associated with the HMG-CoA reductase genotype was 9 mg/dL and 6 mg/dL, respectively.

References

Chasman DI, Posada D, Subrahmanyan L, et al, "Pharmacogenetic Study of Statin Therapy and Cholesterol Reduction," *JAMA*, 2004, 291(23):2821-7.

- **HMGCR** *see* HMG-CoA Reductase *on page 290*
- **HR1** *see* Histamine 1 and 2 Receptors *on page 289*
- **HR2** *see* Histamine 1 and 2 Receptors *on page 289*

5-HT_{1A} Receptor

Discussion Serotonin receptor subtypes are grouped into several classes. The 5-HT_1 class are G protein receptors and include multiple isoforms within the class. The 5-HT_1 receptor subset includes at least five receptor subtypes (5-$HT_{1A, 1B, 1D, 1E, 1F}$) and is linked to inhibition of adenylyl cyclase activity or to regulation of potassium or calcium channels. The 5-HT_{1A} receptors are most abundant in the dorsal raphe nucleus. They are also found in the hippocampus and amygdala. Activities associated with these receptor locations include temperature regulation, mood changes, and anxiety, respectively. The 5-HT_{1A} receptors are located both presynaptically (somatodendritic autoreceptor) and postsynaptically.

Clozapine:

No significant association with weight gain (Basile, 2001) in the C antinucleotide repeat polymorphism.

May Alter Pharmacodynamics of Aripiprazole, ziprasidone, SSRIs

May Affect Disease Predisposition of Anxiety disorder, affective disorder

References

Basile VS, Masellis M, McIntyre RS, et al, "Genetic Dissection of Atypical Antipsychotic-Induced Weight Gain: Novel Preliminary Data on the Pharmacogenetic Puzzle," *J Clin Psychiatry*, 2001, 62(Suppl 23):45-66.

Serretti A, Lorenzi C, Lilli R, et al, "Serotonin Receptor 2A, 2C, 1A Genes and Response to Lithium Prophylaxis in Mood Disorders," *J Psychiatr Res*, 2000, 34:89-98.

5-HT_{2A} Receptor

Synonyms HTR2

Chromosome Location 13q14-q21

Clinically-Important Polymorphisms T102C, Thr25Asn, His452Tyr, T516C, and -G1438A

Discussion Serotonin receptor subtypes are grouped into several classes. The 5-HT_2 class are G protein receptors and include multiple isoforms within the class. The 5-HT_2 receptor subset includes at least three receptor subtypes (5-$HT_{2A, 2B, 2C}$) and is linked to activation of phospholipase C. Areas of high concentration of 5-HT_{2A} receptors

(Continued)

5-HT_{2A} Receptor *(Continued)*

include the neocortex, olfactory tubercle, and several nuclei arising from the brainstem.

Clozapine:

The *C102/C102* genotype has been associated with a lack of response to clozapine in a cohort of 149 patients with schizophrenia (Arranz, 1995). In 1998 these same authors (Arranz, 1998) found that homozygosity for the *-1438G* allele was also higher among nonresponders than responders (58% vs 32%, p=0.001). The *His452Tyr* polymorphism has also been associated with clozapine response (Arranz, 1996; Badri, 1996) with the presence of the *Tyr452* variant being tied to a poorer response (Arranz, 1998).

Multiple authors have been unable to replicate these findings (Arranz, 1998; Ishigaki, 1996; Jonsson, 1996; Lin, 1999; Malhotra, 1996; Masellis, 1995; Masellis, 1998; Nothen, 1995; Sasaki, 1996).

A meta-analysis was conducted that included 373 patients who responded to clozapine treatment and 360 nonresponders. An association between two 5-HT2A polymorphisms, 102T/C, and His452Tyr, and clozapine response was found. Extreme responders showed a clearer association of the 102T/C polymorphism and clozapine response (Arranz, 1998).

Four allelic variants (T25N, I197V, A447V, and H452Y) of the human 5HT2A receptor were compared to the wild-type allele to determine if clozapine or loxapine altered response. The results indicated that the T25N, A447V, and H452Y mutations did not significantly alter the response of the receptor to loxapine or clozapine. The 197V allele required a twofold higher concentration of clozapine to inhibit serotonin stimulation compared to the wild-type receptor (Harvey, 2003).

Lithium:

No association between lithium's efficacy and polymorphisms of the 5-HT_{2A} receptor was seen in a group of 125 patients with depression or bipolar disorder treated with lithium prophylaxis (Serretti, 2000). In a larger group of 443 patients with bipolar disorder or depression, no association between 5-HT_{2A} receptor polymorphisms and lithium response was found (Cusin, 2002).

Olanzapine:

Negative symptom response has been associated with the *102T/T* genotype and *-1438A/A* genotype (Ellingrod, 2002) in 41 patients treated with olanzapine for 6 weeks.

Risperidone:

One hundred Han Chinese patients with acutely exacerbated schizophrenia were given risperidone for 42 days. Patients with the *C/C* genotype had lower total scores, negative subscale scores, and general psychopathology scores, but not positive subscale scores measured by the Positive and Negative Syndrome Scale than patients with the *102-T/C* genotype. Patients with the *T/C* and *T/T* genotypes had comparable total and subscale scores (Lane, 2002).

A pilot study evaluating 16 patients treated with risperidone, haloperidol or placebo showed that the *102T/C* polymorphism of the 5-HT$_{2A}$ receptor modulated the efficacy of antipsychotic treatment in patients with Alzheimer's disease and behavioral and psychological symptoms of dementia (Engelborghs, 2004).

SSRIs:

A marginal association between 5-HT$_{2A}$ variants (*T102C*, *C-1420T*) and antidepressant response to fluvoxamine and paroxetine. These variants do not seem to play a role in response to SSRI therapy (Cusin, 2002).

Tardive dyskinesia:

Two studies have found a relationship between SNPs of the 5-HT$_{2A}$ receptor and tardive dyskinesia (Segman, 2001; Tan, 2001), although subsequent studies were unable to replicate these results (Basile, 2000; Herken, 2003). In comparing patients with tardive dyskinesia to normal controls, there was a significant excess of the *102C* and *-1438G* alleles in patients with tardive dyskinesia. The *102C/C* and *-1438G/G* genotypes were also significantly associated with higher abnormal involuntary movement scale (AIMS) trunk dyskinesia scores.

Typical antipsychotics:

The *C/C* genotype was more frequent in male patients with schizophrenia who had poor long-term outcome and poor response to typical antipsychotics. Further, the *C/C* genotype was associated with a significantly younger age for the first psychiatric contact compared to those with the *T/T* genotype (Joober, 1999).

A pilot study evaluating 16 patients treated with risperidone, haloperidol or placebo showed that the *102T/C* polymorphism of the 5-HT$_{2A}$ receptor modulated the efficacy of antipsychotic treatment in patients with Alzheimer's disease and behavioral and psychological symptoms of dementia (Engelborghs, 2004).

May Alter Pharmacodynamics of Atypical antipsychotics (except quetiapine)

May Affect Disease Predisposition of Schizophrenia

References

Arranz M, Collier D, Sodhi M, et al, "Association Between Clozapine Response and Allelic Variation in 5-HT2A Receptor Gene," *Lancet*, 1995, 346(8970):281-2.

Arranz MJ, Collier DA, Munro J, et al, "Analysis of the Structural Polymorphisms in the 5-HT$_{2A}$ Receptor and Clinical Response to Clozapine," *Neurosci Lett*, 1996, 217(2-3):177-8.

Arranz MJ, Dawson E, Shaikh S, et al, "Cytochrome P4502D6 Genotype Does Not Determine Response to Clozapine," *Br J Clin Pharmacol*, 1995, 39(4):417-20.

Arranz MJ, Munro J, Owen MJ, et al, "Evidence for Association Between Polymorphisms in the Promoter and Coding Regions of the 5-HT$_{2A}$ Receptor Gene and Response to Clozapine," *Mol Psychiatry*, 1998, 3(1):61-6.

Arranz MJ, Munro J, Sham P, et al, "Meta-Analysis of Studies on Genetic Variation in 5-HT2A Receptors and Clozapine Response," *Schizophr Res*, 1998, 32(2):93-9.

Badri F, Masellis M, Petronis A, et al, "Dopamine and Serotonin System Genes May Predict Clinical Response to Clozapine," *Am J Hum Genet*, 1996, 59:A247.

Basile VS, Ozdemir V, Masellis M, et al, "Lack of Association Between Serotonin-2A Receptor Gene (HTR2A) Polymorphisms and Tardive Dyskinesia in Schizophrenia," *Mol Psychiatry*, 2001, 6(2):230-4.

(Continued)

5-HT_{2A} Receptor *(Continued)*

Cusin C, Serretti A, Zanardi R, et al, "Influence of Monoamine Oxidase A and Serotonin Receptor 2A Polymorphisms in SSRI Antidepressant Activity," *Int J Neuropsychopharmacol*, 2002, 5(1):27-35.

Ellingrod VL, Perry PJ, Lund BL, et al, "5-HT_{2A} and 5-HT_{2C} Receptor Polymorphisms and Predicting Clinical Response to Olanzapine in Schizophrenia," *J Clin Psychopharmacol*, 2002, 22(6):622-4.

Engelborghs S, Holmes C, McCulley M, et al, "5-HT2A Receptor Polymorphism May Modulate Antipsychotic Treatment Response in Alzheimer's Disease," *Int J Geriatr Psychiatry*, 2004, 19(11):1108-9.

Harvey L, Reid RE, Ma C, et al, "Human Genetic Variations in the 5-HT2A Receptor: A Single Nucleotide Polymorphism Identified With Altered Response to Clozapine," *Pharmacogenetics*, 2003, 13(2):107-18.

Herken H, Erdal ME, Boke O, et al, "Tardive Dyskinesia Is Not Associated With the Polymorphisms of 5-HT2A Receptor Gene, Serotonin Transporter Gene and Catechol-O-methyltransferase Gene," *Eur Psychiatry*, 2003, 18(2):77-81.

Ishigaki T, Xie DW, Liu JC, et al, "Intact 5-HT_{2A} Receptor Exons and the Adjoining Intron Regions in Schizophrenia," *Neuropsychopharmacology*, 1996, 14(5):339-47.

Jonsson E, Nothen MM, Bunzel R, et al, "5-HT_{2A} Receptor T102C Polymorphism and Schizophrenia," *Lancet*, 1996, 347(9018):1831.

Joober R, Benkelfat C, Brisebois K, et al, "T102C Polymorphism in the 5-HT_{2A} Gene and Schizophrenia: Relation to Phenotype and Drug Response Variability," *J Psychiatry Neurosci*, 1999, 24(2):141-6.

Lane HY, Chang YC, Chiu CC, et al, "Association of Risperidone Treatment Response With a Polymorphism in the 5-HT_{2A} Receptor Gene," *Am J Psychiatry*, 2002, 159(9):1593-5.

Lin CH, Tsai SJ, Yu YW, et al, "No Evidence for Association of Serotonin-2A Receptor Variant (102T/C) With Schizophrenia or Clozapine Response in a Chinese Population," *Neuroreport*, 1999, 10(1):57-60.

Malhotra AK, Goldman D, Ozaki N, et al, "Lack of Association Between Polymorphisms in the 5-HT_{2A} Receptor Gene and the Antipsychotic Response to Clozapine," *Am J Psychiatry*, 1996, 153(8):1092-4.

Malhotra AK, Goldman D, Buchanan R, et al, "5-HT_{2A} Receptor T102C Polymorphism and Schizophrenia," *Lancet*, 1996, 347(9018):1830-1.

Masellis M, Paterson AD, Badri F, et al, "Genetic Variation of 5-HT_{2A} Receptor and Response to Clozapine," *Lancet*, 1995, 346(8982):1108.

Masellis M, Basile VS, Meltzer HY, et al, "Serotonin Subtype 2 Receptor Genes and Clinical Response to Clozapine in Schizophrenia Patients," *Neuropsychopharmacology*, 1998, 19(2):123-32.

Nothen MM, Rietschel M, Erdmann J, et al, "Genetic Variation of the 5-HT_{2A} Receptor and Response to Clozapine," *Lancet*, 1995, 346(8979):908-9.

Sasaki T, Hattori M, Fukuda R, et al, "5-HT_{2A} Receptor T102C Polymorphism and Schizophrenia," *Lancet*, 1996, 347(9018):1832.

Segman RH, Heresco-Levy U, Finkel B, et al, "Association Between the Serotonin 2A Receptor Gene and Tardive Dyskinesia in Chronic Schizophrenia," 2001, *Mol Psychiatry*, 6(2):225-9.

Serretti A, Lorenzi C, Lilli R, et al, "Serotonin Receptor 2A, 2C, 1A Genes and Response to Lithium Prophylaxis in Mood Disorders," *J Psychiatr Res*, 2000, 34:89-98.

Tan EC, Chong SA, Mahendran R, et al, "Susceptibility to Neuroleptic-Induced Tardive Dyskinesia and the T102C Polymorphism in the Serotonin Type 2A Receptor," *Biol Psychiatry*, 2001, 50(2):144-7.

5-HT_{2C} Receptor

Synonyms HTR2C

Chromosome Location Xq24

Clinically-Important Polymorphisms Cys23Ser, -759C/T

Discussion Serotonin receptor subtypes are grouped into several classes. The 5-HT_2 class are G protein receptors and include multiple isoforms within the class. The 5-HT_2 receptor subset includes at least three receptor subtypes (5-$HT_{2A, 2B, 2C}$) and is linked to activation of phospholipase C. 5-HT_{2C} receptors are abundant in the choroid plexus and its pharmacology is similar to the 5-HT_{2A} receptor.

This receptor has been associated with weight gain. Significantly less weight gain was noted in patients with the *-759T* variant allele than in those without this allele. This was noted in first-episode patients with schizophrenia (Reynolds, 2002).

Clozapine:

The *Ser* allele has been associated with a positive change in GAS scores (Sodhi, 1995). Other authors were unable to confirm these results (Rietschel, 1997; Masellis, 1998; Malhotra, 1996). There was a trend for patients carrying only the serine variant to have higher mean weight gain following treatment with clozapine (Basile, 2001). Patients with the *-759T* variant allele showed significantly less weight gain than those without this allele. The effect was strongest in male patients and not apparent in female patients (Reynolds, 2003). Baseline BMI and the presence or absence of the *-759T* allele had significant effects on BMI at 6 months. The T allele may provide a protective effect in preventing weight gain from clozapine (Miller, 2005). At least three authors have found a relationship between weight gain from clozapine and presence of the *-759C* allele (Basile, 2003; Reynolds, 2003), while one research group was unable to find an association (Tsai, 2003).

Lithium:

No association between lithium's efficacy and polymorphisms of the 5-HT_{2C} receptor was seen in a group of 125 patients with depression or bipolar disorder treated with lithium prophylaxis (Serretti, 2000).

Olanzapine:

Presence of a *-759T* allele has been associated with lack of weight gain of greater than 10% over baseline in 6 weeks (Ellingrod, 2005).

Tardive dyskinesia:

The frequency of the 5-HT_{2C} *Ser* allele has been found to be significantly higher in patients with tardive dyskinesia, versus those without tardive dyskinesia and normal controls (27.2% vs 14.6%, 14.2%, respectively). The 5-HT_{2C} *Ser* and DRD3 *Gly* alleles contributed to 4.2% and 4.7% of the variance seen in orofacial dyskinesia scores (Segman, 2000).

May Alter Pharmacodynamics of Atypical antipsychotics (except quetiapine)

May Affect Disease Predisposition of Schizophrenia

References

Basile VS, Masellis M, DeLuca V, et al, "-759C/T Genetic Variation of the 5-HT_{2C} Receptor and Clozapine Induced Weight Gain," *Lancet*, 2003, 360:1790-1.

Basile VS, Masellis M, McIntyre RS, et al, "Genetic Dissection of Atypical Antipsychotic-Induced Weight Gain: Novel Preliminary Data on the Pharmacogenetic Puzzle," *J Clin Psychiatry*, 2001, 62(Suppl 23):45-66.

Ellingrod VL, Perry PJ, Ringold JC, et al, "Weight Gain Associated With the -759 C/T Polymorphism of the 5-HT_{2C} Receptor and Olanzapine," *Am J Med Genet B Neuropsychiatr Genet*, 2005, 134B(1):76-8.

(Continued)

5-HT_{2C} Receptor *(Continued)*

Malhotra AK, Goldman D, Ozaki N, et al, "Clozapine Response and the 5-HT_{2C} Cys23Ser Polymorphism," *Neuroreport*, 1996, 7(13):2100-2.

Masellis M, Basile VS, Meltzer HY, et al, "Serotonin Subtype 2 Receptor Genes and Clinical Response to Clozapine in Schizophrenia Patients," *Neuropsychopharmacology*, 1998, 19(2):123-32.

Miller DD, Ellingrod VL, Holman TL, et al, "Clozapine-Induced Weight Gain Associated With The 5-HT_{2C} Receptor -759C/T Polymorphism," *Am J Med Genet B Neuropsychiatr Genet*, 2005, 133B(1):97-100.

Reynolds GP, Zhang ZJ, and Zhang XB, "Association of Antipsychotic Drug-Induced Weight Gain With 5-HT_{2C} Receptor Gene Polymorphism," *Lancet*, 2002, 359(9323):2086-7.

Reynolds GP, Zhang Z, and Zhang X, "Polymorphism of the Promoter Region of the Serotonin 5-HT_{2C} Receptor Gene and Clozapine-Induced Weight Gain," *Am J Psychiatry*, 2003, 160(4):677-9.

Rietschel M, Naber D, Fimmers R, et al, "Efficacy and Side Effects of Clozapine Not Associated With Variation in the 5-HT_{2C} Receptor," *Neuroreport*, 1997, 8(8):1999-2003.

Segman RH, Heresco-Levy U, Finkel B, et al, "Association Between the Serotonin 2C Receptor Gene and Tardive Dyskinesia in Chronic Schizophrenia: Additive Contribution of the 5-HT_{2C}ser and DRD3gly to Susceptibility," *Psychopharmacology (Berl)*, 2000, 152(4):408-13.

Serretti A, Lorenzi C, Lilli R, et al, "Serotonin Receptor 2A, 2C, 1A Genes and Response to Lithium Prophylaxis in Mood Disorders," *J Psychiatr Res*, 2000, 34:89-98.

Sodhi MS, Arranz MJ, Curtis D, et al, "Association Between Clozapine Response and Allelic Variation in the 5-HT_{2C} Receptor Gene," *Neuroreport*, 1995, 7(1):169-72.

Tsai SJ, Hong CJ, Yu YW, et al, "-759C/T Genetic Variation of the 5-HT_{2C} Receptor and Clozapine Induced Weight Gain," *Lancet*, 2002, 360(9347):1790.

5-HT_3 Receptor

Synonyms HTR3A; HTR3B

Chromosome Location 11q23.1-q23.2

Clinically-Important Polymorphisms 178-C/T, 1596-A/G (5-HT_{3A}) CA-repeat (5-HT_{3B})

Discussion 5-HT_3 receptors are ligand-gated ion channels whereas other serotonin receptors are G-protein receptors. 5-HT_3 receptors are involved in rapid excitatory responses in peripheral and central nervous systems. The receptors are located in the GI tract and CNS. In the GI tract the receptors are located on parasympathetic terminals including the vagal and splanchnic afferents. In the CNS, a high density of receptors is located in the nucleus tractus solitarii and in the area postrema.

Clozapine:

Two-hundred and sixty-six clozapine treated patients were screened for the 5-HT_{3A} and 5-HT_{3B} variants to determine the association between polymorphisms and clozapine response. Similar allele and genotype distributions among clozapine responders and nonresponders was found suggesting that 5-HT_{3A} and 5-HT_{3B} do not play a role in determining variation of clinical response to clozapine (Gutierrez, 2002).

References

Gutierrez B, Arranz MJ, Huezo-Diaz P, et al, "Novel Mutations in 5-HT3A and 5-HT3B Receptor Genes Not Associated With Clozapine Response," *Schizophr Res*, 2002, 58(1):93-7.

5-HT_6 Receptor

Synonyms HTR6

Chromosome Location 1p36-p35

Clinically-Important Polymorphisms The *T267C* polymorphism was evaluated, and a larger change in BPRS score was associated with the *T/T* genotype (Yu, 1999). This has not been replicated (Masellis, 2000).

Discussion The 5-HT_6 receptor is a G protein receptor and is linked to activation of adenylyl cyclase. Clozapine has a high affinity for 5-HT_6 receptors.

May Alter Pharmacodynamics of Clozapine, olanzapine

References

Masellis M, Basile VS, Meltzer HY, et al, "Lack of Association Between the T.C267 Serotonin 5HT6 Receptor Gene (HTR6) Polymorphism and Prediction of Response to Clozapine in Schizophrenia," *Schizophr Res*, 2001, 47(1):49-58.

Yu YW, Tsai SJ, Lin CH, et al, "Serotonin-6 Receptor Variant (C267T) and Clinical Response to Clozapine," *Neuroreport*, 1999, 10(6):1231-3.

- ♦ **HTR2** *see* 5-HT_{2A} Receptor *on page 291*
- ♦ **HTR2C** *see* 5-HT_{2C} Receptor *on page 294*
- ♦ **HTR3A** *see* 5-HT_3 Receptor *on page 296*
- ♦ **HTR3B** *see* 5-HT_3 Receptor *on page 296*
- ♦ **HTR6** *see* 5-HT_6 Receptor *on page 297*
- ♦ **HTT** *see* 5-HT Transporter *on page 297*
- ♦ **5HTT** *see* 5-HT Transporter *on page 297*
- ♦ **5HTTLPR** *see* 5-HT Transporter *on page 297*

5-HT Transporter

Synonyms 5HTT; 5HTTLPR; HTT; SERT; SLC6A4

Chromosome Location 17q11.1-q12

Clinically-Important Polymorphisms The 5HTT gene (SLC6A4) has 2 known polymorphisms. A functional polymorphism in the promoter region of 5HTT (5HTTLPR) has been identified resulting in two variants, an insertion (long allele) and a deletion (short allele). A 44 bp insertion results in a long variant (l) of this gene. Additionally an intronic variable number of tandem repeats (VNTR) polymorphism has been found in intron 2. This polymorphism has three alleles (*Stin2.9*, *Stin2.10*, and *Stin2.12*).

Discussion The serotonin transporter is selective for serotonin and is in part responsible for the termination of its action at the postsynaptic receptors.

The selective serotonin reuptake inhibitors (SSRIs) bind to the serotonin transporter (5-HTT) and inhibit its capacity to transport serotonin (5-HT). The long allele is associated with higher expression of brain 5-HTT. The short variant has been associated with a reduced transcriptional efficiency of the 5-HTT gene promoter. The "s" variant has also been linked to a greater risk of "switching" in bipolar patients. In addition, an association between this polymorphism and the development of mental disorders has been reported by some investigators. These findings have not been replicated in all studies. Gene polymorphisms have been associated with greater response to SSRIs.

(Continued)

5-HT Transporter *(Continued)*

Further investigation is warranted to evaluate the relationships between genotype, susceptibility to mental disorders, and response to antidepressants (Weizman, 2000).

Variants have been correlated to the pathogenesis of antidepressant-induced mania in bipolar disorder (promoter polymorphism and the short allele). If replicated, polymorphism in the 5-HTT gene may be useful as a predictor of mania/hypomania in bipolar patients (Mundo, 2001).

Antidepressants:

No association was found between the *s* allele of the 5-HTTLPR and antidepressant-induced mania. However, an association between the 5-HTTLPR and lifetime history of rapid cycling in a subsample of patients was found (Rousseva, 2003).

Clozapine:

No relationship between clozapine response and these polymorphisms have been found (Arranz, 2000; Tsai, 2000).

Lithium:

In a group of approximately 200 patients with bipolar disorder or depression, a positive association between lithium efficacy and polymorphisms at the SLC6A4 promoter region was found (Serretti, 2001).

SSRIs:

The long form of this gene has been associated with a greater response to fluvoxamine, paroxetine, and fluvoxamine in unipolar and bipolar depression (Smeraldi, 1998; Zanardi, 2000; Pollock, 2000; Kim, 2000). Response to SSRIs for major depressive disorder, has been reported to be associated with genotype, however the associations have been inconsistent. Minov found no differences in outcome among genotypes (Minov, 2001). In some studies, the presence of the *l* allele has been linked to enhanced response (Smeraldi, 1998; Zanardi, 2000; Pollock, 2000), while in other reports the *s/s* genotype was reported to have an improved response (Kim, 2000; Yoshida, 2002). Clomipramine-induced prolactin release (an index for serotonin neurotransmission) was significantly greater in patients with the *ll* genotype. These results support the data suggesting that patients with the *ss* genotype have a poorer therapeutic response to SSRIs (Whale, 2000). Further, the ss genotype was associated with nonremission and patients were three times more likely to not reach remission of depressive episode after citalopram treatment than patients with other transporter genotype combinations (Arias, 2003). Additionally, no relationship between nortriptyline and 5-HTTLPR genotype has been found (Pollock, 2000).

Two hundred and six elderly depressed patients genotyped for 5HTTLPR polymorphism were treated with sertaline or placebo in an 8-week study to determine if this polymorphism is associated with rapidity of response. Patients homozygous for the long allele of 5HTTLPR showed a significant increase in response to sertraline compared to patients carrying one or two copies of the short allele (p=0.01). No difference was observed in the placebo group (Durham, 2004). In patients under 25 years of age, antidepressant response was not predicted for depressed patients receiving nortriptyline. However, in patients over age 25, the *ss* genotype of the serotonin transporter was associated with poorer response to both fluoxetine and nortriptyline (Joyce, 2003).

In obsessive compulsive disorder, a negative response to medication has been associated with the *l* variant (McDougle, 1998). Additionally, no relationship between 5-HTTLPR genotype and response to SSRIs or clomipramine was found in OCD by other authors (Billet, 1997).

No differences in fluvoxamine response in OCD were found, considering Yale-Brown Obsessive Compulsive Scale (YBOCS) total scores. However, a significant time per genotype interaction was found for the YBOCS subtotal compulsion scores. In patients without a tic disorder codiagnosis, a significant time per genotype interaction for both YBOCS total scores and compulsion scores was found (DiBella, 2002).

Thirty-six patients with major depressive disorder were genotyped at 5HTTLPR and treated with open-label fluoxetine up to 60 mg/day. Seven of nine patients (78%) homozyogous for the s allele developed new or worsening insomnia versus 22% (6/27) non-*s*-homozygous patients (p=0.005). Six of nine (67%) patients homozygous for the s allele developed agitation versus 7% (2/27) of non-*s*-homozygous patients (p=0.001). These finding suggest that the *s* allele of the 5HTTLPR may identify patients at risk for developing insomnia or agitation with fluoxetine (Perlis, 2003).

Two hundred and forty-six patients 65 years of age or older with major depression received mirtazapine or paroxetine in a randomized, double-blind 8-week study. Outcomes were stratified according to 5HTTLPR genotypes. The *s* allele had little impact on efficacy but dramatic effects on adverse effects. The paroxetine treated patients experienced more severe adverse reactions, achieved lower final daily doses, and had more discontinuations. However, mirtazapine treated patients had fewer discontinuations due to adverse reactions, experienced less severe adverse reactions, and achieved higher final daily doses (Murphy, 2004).

Tardive dyskinesia:

No relationship has been found between this polymorphism of 5-HTTLPR, AIMS score, or the diagnosis of tardive dyskinesia (Chong, 2000). Tardive dyskinesia was not associated with polymorphisms of the 5-HT_{2A} receptor gene, serotonin transporter gene, and catechol-O-methyltransferase gene (Herken, 2003).

May Alter Pharmacodynamics of SSRIs

May Affect Disease Predisposition of Depression

References

Arias B, Catalan R, Gasto C, et al, "5-HTTLPR Polymorphism of the Serotonin Transporter Gene Predicts Non-Remission in Major Depression Patients Treated With

(Continued)

5-HT Transporter *(Continued)*

Citalopram in a 12-Weeks Follow Up Study," *J Clin Psychopharmacol*, 2003, 23(6):563-7.

Arranz MJ, Bolonna AA, Munro J, et al, "The Serotonin Transporter and Clozapine Response," *Mol Psychiatry*, 2000, 5(2):124-5.

Billett EA, Richter MA, King N, et al, "Obsessive-Compulsive Disorder, Response to Serotonin Reuptake Inhibitors and Serotonin Transporter Gene," *Mol Psychiatry*, 1997, 2(5):403-6.

Chong SA, Tan EC, Tan CH, et al, "Tardive Dyskinesia Is Not Associated With the Serotonin Gene Polymorphism (5-HTTLPR) in Chinese," *Am J Med Genet*, 2000, 96(6):712-5.

DiBella D, Erzegovesi S, Cavallini MC, et al, "Obsessive-Compulsive Disorder, 5-HTTLPR Polymorphism and Treatment Response," *Pharmacogenomics J*, 2002, 2(3):176-81.

Durham LK, Webb SM, Milos PM, et al, "The Serotonin Transporter Polymorphism, 5HTTLPR, is Associated With a Faster Response Time to Sertraline in an Elderly Population With Major Depressive Disorder," *Psychopharmacology (Berl)*, 2004, 174(4):525-9.

Herken H, Erdal ME, Boke O, et al, "Tardive Dyskinesia Is Not Associated With the Polymorphisms of 5-HT_{2A} Receptor Gene, Serotonin Transporter, Gene, and Catechol-O-Methyltransferase Gene," *Eur Psychiatry*, 2003, 18(2):77-81.

Joyce PR, Mulder RT, Luty SE, et al, "Age-Dependent Antidepressant Pharmacogenomics: Polymorphisms of the Serotonin Transporter and G Protein Beta Subunit as Predictors of Response to Fluoxetine and Nortriptyline," *Int J Neuropsychopharmacol*, 2003, 6(4):339-46.

Kim DK, Lim SW, Lee S, et al, "Serotonin Transporter Gene Polymorphism and Antidepressant Response," *Neuroreport*, 2000, 11(1):215-9.

McDougle CJ, Epperson CN, Price LH, et al, "Evidence for Linkage Disequilibrium Between Serotonin Transporter Gene (SLC6A4) and Obsessive Compulsive Disorder," *Mol Psychiatry*, 1998, 3(3):270-3.

Minov C, Baghai TC, Schule C, et al, "Serotonin-2A-Receptor and -Transporter Polymorphisms: Lack of Association in Patients With Major Depression," *Neurosci Lett*, 2001, 303(2):119-22.

Mundo E, Walker M, Cate T, et al, "The Role of Serotonin Transporter Protein Gene in Antidepressant-Induced Mania in Bipolar Disorder: Preliminary Findings," *Arch Gen Psychiatry*, 2001, 58(6):539-44.

Murphy GM Jr, Hollander SB, Rodrigues HE, et al, "Effects of the Serotonin Transporter Gene Promoter Polymorphism on Mirtazapine and Paroxetine Efficacy and Adverse Events in Geriatric Major Depression," *Arch Gen Psychiatry*, 2004, 61(11):1163-9.

Perlis RH, Mischoulon D, Smoller JW, et al, "Serotonin Transporter Polymorphisms and Adverse Effects With Fluoxetine Treatment," *Biol Psychiatry*, 2003, 54(9):879-83.

Pollock BG, Ferrell RE, Mulsant BH, et al, "Allelic Variation in the Serotonin Transporter Promoter Affects Onset of Paroxetine Treatment Response in Late Life Depression," *Neuropsychopharmacology*, 2000, 23(5):587-90.

Rousseva A, Henry C, van den Bulke D, et al, "Antidepressant-Induced Mania, Rapid Cycling, and the Serotonin Transporter Gene Polymorphism," *Pharmacogenomics J*, 2003, 3(2):101-4.

Serretti A, Lilli R, Mandelli L, et al, "Serotonin Transporter Gene Association With Lithium Prophylaxis in Mood Disorders," *Pharmacogenomics J*, 2001, 1:71-7.

Smeraldi E, Zanardi R, Benedetti F, et al, "Polymorphism Within the Promoter of the Serotonin Transporter Gene and Antidepressant Efficacy of Fluvoxamine," *Mol Psychiatry*, 1998, 3(6):508-11.

Tsai SJ, Hong CJ, Yu YW-Y, et al, "Association Study of a Functional Serotonin Transporter Gene Polymorphism With Schizophrenia, Psychopathology, and Clozapine Response," *Schizophr Res*, 2000, 44:177-81.

Weizman A and Weizman R, "Serotonin Transporter Polymorphism and Response to SSRIs in Major Depression and Relevance to Anxiety Disorders and Substance Abuse," *Pharmacogenomics*, 2000, 1(3):335-41.

Whale R, Quested DJ, Laver D, et al, "Serotonin Transporter (5-HTT) Promoter Genotype May Influence the Prolactin Response to Clomipramine," *Psychopharmacology (Berl)*, 2000, 150(1):120-2.

Yoshida K, Ito K, Sato K, et al, "Influence of the Serotonin Transporter Gene-Linked Polymorphic Region on the Antidepressant Response to Fluvoxamine in Japanese Depressed Patients," *Prog Neuropsychopharmacol Biol Psychiatry*, 2002, 26(2):383-6.

Zanardi R, Benedetti F, DiBella D, et al, "Efficacy of Paroxetine in Depression Is Influenced by a Functional Polymorphism Within the Promoter of the Serotonin Transporter Gene," *J Clin Psychopharmacol*, 2000, 20(1):105-7.

♦ **HUG-BR1** *see* UDP-Glucuronosyltransferase 1 Family, Polypeptide A1 *on page 322*

Human Leukocyte Antigen

Synonyms HLA

Chromosome Location 6p21.3

Clinically-Important Polymorphisms HLA-B*5701, HLA-DR7, HLA-DQ3 haplotype

Discussion

Abacavir:

Life-threatening hypersensitivity reactions to abacavir are known to occur in about 5% of all patients. The gene for HLA is polymorphic and believed to contribute to the interpatient variability in antigen interaction with T cells. Researchers have noted a strong association between the HLA gene and hypersensitivity reactions to abacavir. In a study of 200 patients, the HLA-B*5701, HLA-DR7, HLA-DQ3 haplotype was present in 13 (72%) of the 18 patients with abacavir hypersensitivity, and none of the 167 patients who tolerated abacavir. It is unclear whether this gene participates in triggering the hypersensitivity or is closely linked to a gene that mediates this reaction. The presence of HLA-B5701, HLA-DR7, and HLA-DQ3 had a positive predictive value for hypersensitivity of 100%, and a negative predictive value of 97%. The researchers concluded that withholding abacavir in patients with HLA-B5701, HLA-DR7, and HLA-DQ3 would substantially reduce the prevalence of hypersensitivity (estimating a reduction from 9% to 2.5% in this study population), without denying the use of the agent inappropriately. It remains to be seen whether genetic screening for these markers, or perhaps additional genes, will become a standard for patients who may be candidates for this therapy. However, this study indicates the potential for these procedures to improve the safety of drug therapy (Mallal, 2002).

May Alter Pharmacodynamics of Abacavir

References

Mallal S, Nolan D, Witt C, et al, "Association Between Presence of HLA-B*5701, HLA-DR7, and HLA-DQ3 and Hypersensitivity to HIV-1 Reverse-Transcriptase Inhibitor Abacavir," *Lancet*, 2002, 359(9308):727-32.

♦ **3-hydroxy-3-methylglutaryl-Coenzyme A Reductase** *see* HMG-CoA Reductase *on page 290*

Inositol Polyphosphate 1-Phosphatase

Synonyms IP

Clinically-Important Polymorphisms C973A

(Continued)

Inositol Polyphosphate 1-Phosphatase *(Continued)*

Discussion Inositol phosphates are second messengers. Lithium inhibits the phosphatase (inositol monophosphatase) that liberates inositol from inositol phosphate. Therefore, lithium interferes with the phosphatidylinositol pathway (Berridge, 1989).

Lithium:

An association between the inositol polyphosphate 1-phosphatase C973A variant and bipolar disorder was found in 23 patients. However, in a second group of 54 patients no association was found (Steen, 1998).

May Alter Pharmacodynamics of Lithium

References

Berridge MJ, Downes CP, and Hanley MR, "Neural and Developmental Actions of Lithium: A Unifying Hypothesis," *Cell*, 1989, 59:411-9.

Steen VM, Lovlie R, Osher Y, et al, "The Polymorphic Inositol Polyphosphate 1-phosphatase Gene as a Candidate for Pharmacogenetic Prediction of Lithium-responsive Manic-depressive Illness," *Pharmacogenetics*, 1998, 8:259-68.

♦ **IP** *see* Inositol Polyphosphate 1-Phosphatase *on page 301*

♦ **k-channel** *see* Cardiac Potassium Ion Channel *on page 241*

♦ **LDLR** *see* Low-Density Lipoprotein Receptor *on page 304*

Leukotriene C4 Synthase

Synonyms LTC(4) Synthase

Chromosome Location 5q35

Clinically-Important Polymorphisms A-444C in the promoter region

Discussion Leukotrienes are important mediators of inflammation, and have been implicated in the pathogenesis of allergic disorders, asthma and other inflammatory diseases. Leukotrienes have been implicated as a contributing factor in a number of disease states, including Alzheimer's disease (Manev, 2000).

The synthesis of leukotrienes may be influenced by polymorphisms of the promoter regions for leukotriene C(4) synthase. Leukotriene C(4) synthase is the initial enzyme in the pathway which produces leukotrienes from arachidonic acid. Although leukotrienes synthesized by LTC(4) play a role in the pathogenesis of asthma, the pathogenesis of this disorder, as well as other inflammatory diseases, is complex. The association between individual polymorphisms and the asthmatic phenotype has not been adequately defined.

Aspirin (sensitivity and asthma):

Approximately 10% of patients with asthma have a form in which symptoms are exacerbated by aspirin (as well as most other nonsteroidal anti-inflammatory agents). This syndrome is characterized by significant basal overproduction of cysteinyl leukotrienes (cysLT). This has been correlated to elevated expression of leukotriene C(4) synthase. The exacerbation of symptoms by aspirin-like drugs is related to inhibition of cyclooxygenase, the second pathway for arachidonic acid conversion, and results in overproduction of cysteinyl leukotrienes.

Several investigations have attempted to evaluate the relationship between polymorphisms and aspirin-sensitive asthma. The frequency of the (*-444*) allele appears to correlate with upregulation of the cys-leukotriene pathway. However, associations with the development of aspirin-induced asthma have been inconsistent. For example, this polymorphism was associated with a relative risk of 3.89 for the aspirin-intolerant phenotype in Polish patients. A subsequent study in the United States demonstrated that the *C-444* allele was not statistically different among patients between aspirin-intolerant asthmatics, aspirin-tolerant asthmatics, and unaffected control subjects. In addition, functional studies have been unable to demonstrate significant upregulatory or downregulatory effects in the transcription of the leukotriene C4 synthetase gene related to the *-444* allele (Van Sambeek, 2000). Basal levels of specific leukotrienes (LTE4) and the increment of urinary LTE4 on venous aspirin challenge did not differ between wild-type homozygotes and carriers of the *C*-allele (Kawagishi, 2002).

May Alter Pharmacodynamics of Aspirin (exacerbation of asthma), nonsteroidal anti-inflammatory agents (exacerbation of asthma), leukotriene receptor antagonists

May Affect Disease Predisposition of Asthma

Clinical Recommendations While a polymorphism in leukotriene C4 synthetase may contribute to the development of aspirin-intolerant asthma, it does not appear to be a single factor in regulating this response. It has been suggested that this gene may be in linkage disequilibrium with another mutation which may be more directly related to the phenomenon.

References

Coffey M and Peters-Golden M, "Extending the Understanding of Leukotrienes in Asthma," *Curr Opin Allergy Clin Immunol*, 2003, 3(1):57-63.

Fowler SJ, Hall IP, Wilson AM, et al, "5-Lipoxygenase Polymorphism and *in vivo* Response to Leukotriene Receptor Antagonists," *Eur J Clin Pharmacol*, 2002, 58(3):187-90.

Kawagishi Y, Mita H, Taniguchi M, et al, "Leukotriene C4 Synthase Promoter Polymorphism in Japanese Patients With Aspirin-Induced Asthma," *J Allergy Clin Immunol*, 2002, 109(6):936-42.

Manev H, "5-Lipoxygenase Gene Polymorphism and Onset of Alzheimer's Disease," *Med Hypotheses*, 2000, 54(1):75-6.

Nanavaty U, Goldstein AD, and Levine SJ, "Polymorphisms in Candidate Asthma Genes," *Am J Med Sci*, 2001, 321(1):11-6.

Palmer LJ, Silverman ES, Weiss ST, et al, "Pharmacogenetics of Asthma," *Am J Respir Crit Care Med*, 2002, 165(7):861-6.

Sanak M, Pierzchalska M, Bazan-Socha S, et al, "Enhanced Expression of the Leukotriene C(4) Synthase Due to Overactive Transcription of an Allelic Variant Associated With Aspirin-Intolerant Asthma," *Am J Respir Cell Mol Biol*, 2000, 23(3):290-6.

♦ **5-LO** *see* Arachidonate 5-Lipoxygenase *on page 223*

♦ **LOG5** *see* Arachidonate 5-Lipoxygenase *on page 223*

Low-Density Lipoprotein Receptor

Synonyms LDLR

Chromosome Location 19p13.3

Clinically-Important Polymorphisms AvaII (exon 13), HincII (exon 12), PvuII (intron 15) restriction fragment length polymorphisms

Discussion The LDLR is responsible for the hepatic uptake of low density lipoproteins from the plasma. Many mutations have been reported, and have been associated with forms of familial hypercholesterolemia. Familial hypercholesterolemia is an autosomal dominant disorder characterized by elevated low-density lipoproteins, as well as premature coronary artery disease.

HMG CoA reductase inhibitors:

The AvaII and PvuII polymorphisms were associated with the cholesterol-lowering response to fluvastatin in patients with primary hypercholesterolemia, with less reduction in total cholesterol, LDL cholesterol, and apolipoprotein B levels after 16 weeks among A+A+ (AvaII) and P+P+ (PvuII) homozygotes (Salazar, 2000).

May Alter Pharmacokinetics of LDLR is not known to alter the metabolism of any drugs.

May Alter Pharmacodynamics of HMG CoA reductase inhibitors

May Affect Disease Predisposition of Hypercholesterolemia

Clinical Recommendations The association between the LDLR gene and clinical outcomes during HMG CoA reductase therapy should be determined before genotyping for this polymorphism is considered clinically useful.

Counseling Points Carrier status for a variant *LDLR* allele may increase the risk for hypercholesterolemia. Individuals should discuss the implications of carrier status with their clinician or another health-care professional. In addition, carriers of the variant allele should be encouraged to follow recommended guidelines for cholesterol screening.

References

Salazar LA, Hirata MH, Forti N, et al, "Pvu II Intron 15 Polymorphism at the LDL Receptor Gene Is Associated With Differences in Serum Lipid Concentrations in Subjects With Low and High Risk for Coronary Artery Disease From Brazil," *Clin Chim Acta*, 2000, 293(1-2):75-88.

♦ **5-LOX** *see* Arachidonate 5-Lipoxygenase *on page 223*

♦ **5LPG** *see* Arachidonate 5-Lipoxygenase *on page 223*

♦ **LTC(4) Synthase** *see* Leukotriene C4 Synthase *on page 302*

♦ **LUGP4** *see* UDP-Glucuronosyltransferase 1 Family, Polypeptide A9 *on page 326*

♦ **MAO A** *see* Monoamine Oxidase A *on page 307*

♦ **Matrix Metalloproteinase 3** *see* Stromelysin-1 *on page 316*

♦ **MDR-1** *see* ATP-Binding Cassette, Sub-Family B, Member 1 *on page 224*

5,10-Methylenetetrahydrofolate Reductase

Synonyms MHFR; MTHFR

Chromosome Location 1p36.3

Clinically-Important Polymorphisms C677T

Discussion Methylenetetrahydrofolate reductase regulates the intracellular folate pool which is used in the synthesis of DNA and protein. A homozygous variant, *C677T*, occurs in up to 10% of Caucasians. Homozygotes for this variant exhibit diminished activity (only 35% of normal enzyme capacity) and accumulate 5,10-methylenetetrahydrofolate, or CH2THF (Schwahn, 2001).

Fluorouracil:

Severe myelosuppression was reported in breast cancer patients with the *C677T* polymorphism after receiving CMF (cyclophosphamide, methotrexate, and 5FU). An excess of CH2THF may increase the ability of 5FU to inhibit thymidylate synthetase, resulting in increased myelosuppression.

Raletrexid:

In a phase 1 trial with the thymidylate synthetase inhibitor, raletrexid, individuals with polymorphism of this enzyme had no toxicities associated with raletrexid (Schwahn, 2001).

Methotrexate:

In a study of 220 chronic myelogenous leukemia patients treated with MTX, patients expressing the homozygous C677T mutation experienced a 36% increase in oral mucositis and a 34% slower platelet recovery phase (Ulrich, 2001). This observation has been confirmed in other studies.

May Alter Pharmacodynamics of Fluorouracil, capecitabine, methotrexate

May Affect Disease Predisposition of Hyperhomocysteinemia and coronary artery disease

Clinical Recommendations Pending additional clinical investigation, analysis of MHFR polymorphisms are not recommended for routine clinical use.

References

Schwahn B and Rozen R, "Polymorphisms in the Methylenetetrahydrofolate Reductase Gene: Clinical Consequences," *Am J Pharmacogenomics*, 2001, 1(3):189-201.

Ulrich CM, Yasui Y, Storb R, et al, "Pharmacogenetics of Methotrexate: Toxicity Among Marrow Transplantation Patients Varies With the Methylenetetrahydrofolate Reductase C677T Polymorphism," *Blood*, 2001, 98(1):231-4.

Methylguanine-DNA Methyltransferase

Synonyms MGMT; O^6-Alkylguanine-DNA Alkyltransferase; O^6-Methylguanine-DNA Methyltransferase

Chromosome Location 10q26

Clinically-Important Polymorphisms Promoter methylation status has been demonstrated to influence response to chemotherapy. The epigenetic basis of this phenotypic variation has not been established.

Discussion Methylguanine-DNA methyltransferase (MGMT) is an important enzyme responsible for repairing DNA damaged by alkylation of the O-6 position of guanine. Methylation at this position can induce a mispairing polymorphism of G:C>A:T, whereas general alkylation can cause subsequent cross-linking of DNA leading to strand breakage and apoptosis. As guanine residues represent a major target

(Continued)

Methylguanine-DNA Methyltransferase *(Continued)*

for chemotherapeutic alkylating agents, the normal reparative activity of MGMT has been postulated to account for resistance to these agents, essentially by reversing the cytotoxic effects of these drugs. MGMT is transcriptionally silenced by hypermethylation of the CpG islands within its promoter region. Ostensibly, this hypermethylation reduces the functional pool of MGMT, thus permitting unopposed DNA damage induced by alkylating treatments. Interestingly, reduced or absent MGMT phenotypes have been associated with tumorigenicity, particularly cancers of the colorectal region, head and neck, and brain.

Carmustine:

MGMT promoter methylation status was retrospectively evaluated in 47 patients with grade III or IV gliomas treated with carmustine. Promoter methylation was present in 19 or 47 patients (40%). Of these patients, 12 of 19 (63%) showed complete or partial response to carmustine, compared to only 1 of 28 (4%) patients without the methylated promoter (p<0.001). In addition, median time to progression was significantly different between groups, at 21 months and 8 months, respectively (p<0.001) (Esteller, 2000).

Paz and colleagues documented a similar finding in patients receiving carmustine as first-line therapy for primary glioma. A significant association was seen between methylated MGMT status and clinical response (n=35, p=0.041).

Temozolomide:

Hegi et al, conducted a prospective evaluation of 38 patients undergoing resection for glioblastoma and receiving adjunctive temozolomide with radiation. Post-surgical survival rate was 62% for patients with MGMT inactivation (ie, promoter methylation) compared to only 8% of patients with unmethylated tumors. In multivariate analyses, methylation status was an independent predictor of survival, and did not correlate with any other patient variables.

In a randomized trial of 206 glioblastoma patients comparing radiotherapy with or without temozolomide, promoter methylation was an independent prognostic factor showing a 55% reduction of death compared to unmethylated status, irrespective of treatment (p<0.001). Of those patients with methylated MGMT status, concomitant treatment of temozolomide and radiotherapy improved median survival (21.7 months) by 6.4 months compared to radiotherapy alone (15.3 months, p=0.007) (Hegi, 2005).

Another study evaluated 92 patients receiving temozolomide as either first-line therapy or for relapse treatment of primary glioma (Paz, 2004). Of the 40 patients receiving temozolomide first-line, 8 of 12 (67%) showed complete or partial clinical response associated with promoter methylation, while only 7 of 28 (25%) patients with the non-methylated phenotype responded to treatment (p=0.03). Interestingly, there was no positive association between clinical response and methylation status in patients receiving temozolomide for relapse treatment.

May Affect Disease Predisposition of Lung cancer, colorectal cancer, gliomas (astrocytomas, dendritic cell), esophageal cancer

References

Esteller M, Garcia-Foncillas J, Andion E, et al, "Inactivation of the DNA-Repair Gene MGMT and the Clinical Response of Gliomas to Alkylating Agents," *N Engl J Med*, 2000, 343(19):1350-4.

Hegi ME, Diserens AC, Gorlia T, et al, "MGMT Gene Silencing and Benefit from Temozolomide in Glioblastoma," *N Engl J Med*, 2005, 352(10):997-1003.

Hegi ME, Diserens AC, Godard S, et al, "Clinical Trial Substantiates the Predictive Value of O-6-Methylguanine-DNA Methyltransferase Promoter Methylation in Glioblastoma Patients Treated with Temozolomide," *Clin Cancer Res*, 2004, 10(6):1871-4.

Paz MF, Yaya-Tur R, Rojas-Marcos I, et al, "CpG Island Hypermethylation of the DNA Repair Enzyme Methyltransferase Predicts Response to Temozolomide in Primary Gliomas," *Clin Cancer Res*, 2004, 10(15):4933-8.

♦ **MGMT** *see* Methylguanine-DNA Methyltransferase *on page 305*

♦ **MHFR** *see* 5,10-Methylenetetrahydrofolate Reductase *on page 304*

♦ **MMC-IA** *see* HLA-A1 *on page 289*

♦ **MMP3** *see* Stromelysin-1 *on page 316*

Monoamine Oxidase A

Synonyms MAO A

Chromosome Location Xp11.23

Clinically-Important Polymorphisms VNTR, G941T, C1077A, T1460C, 30 bp

Discussion Monoamine oxidase inhibitors are effective antidepressants. Their pharmacological effects mediate the action of dopamine, norepinephrine, and serotonin by inhibition of their breakdown.

Lithium:

In a group of approximately 200 patients with bipolar disorder or depression, no association between lithium efficacy and polymorphisms at the MAO-A loci was found (Serretti, 2001). In a larger group of 443 patients with bipolar disorder or depression, no association between MAO-A polymorphisms and lithium response was found (Cusin, 2002).

SSRIs:

No association with MAO-A genotypes and antidepressant response to fluvoxamine and paroxetine was observed. MAO-A does not seem to play a role in response to SSRI therapy (Cusin, 2002).

References

Cusin C, Serretti A, Zanardi R, et al, "Influence of Monoamine Oxidase A and Serotonin Receptor 2A Polymorphisms in SSRI Antidepressant Activity," *Int J Neuropsychopharmacol*, 2002, 5(1):27-35.

Serretti A, Lilli R, Mandelli L, et al, "Serotonin Transporter Gene Association With Lithium Prophylaxis in Mood Disorders," *Pharmacogenomics J*, 2001, 1:71-7.

♦ **MTHFR** *see* 5,10-Methylenetetrahydrofolate Reductase *on page 304*

♦ **Multidrug Resistance Gene** *see* ATP-Binding Cassette, Sub-Family B, Member 1 *on page 224*

N-Acetyltransferase 2 Enzyme

Synonyms NAT2

Chromosome Location 8p22

Clinically-Important Polymorphisms At least 11 single nucleotide polymorphisms contributing to the slow, rapid, and intermediate acetylator phenotypes

Discussion Acetylator phenotype may influence the activation and/or metabolism of a variety of compounds. For a number of medications metabolized by NAT2, the development of specific adverse events has been correlated to acetylator phenotype (see below).

Isoniazid:

Isoniazid (INH) is metabolized by hepatic N-acetylation to yield a variety of metabolites. These compounds include acetylhydrazine, which has been characterized as a potent hepatotoxin. INH can cause clinically-significant and even fatal hepatic injury in 1% of patients and elevated liver enzymes in 10% to 20% of patients. The frequency of hepatic injury has been correlated to acetylator phenotype.

Procainamide:

Slow acetylators are at risk of developing antinuclear antibodies and lupus-like syndrome during hydralazine or procainamide therapy (Woosley, 1978).

Fast acetylators have increased conversion of procainamide to N-acetylprocainamide, its active metabolites possessing potent class III antiarrhythmic effects. In fast acetylators, a normal procainamide dose can lead to supratherapeutic levels of N-acetylprocainamide (NAPA), prolongation of the QT interval, and an increased risk for ventricular arrhythmias.

Hydralazine:

Slow acetylators are at risk of developing antinuclear antibodies and lupus-like syndrome during hydralazine therapy (Mansilla-Tinoco, 1982).

Sulfonamides:

Adverse effects to sulfamethoxazole-trimethoprim, such as rash, granulocytopenia, or liver impairment, were noted to be considerably higher in children with mutations of the *NAT2* encoding gene. It has been suggested that the *NAT2* genotype may provides the basis for the detection of hypersensitivity to TMP-SMX (Zielinska, 1998). No association was evident between the slow acetylator phenotype and leprosy treatment outcome, although the mean percentage of sulfamethazine acetylated in patients with the slow acetylator phenotype was significantly higher than that observed for the same phenotype in controls.

May Alter Pharmacokinetics of Hydralazine, isoniazid, procainamide, sulfonamides

References

Mansilla-Tinoco R, Harland SJ, Ryan PJ, et al, "Hydralazine, Antinuclear Antibodies, and the Lupus Syndrome," *Br Med J (Clin Res Ed)*, 1982, 284(6320):936-9.

Woosley RL, Drayer DE, Reidenberg MM, et al, "Effect of Acetylator Phenotype on the Rate at Which Procainamide Induces Antinuclear Antibodies and the Lupus Syndrome," *N Engl J Med*, 1978, 298(21):1157-9.

Zielinska E, Niewiarowski W, Bodalski J, et al, "Genotyping of the Arylamine N-Acetyltransferase Polymorphism in the Prediction of Idiosyncratic Reactions to Trimethoprim-Sulfamethoxazole in Infants," *Pharm World Sci*, 1998, 20(3):123-30.

NAD(P)H Quinone Oxidoreductase

Synonyms DT-Diaphorase; Diaphorase-4; EC 1.6.99.2; NQO1; Quinone Oxidoreductase

Chromosome Location 16q22.1

Clinically-Important Polymorphisms Three alleles of the human reduced nicotinamide adenine dinucleotide phosphate:quinone oxidoreductase-1 (NQO1) gene are known: Wild-type, *609C>T* variant, and *465C>T* variant; these are designed as NQO1*1 and NQO1*2, and NQO1*3

Discussion Mammalian NAD(P)H:quinone oxidoreductase (NQO1) catalyzes the two-electron reduction of quinones and plays one of the main roles in the bioactivation of quinoidal drugs. NQO1 has often been suggested to be involved in cancer prevention by means of detoxification of electrophilic quinones. Underactive variants of NQO1 seem to increase the risk of AML. NQO1 has been associated with the development of ALL (along with many other genetic factors), and the prognosis of patients with CYPIA1 and NQO1 variants has been noted to be worse than that of patients who lack these variants (Krajinovic, 2001). NQO1 C609T has also been reported to be associated with lung cancer, colorectal cancer, and urological malignancies.

Mitomycin-C:

Studies have suggested that patients homozygous for a C to T transition at position 609 of the cDNA sequence of NQO1 may be resistant to mitomycin C. Resistance appears to result from a diminished activation of mitomycin C. In addition, gene expression has been shown to correlate with chemosensitivity (Pan, 1995). However, several enzyme systems, including DTD, P450 reductase, GSH and GST may act in concert to determine chemosensitivity. This may include additive or antagonistic effects, depending on intracellular concentrations. An isolated mutation in NQO1 may not result in predictable effect on MMC activity (Phillips, 2001).

May Alter Pharmacodynamics of Mitomycin C

May Affect Disease Predisposition of Secondary AML carcinogenesis

References

Krajinovic M, Labuda D, and Sinnett D, "Childhood Acute Lymphoblastic Leukemia: Genetic Determinants of Susceptibility and Disease Outcome," *Rev Environ Health*, 2001, 16(4):263-79.

Pan SS, Forrest GL, Akman SA, et al, "NAD(P)H:Quinone Oxidoreductase Expression and Mitomycin C Resistance Developed by Human Colon Cancer HCT 116 Cells," *Cancer Res*, 1995, 55(2):330-5.

Phillips RM, Burger AM, Fiebig HH, et al, "Genotyping of NAD(P)H:Quinone Oxidoreductase (NQO1) in a Panel of Human Tumor Xenografts: Relationship Between Genotype Status, NQO1 Activity, and the Response of Xenografts to Mitomycin C Chemotherapy *in vivo*(1)," *Biochem Pharmacol*, 2001, 62(10):1371-7.

♦ **NAT2** *see* N-Acetyltransferase 2 Enzyme *on page 308*

♦ **NQO1** *see* NAD(P)H Quinone Oxidoreductase *on page 309*

♦ **O[6]-Alkylguanine-DNA Alkyltransferase** *see* Methylguanine-DNA Methyltransferase *on page 305*

♦ **O[6]-Methylguanine-DNA Methyltransferase** *see* Methylguanine-DNA Methyltransferase *on page 305*

P2RY12

Synonyms P2Y12; P2Y; Platelet ADP Receptor; Purinergic Receptor

Chromosome Location 3q24-q25

Clinically-Important Polymorphisms Five polymorphisms have been recently reported. Two SNPs (C139T and T744C) and one nucleotide insertion (ins801A) have been identified in the only intron of this gene, occurring with an allelic frequency of 14% in a small European sample population. Two additional synonymous polymorphisms in exon 2, G52T and C34T, have also been described in this sample group with frequencies of 14% and 28%, respectively.

Discussion P2Y12 is an inhibitory G-protein coupled receptor responsible for the sustained, irreversible activation of platelet aggregation induced by the endogenous ligand ADP. This receptor is the target of the antiplatelet drugs clopidogrel and ticlopidine. Several polymorphisms of the gene encoding this receptor have been identified which influence the efficacy of ADP-mediated platelet aggregation. In a study of 98 white male European patients, Fontana et al, reported that 4 polymorphisms (C139T, T744C, ins801A, and G52T) occurred in linkage disequilibrium with a frequency of 14% in this sample population. Blood samples from patients exhibiting this polymorphic haplotype were associated with a significantly greater maximal ADP-induced aggregation response as compared to wild type ($p<0.007$). As the variant haplotype was linked to a sequence variation in the promoter region, the investigators theorized that an upregulation of receptor number may account for this augmented aggregation response.

Clopidogrel:

Ziegler et al, evaluated 473 patients with symptomatic peripheral artery disease treated with clopidogrel (n=137) or aspirin (n=336). Patients were followed for 21 months and monitored for the occurrence of neurological events (ischemic stroke and/or carotid revascularization). These events occurred in 8% of all patients. Genotype analysis for G52T and C34T polymorphisms revealed that neither SNP correlated with aspirin-related vascular events; however, presence of the 34T allele was associated with a 4.02-fold increased risk (95% CI: 1.08-14.9) of neurologic vascular events in clopidogrel-treated patients. These observations suggest that the variant ADP receptor phenotype selectively influences the efficacy of clopidogrel and possibly ticlopidine.

It is unclear at this time how the reportedly synonymous coding polymorphism of C34T results in a significant association with neurovascular events. Although the authors hypothesized that these clinical observations reflected altered ADP receptor responses, unfortunately, this correlate was not specifically studied. It is possible, however, that this SNP defines an alternate haplotype associated with coding changes in the Austrian population studied by Ziegler.

May Alter Pharmacodynamics of Clopidogrel, ticlopidine

May Affect Disease Predisposition of Coronary thrombosis, cerebrovascular events, percutaneous coronary interventions

Clinical Recommendations As these data represent isolated studies without large, prospective trial confirmation, evaluating patients for the presence of these polymorphisms is not recommended at this time.

References

Fontana P, Dupont A, Gandrille S, et al, "Adenosine Diphosphate-Induced Platelet Aggregation is Associated with P2Y12 Gene Sequence Variations in Healthy Subjects," *Circulation*, 2003, 108(8):989-95.

Nguyen TA, Diodati JG, and Pharand C, "Resistance to Clopidogrel: A Review of the Evidence," *J Am Coll Cardiol*, 2005, 45(8):1157-64.

Ziegler S, Schillinger M, Funk M, et al, "Association of a Functional Polymorphism in the Clopidogrel Target Receptor Gene, P2Y12, and the Risk for Ischemic Cerebrovascular Events in Patients With Peripheral Artery Disease," *Stroke*, 2005, 36(7):1394-9.

♦ **P2Y** *see* P2RY12 *on page 310*

♦ **P2Y12** *see* P2RY12 *on page 310*

p53

Synonyms TP53; TRP53

Chromosome Location 17p13.1

Clinically-Important Polymorphisms Arg72Pro

Discussion The p53 gene encodes a nuclear protein which regulates cell growth and division. The protein serves as a tumor suppressor by regulating gene transcription. It is believed to form a tetramer which binds DNA at a specific receptor site to activate expression of specific genes which inhibit growth. The more common mutants fail to bind to the recognized p53 DNA binding site, resulting in a loss of tumor suppressor activity.

Many forms of cancer, both inherited and sporadic, have been associated with mutations of the p53 gene. Bladder, breast, colorectal, lung, and brain cancers have been shown to have a relationship with the activity of this gene's product. Mutations of the p53 gene occur as somatic mutations as well as germline mutations in families with a high cancer incidence (such as in Li-Fraumeni syndrome).

The pathways which are affected by p53 polymorphisms and the clinical consequences of these polymorphisms continue to be investigated. A common polymorphism involves either proline or arginine at position 72, which results in a dramatic change in the primary structure of the protein. Mutations of the p53 gene have been shown to result in a loss of its ability to transactivate Bax, an apoptosis-inducing gene (Perego, 1996). The *Arg72* form has been shown to have greater efficiency in the induction of apoptosis, while the *Pro72* form has been shown to cause a higher level of G1 arrest.

Related transcription-regulating proteins such as p63 and p73 may also mediate response, and are inter-related with p53 activities. P53 may regulate the activity of additional DNA repair enzymes, including

(Continued)

p53 *(Continued)*

members of the XP family. P53 status may be a determinant of chemosensitivity of some tumor cells.

Cisplatin:

Clinical response following cisplatin-based chemoradiotherapy for advanced head and neck cancer has been shown to be influenced by a polymorphism in the p53 gene, with cancers expressing 72R having lower response rates than those expressing 72P. In patients with ovarian cancer, p53 alterations have been correlated with resistance to platinum-based chemotherapy, early relapse, and shortened overall survival. However, in multivariate analysis this was not an independent prognostic factor (Reles, 2001).

May Alter Pharmacodynamics of Cisplatin

May Affect Disease Predisposition of A wide variety of cancers have been associated with p53

Laboratory Evaluation Functional and sequencing assays are commercially available to assess p53 mutations

Clinical Recommendations Commercial tests are available for p53 mutations; however, clinical correlations have not been validated. P53 analysis is not currently recommended for routine clinical use.

References

Bergamaschi D, Gasco M, Hiller L, et al, "p53 Polymorphism Influences Response in Cancer Chemotherapy Via Modulation of p73-dependent Apoptosis," *Cancer Cell*, 2003, 3(4):387-402.

Perego P, Giarola M, Righetti SC, et al, "Association Between Cisplatin Resistance and Mutation of p53 Gene and Reduced Bax Expression in Ovarian Carcinoma Cell Systems," *Cancer Res*, 1996, 56(3):556-62.

Pim D and Banks L, "p53 Polymorphic Variants at Codon 72 Exert Different Effects on Cell Cycle Progression," *Int J Cancer*, 2004, 108(2):196-9.

Reles A, Wen WH, Schmider A, et al, "Correlation of p53 Mutations With Resistance to Platinum-based Chemotherapy and Shortened Survival in Ovarian Cancer," *Clin Cancer Res*, 2001, 7(10):2984-97.

- ♦ **P-450 C18 11-Beta Hydroxylase** *see* Aldosterone Synthase *on page 208*
- ♦ **P450 MP-12/MP-20** *see* CYP2C8 *on page 248*
- ♦ **P-gp** *see* ATP-Binding Cassette, Sub-Family B, Member 1 *on page 224*
- ♦ **PGY1** *see* ATP-Binding Cassette, Sub-Family B, Member 1 *on page 224*
- ♦ **PI** *see* Glutathione-S-Transferase Pi *on page 283*
- ♦ **platelet ADP receptor** *see* P2RY12 *on page 310*

Platelet Fc Gamma Receptor

Synonyms FCG R2A; Fc Gamma RIIa

Chromosome Location 1q23

Clinically-Important Polymorphisms Nonsynonymous SNP in the extracellular domain of the receptor *(Arg131His)*

Discussion The platelet Fc gamma receptor is widely expressed on hematopoietic cells. There are two known alleles (*131Arg* and *131His*). These differ in their ability to bind to specific proteins. Clearance of autoantibody-sensitized platelets through Fc gamma receptors on phagocytic cells is one of the main mechanisms of thrombocytopenia in idiopathic thrombocytopenic purpura (ITP).

Heparin-induced thrombocytopenia (HIT) is a severe complication of heparin treatment. HIT antibodies activate platelets via the platelet Fc gamma receptor. The impact of this polymorphism on the clinical presentation and course of HIT is under investigation. It has been speculated that reduced clearance of immune complexes in patients with the *131Arg* allele may result in prolonged activation of endothelial cells and platelets, which may lead to thrombotic complications.

Heparin:

The *Arg131His* polymorphism has been associated with an increased risk of type II heparin-induced thrombocytopenia (HIT) (Carlsson, 1998). In a study comparing healthy individuals, patients with a history of HIT, and patients with a history of thrombocytopenia from other causes, the frequency of the *131Arg/Arg* genotype was greater among those with a history of HIT than among the other two groups. In a subgroup of HIT patients studied prospectively, the *131Arg/Arg* genotype was more common among those who developed thromboembolic complications (Carlsson, 1998).

May Alter Pharmacokinetics of Platelet Fc gamma receptor gene is not known to alter the metabolism of any drugs.

May Alter Pharmacodynamics of Heparin

Clinical Recommendations Data suggest that the Fc gamma receptor gene may be useful in identifying patients at high risk for developing HIT in whom alternative anticoagulant therapy should be initiated.

References

Carlsson LE, Santoso S, Baurichter G, et al, "Heparin-Induced Thrombocytopenia: New Insights Into the Impact of the FcgammaRIIa-R-H131 Polymorphism," *Blood*, 1998, 92(5):1526-31.

♦ **PROC** *see* Protein C *on page 313*

Protein C

Synonyms PROC

Chromosome Location 2q13-14

Clinically-Important Polymorphisms Numerous functional defects have been described which result in defective interaction with one or more substrate molecules, including thrombomodulin, phospholipids, factor Va, and factor VIIIa (type II deficiencies). In addition, decreased synthesis of normally functioning protein C has been described (type I).

SNPs at nucleotides -1654 (C/T), -1641 (A/G), and -1476 (A/T) have been identified in the protein C gene promoter region.

Discussion Protein C deficiency predisposes an individual to venous thrombosis and embolic events. First described in 1981, protein C is required to inactivate factor Va and factor VIIIa. Initially thrombomodulin is activated by thrombin. Protein C then combines with thrombomodulin resulting in the activation of Protein C. Activated protein C

(Continued)

Protein C *(Continued)*

may combine with an additional molecule, protein S, on the platelet surface, where it inactivates factor Va and factor VIIIa.

Protein C deficiency is classified as a deficiency of functional protein (type I deficiency), or a functional defect in the synthesized protein in spite of normal circulating concentrations (type II deficiency). Approximately 0.2% of the general population are estimated to have a deficiency of protein C.

The combination of the *-C1654T* and *-A1641G* polymorphisms has been associated with protein C concentrations and risk of venous thromboembolism (Aiach, 1999).

Warfarin:

Skin necrosis is a rare, but potentially severe, complication of warfarin therapy. The risk of this reaction is increased in patients with deficiency in protein C and/or S.

May Alter Pharmacodynamics of Warfarin

Laboratory Evaluation Future studies may support genotyping for the protein C polymorphisms in potential warfarin users with a family history of thrombosis.

Clinical Recommendations Warfarin should be avoided or started in low doses with concurrent heparin therapy and gradually dose increases over several weeks in patients with a genetic predisposition for protein C deficiency.

References

Aiach M, Nicaud V, Alhenc-Gelas M, et al, "Complex Association of Protein C Gene Promoter Polymorphism With Circulating Protein C Levels and Thrombotic Risk," *Arterioscler Thromb Vasc Biol*, 1999, 19(6):1573-6.

Protein S

Chromosome Location 3p11-11.2

Clinically-Important Polymorphisms Numerous abnormalities have been reported, including deficiency in circulating concentrations (type I), unbound form of the protein (type III), and functional defects despite adequate circulating concentrations of protein (type II).

Discussion Protein S is a cofactor for the inactivation of factor Va and factor VIIIa. It acts in conjunction with protein C, which is the protein which is responsible for this inactivation (also see Protein C listing). Activated protein C combines with protein S on platelet surfaces to degrade factor Va and factor VIIIa. Protein S circulates in bound and unbound (free) forms.

Protein S deficiency may be classified according to the nature of the deficiency. Type I protein S deficiency results from inadequate synthesis of protein S, leading to low circulating levels of fully-functional protein. Type II deficiency is defined by functional defects in protein S molecules, which circulate in normal amounts. An unusual deficiency, type III, is related to altered protein binding of protein S, resulting in low concentrations of unbound protein S, although total concentrations are normal. In Caucasians, the incidence of protein S deficiency is between 1% to 5% of persons who experience a venous thrombotic event.

Warfarin:

Skin necrosis is a rare by potentially severe complication of warfarin therapy. The risk of this reaction is increased in patients with deficiency in protein C and/or S.

May Alter Pharmacodynamics of Warfarin

Laboratory Evaluation Future studies may support genotyping for the protein S polymorphisms in potential warfarin users with a family history of thrombosis.

Clinical Recommendations Warfarin should be avoided or started in low doses with concurrent heparin therapy and gradually dose increases over several weeks in patients with a genetic predisposition for protein S deficiency.

Prothrombin

Synonyms PT

Chromosome Location 11p11-12

Clinically-Important Polymorphisms G20210A

Discussion Prothrombin is the circulating precursor to thrombin, which catalyzes the conversion of fibrinogen into fibrin. The variant prothrombin gene results in higher circulating concentrations of thrombin, and results in a hypercoagulable state. Approximately 1% to 2% of the general population is heterozygous for the prothrombin gene mutation. It appears to be more common in Caucasians, and has been found to be relatively uncommon in the native populations of India, Korea, Africa and North America. The highest rate of carriage has been in Spain, where rates as high as 6% have been reported. The G20210A mutation in the prothrombin gene is an established risk factor for venous thrombosis.

Oral contraceptives:

The risk of cerebral vein thrombosis is increased in patients with the prothrombin gene mutation. When coupled with oral contraceptive use, the risk of cerebral vein thrombosis in patients with the G20210A mutation was increased nearly 20-fold, resulting in an odds ratio of 149.3. Since cerebral vein thrombosis is a rare event, the authors concluded that screening for the prothrombin mutation would not be cost-effective (Martinelli, 1998).

May Alter Pharmacokinetics of The prothrombin gene is not known to alter the pharmacokinetics of any drugs

May Alter Pharmacodynamics of Oral contraceptives, estrogen

May Affect Disease Predisposition of Thrombosis

Laboratory Evaluation Screening for the *G20210A* polymorphism should be considered in potential oral contraceptive users with a positive family history of thrombosis.

Clinical Recommendations Individuals with the *20210A* allele who use oral contraceptives are at a markedly increased risk for thromboembolic events. Clinicians should consider alternative contraceptive methods in *20210A* allele carriers, especially if the factor V Leiden mutation is also present.

(Continued)

Prothrombin *(Continued)*

References

Martinelli I, Sacchi E, Landi G, et al, "High Risk of Cerebral-Vein Thrombosis in Carriers of a Prothrombin-Tene Mutation and in Users of Oral Contraceptives," *N Engl J Med*, 1998, 338(25):1793-7.

- **PT** *see* Prothrombin *on page 315*
- **purinergic receptor** *see* P2RY12 *on page 310*
- **Quinone Oxidoreductase** *see* NAD(P)H Quinone Oxidoreductase *on page 309*
- **RCC** *see* XRCC1 *on page 331*
- **RHR** *see* Beta$_1$-Adrenergic Receptor *on page 230*
- **SCN5A** *see* Cardiac Sodium Channel *on page 242*
- **SERT** *see* 5-HT Transporter *on page 297*
- **SLC6A4** *see* 5-HT Transporter *on page 297*

Stromelysin-1

Synonyms MMP3; Matrix Metalloproteinase 3

Chromosome Location 11q22.3

Clinically-Important Polymorphisms Presence of five (5A) or 6 (6A) adenines in the promoter region at nucleotide -1612 [-1612 (5A/6A)]

Discussion Stromelysin-1 is a member of the matrix metalloproteinase family and is believed to be involved in the remodeling of the extracellular matrix of atherosclerotic lesions. The *6A* allele has been associated with reduced stromelysin-1 activity and a faster progression of coronary atherosclerosis (as determined by angiography) (Ye, 1996; de Maat, 1999). The *5A* allele has been associated with an increased risk of acute myocardial infarction in patients with unstable angina.

HMG CoA reductase inhibitors:

Among men with coronary artery disease, pravastatin reduced the incidence of coronary artery restenosis and repeat angioplasty in those with the *5A6A* and *6A6A* genotypes, but not in those with the *5A5A* genotype (de Maat, 1999).

May Alter Pharmacokinetics of Stromelysin-I is not known to alter the metabolism of any drugs.

May Alter Pharmacodynamics of HMG CoA reductase inhibitors

May Affect Disease Predisposition of Atherosclerosis

Clinical Recommendations Data suggest that the stromelysin-1 genotype may be useful in predicting regression of atherosclerotic lesions during HMG CoA reductase inhibitor therapy. However, the effect of this gene on clinical outcomes with HMG CoA reductase inhibitor therapy should be determined before genotyping for the stromelysin-1 polymorphism is considered clinically useful.

Counseling Points Carrier status for the *6A* allele has been associated with greater disease progression in individuals with coronary heart disease. Individuals with coronary heart disease who carry this allele should be encouraged to discuss the implications of their carrier status with their clinician or another healthcare professional.

References

de Maat MP, Jukema JW, Ye S, et al, "Effect of the Stromelysin-1 Promoter on Efficacy of Pravastatin in Coronary Atherosclerosis and Restenosis," *Am J Cardiol*, 1999, 83(6):852-6.

Ye S, Eriksson P, Hamsten A, et al, "Progression of Coronary Atherosclerosis Is Associated With a Common Genetic Variant of the Human Stromelysin-1 Promoter Which Results in Reduced Gene Expression," *J Biol Chem*, 1996, 271(22):13055-60.

Thiopurine Methyltransferase

Synonyms TPMT

Chromosome Location 6p22.3

Clinically-Important Polymorphisms Eight TPMT alleles have been described. However, three alleles account for the majority (80% to 95%) of cases with low or intermediate activity. These are *TPMT*2* (G238C), *TPMT*3A*, and *TPMT*3C*.

Discussion Thiopurine methyltransferase is responsible for the S-methylation of a number of compounds, including azathioprine, mercaptopurine, and thioguanine. A deficiency in this enzyme is inherited as an autosomal recessive trait. Approximately 10% of Caucasians exhibit diminished activity of this enzyme, while 0.3% of patients are estimated to carry a complete deficiency of the enzyme. Patients with diminished, but detectable activity, are heterozygous at the TPMT locus. Of note, aminosalicylates have been identified as inhibitors of this enzyme. Individuals with diminished activity are susceptible to severe, and potentially life-threatening, toxicities following exposure to these agents. The use of standard dosages in a patient with a complete deficiency of this enzyme may be fatal.

Azathioprine:

A heart transplant patient receiving azathioprine as part of routine immunosuppression developed severe neutropenia and sepsis. Ultimately, the episode proved to be fatal, and the patient was demonstrated to have very low TPMT activity (Schutz, 1993).

Mercaptopurine:

The inactivation of mercaptopurine requires metabolism by the enzyme thiopurine methyl transferase (TPMT). TPMT polymorphisms were noted to be substantially over-represented in a population of patients with severe adverse reactions to mercaptopurine (Evans, 2001).

Some centers have initiated screening programs for patients who are to receive chemotherapy of ALL (McLeod, 1999; McLeod, 2000). Dosage adjustments, including a 10-fold to 15-fold reduction in TPMT-deficient patients, and a twofold decrease in heterozygotes, has been reported to permit successful treatment without substantial toxicity.

May Alter Pharmacokinetics of Azathioprine, mercaptopurine (6-MP)

Laboratory Evaluation Commercial testing available

References

Black AJ, McLeod HL, Capell HA, et al, "Thiopurine Methyltransferase Genotype Predicts Therapy-Limiting Severe Toxicity From Azathioprine," *Ann Intern Med*, 1998, 129(9):716-8.

(Continued)

Thiopurine Methyltransferase *(Continued)*

Evans WE, Hon YY, Bomgaars, et al, "Preponderance of Thiopurine S-Methyltransferase Deficiency and Heterozygosity Among Patients Intolerant to Mercaptopurine or Azathioprine," *J Clin Oncol*, 2001, 19(8):2293-301.

McLeod HL, Coulthard S, Thomas AE, et al, "Analysis of Thiopurine Methyltransferase Variant Alleles in Childhood Acute Lymphoblastic Leukaemia," *Br J Hem*, 1999, 105(3):696-700.

McLeod HL, Krynetski EY, Relling MV, et al, "Genetic Polymorphism of Thiopurine Methyltransferase and Its Clinical Relevance for Childhood Acute Lymphoblastic Leukemia," *Leukemia*, 2000, 14(4):567-72.

Schutz E, Gummert J, Mohr F, et al, "Azathioprine-Induced Myelosuppression in Thiopurine Methyltransferase Deficient Heart Transplant Recipient," *Lancet*, 1993, 341(8842):436.

♦ **Thymidylate Synthase** *see* Thymidylate Synthetase *on page 318*

Thymidylate Synthetase

Synonyms TS; TSER; TYMS; Thymidylate Synthase

Chromosome Location 18p11.32

Clinically-Important Polymorphisms TSER*2, TSER*3, TSER*4, TSER*9; TS variants reported to occur in approximately 30% of Caucasians and greater than 60% in those of Chinese descent.

Discussion Thymidylate synthetase catalyzes the reductive methylation of 5,10-methylenetetrahydrofolate to dTMP. Thymidylate synthetase is an important synthetic enzyme, since this reaction is a critical step in the synthesis of DNA.

Fluorouracil:

Thymidylate synthetase is the intracellular target of 5FU. Several studies have demonstrated that induction of this enzyme is associated with fluorouracil resistance, while decreases in tumor expression of thymidylate synthetase are associated with improved sensitivity (Wang, 2001). Endogenous expression is regulated by polymorphic variation in the enhancer region of the thymidylate synthetase gene. A tandem repeat sequence of 28 base pairs may be repeated for two, three, four, or nine copies (*TSER*2, TSER*3, TSER*4, TSER*9*). The presence of these repeated sequences alters enzyme activity. *In vitro* assays demonstrate that thymidylate synthetase expression of the *TSER*3* is 2.6 times that of the *TSER*2* allele.

In an analysis of patients with colon cancer, 29% of patients were homozygous for *TSER*3*, 16% were homozygous for the *TSER*2*, and 55% were heterozygous (Marsh, 2001). From a total of 24 patients who received 5FU, 40% of responders were homozygous for the *TSER*2*, compared to 22% of nonresponders. Individuals with the *TSER*2* polymorphism had an improvement in median survival as compared to the *TSER*3* (16 months vs 12 months).

In 50 patients with disseminated colorectal cancer, those individuals homozygous for the triple repeat (*TSER*3*) showed a 3.6-fold increase in mRNA expression for TS compared to those homozygous for the double repeat. Furthermore, a clinical response to 5FU was observed in 50% (4/8) of patients with the *TSER*2* genotype compared to 9% (2/22) of those with the *TSER*3* (Pullarkat, 2001).

Conflicting data were reported by Jakobsen et al in which 88 patients with metastatic colorectal cancer were retrospectively evaluated for 5FU response rate relative to TSER genotype. Significantly more patients (52%) exhibiting homozygosity for the TSER*3 variant showed clinical response to 5FU, compared to those who were heterozygous (28%) or homozygous wild-types (24%) (p =0.03).

The discrepancy of these data from previous studies may reflect two key elements of experimental design. First, normal tissue samples were used for genotyping in the Jakobsen study as opposed to tumor tissue for the others. The use of normal tissue was cited as a potential advantage for ease in biopsy and reduced contaminatory issues. However, as the site of action for 5FU is in tumor cells, genotyping of normal cells may provide misleading results.

The second issue was the rate of drug administration. Jakobsen's study used a bolus dose of 5FU, rather than continuous infusion. It has been reported that rapid administration of 5FU may preferentially target RNA, while an extended infusion may selectively influence the thymidylate synthase enzyme.

Capecitabine:

As a prodrug, capecitabine is metabolized to 5-fluorouracil in tumor tissues. In a retrospective pilot study of 24 patients with disseminated colorectal cancer, patients were genotyped for the *TSER*2* and *TSER*3* variants of TS. Three of four patients homozygous for *TSER*2* achieved clinical response to capecitabine compared to 2 of 8 homozygous for *TSER*3* and 1 of 12 who were heterozygous (Park, 2002).

May Alter Pharmacokinetics of Fluorouracil, capecitabine

Clinical Recommendations Currently, routine clinical assessment of TS polymorphisms is not recommended.

References

Jakobsen A, Nielsen JN, Gyldenkerne N, et al, "Thymidylate Synthase and Methylenetetrahydrofolate Reductase Gene Polymorphism in Normal Tissue as Predictors of Fluorouracil Sensitivity," *J Clin Oncol*, 2005, 23(7):1365-9.

Marsh S, McKay JA, Cassidy J, et al, "Polymorphism in the Thymidylate Synthase Promoter Enhancer Region in Colorectal Cancer," *Int J Oncol*, 2001, 19(2):383-6.

Park DJ, Stoehlmacher J, Zhang W, et al, "Thymidylate Synthase Gene Polymorphism Predicts Response to Capecitabine in Advanced Colorectal Cancer," *Int J Colorectal Dis*, 2002, 17(1):46-9.

Pullarkat ST, Stoehlmacher J, Ghaderi V, et al, 'Thymidylate Synthase Gene Polymorphism Determines Response and Toxicity of 5-FU Chemotherapy," *Pharmacogenomics J*, 2001, 1(1):65-70.

Wang W, Marsh S, Cassidy J, et al, "Pharmacogenomic Dissection of Resistance to Thymidylate Synthase Inhibitors," *Cancer Res*, 2001, 61(14):5505-10.

TNF-Alpha

Clinically-Important Polymorphisms The *-308G/A* polymorphism has been associated with schizophrenia and a recent report showed a trend of significance between the *A* allele and weight gain from antipsychotics (Basile, 2001). Those genotyped as *A/A* homozygous had a twofold greater weight gain.

(Continued)

TNF-Alpha *(Continued)*

Discussion TNF-alpha is a cytokine that mediates local phagocytic-cell emigration and activation as well as release of lipid-derived mediators such as prostaglandin E2, thromboxane, and platelet-activating factor.

TNF-alpha has been shown to be expressed in adipose tissue and skeletal muscle and TNF-alpha receptors have been discovered in adipocytes (Hotamisligil; 1995; Saghizadeh; 1996). Increased levels of TNF-alpha are known to cause sedation, hyperinsulinemia, insulin resistance, and hypertriglyceridemia (Hotamisligil, 1995; Argiles, 1997).

Clozapine:

Clozapine increases serum levels of TNF-alpha (Hinze-Selch, 2000; Haack, 1999; Pollmacher, 1996). However, 99 schizophrenic patients treated with clozapine and tested for genetic effects of the -308G/A polymorphism suggests that the TNF-alpha gene -308G/A variants do not play a significant role in response to clozapine in patients with schizophrenia (Tsai, 2003).

Olanzapine:

Olanzapine produced a rapid increase in soluble TNF-alpha receptor 1 and TNF-alpha receptor 2 following 1 week of treatment in patients with schizophrenia (Schuld, 2000).

Tricyclic antidepressants:

Activate the TNF-alpha system by increasing TNF-alpha or its soluble receptors (Hinze-Selch, 2000).

May Alter Pharmacodynamics of Clozapine, olanzapine, amitriptyline, paroxetine

References

Argiles JM, Lopez-Soriano J, Busquets S, et al, "Journey From Cachexia to Obesity by TNF," *FASEB J*, 1997, 11(10):743-51.

Basile VS, Masellis M, McIntyre RS, et al, "Genetic Dissection of Atypical Antipsychotic-Induced Weight Gain: Novel Preliminary Data on the Pharmacogenetic Puzzle," *J Clin Psychiatry*, 2001, 62(Suppl 23):45-66.

Haack M, Hinze-Selch D, Fenzel T, et al, "Plasma Levels of Cytokines and Soluble Cytokine Receptors in Psychiatric Patients Upon Hospital Admission: Effects of Confounding Factors and Diagnosis," *J Psychiatr Res*, 1999, 33(5):407-18.

Hinze-Selch D, Schuld A, Kraus T, et al, "Effects of Antidepressants on Weight and on the Plasma Levels of Leptin, TNF-Alpha and Soluble TNF Receptors: A Longitudinal Study in Patients Treated With Amitriptyline or Paroxetine," *Neuropsychopharmacology*, 2000, 23(1):13-9.

Hotamisligil GS, Arner P, Caro JF, et al, "Increased Adipose Tissue Expression of Tumor Necrosis Factor-Alpha in Human Obesity and Insulin Resistance," *J Clin Invest*, 1995, 95(5):2409-15.

Pollmacher T, Hinze-Selch D, and Mullington J, "Effects of Clozapine on Plasma Cytokine and Soluble Cytokine Receptor Levels," *J Clin Psychopharmacol*, 1996, 16(5):403-9.

Saghizadeh M, Ong JM, Garvey WT, et al, "The Expression of TNF Alpha by Human Muscle. Relationship to Insulin Resistance," *J Clin Invest*, 1996, 97(4):1111-6.

Schuld A, Kraus T, Haack M, et al, "Plasma Levels of Cytokines and Soluble Cytokine Receptors During Treatment With Olanzapine," *Schizophr Res*, 2000, 43(2-3):164-6.

Tsai SJ, Hong CJ, Yu YW, et al, "No Association of Tumor Necrosis Factor Alpha Gene Polymorphisms With Schizophrenia or Response to Clozapine," *Schizophr Res*, 2003, 65(1):27-32.

♦ **TP53** *see* p53 *on page 311*

- **TPH** *see* Tryptophan Hydroxylase *on page 321*
- **TPMT** *see* Thiopurine Methyltransferase *on page 317*
- **TRP53** *see* p53 *on page 311*

Tryptophan Hydroxylase

Synonyms TPH

Chromosome Location 12q15 (neuronal); 11p15.3-p14

Clinically-Important Polymorphisms A218C in intron 7

Discussion Tryptophan hydroxylase is the enzyme responsible for the conversion of tryptophan to 5-hydroxytryptophan. It is the rate-limiting enzyme in the production of serotonin. It is not regulated by end product inhibition and brain tryptophan hydroxylase is not saturated with substrate. Therefore, the amount of substrate, tryptophan, controls the amount of serotonin produced.

Several studies have evaluated the role of tryptophan hydroxylase in affective disorders and suicidal behavior. The *A218C* polymorphism was evaluated in 927 patients (527 bipolar, 400 unipolar) in the European Collaborative Project on Affective Disorder study. This study failed to detect an association between the *A218C* polymorphism of the tryptophan hydroxylase gene and bipolar and unipolar disorders in the samples (Souery, 2001).

Fluvoxamine:

A study of the possible effects of the *A218C* variant on the antidepressant activity of fluvoxamine was assessed in 217 inpatients with major and bipolar depression. Patients received fluvoxamine and either placebo or pindolol. No significant finding was observed in the overall sample and the pindolol group. Those patients not taking pindolol with the *TPH*A/A* variant, showed a slower response to fluvoxamine (p=0.001) (Serretti, 2001).

Lithium:

A less than significant association was found with the tryptophan hydroxylase *A/A* genotype and lithium response (Serretti, 1999). One hundred and eight patients with bipolar disorder (n=90) and major depression (n=18) were followed prospectively for an average of 50.4 months to determine the role of tryptophan hydroxylase variants and lithium outcome. Patients with the *A/A* variant showed a trend toward a worse response compared to both the *A/C* and *C/C* variants (Serretti, 1999).

Paroxetine:

Genetic variation in the tryptophan hydroxylase gene has been evaluated with respect to a difference in response to paroxetine therapy. The *A218C* variant was characterized in 121 patients with major depression. The *TPH*A/A* and *TPH*A/C* variants were associated with a decreased response to paroxetine as compared to patients with the *TPH*C/C* genotype (p=0.005). Other variables, including the presence of psychotic features, baseline severity of depressive symptoms and paroxetine plasma level, were not associated with the outcome. *TPH* gene variants may be a marker and/or modulator of paroxetine antidepressant activity (Serretti, 2001).

(Continued)

Tryptophan Hydroxylase *(Continued)*

May Alter Pharmacodynamics of Fluvoxamine, lithium, paroxetine

May Affect Disease Predisposition of Affective disorder

References

Serretti A, Lilli R, Lorenzi C, et al, "Dopamine Receptor D2 and D4 Genes, GABA(A) Alpha$_1$ Subunit Genes and Response to Lithium Prophylaxis in Mood Disorders," *Psychiatry Res,* 1999, 87:7-19.

Serretti A, Lilli R, Lorenzi C, et al, "Tryptophan Hydroxylase Gene and Response to Lithium Prophylaxis in Mood Disorders," *J Psychiatr Res*, 1999, 33(5):371-7.

Serretti A, Zanardi R, Cusin C, et al, "Tryptophan Hydroxylase Gene Associated With Paroxetine Antidepressant Activity," *Eur Neuropsychopharmacol*, 2001, 11(5):375-80.

Serretti A, Zanardi R, Rossini D, et al, "Influence of Tryptophan Hydroxylase and Serotonin Transporter Gene on Fluvoxamine Antidepressant Activity," *Mol Psychiatry*, 2001, 6(5):586-92.

Souery D, Van Gestel S, Massat I, et al, "Tryptophan Hydroxylase Polymorphism and Suicidality in Unipolar and Bipolar Affective Disorders: A Multicenter Association Study," *Biol Psychiatry*, 2001, 49(5):405-9.

♦ **TS** *see* Thymidylate Synthetase *on page 318*

♦ **TSER** *see* Thymidylate Synthetase *on page 318*

♦ **TYMS** *see* Thymidylate Synthetase *on page 318*

♦ **UDP-glucuronosyltransferase 1A1** *see* UDP-Glucuronosyltransferase 1 Family, Polypeptide A1 *on page 322*

♦ **UDP-glucuronosyltransferase 1A7** *see* UDP-Glucuronosyltransferase 1 Family, Polypeptide A7 *on page 323*

♦ **UDP-glucuronosyltransferase 1A9** *see* UDP-Glucuronosyltransferase 1 Family, Polypeptide A9 *on page 326*

UDP-Glucuronosyltransferase 1 Family, Polypeptide A1

Synonyms GNT1; HUG-BR1; UDP-glucuronosyltransferase 1A1; UDPGT; UGT 1A1; UGT1*1; UGT1; UGT1A

Chromosome Location 2q37

Clinically-Important Polymorphisms UGT 1A1*28 refers to the insertion of an additional seventh thymine-adenine sequence (T-A) in the promoter (ie, TATA) region of the UGT 1A1 gene. Normally, 6 repeats (ie, $[TA]_6$) are present in the wild type allele. The $[TA]_7$ genotype may occur in 35% of Caucasians and African-Americans.

Discussion Irinotecan's active metabolite, SN-38 is glucuronidated by the 1A1 isoform of UDP-glucuronosyltransferase. A clinically-important variant, UGT *1A1*28*, is a risk factor for both severe neutropenia and diarrhea. Individuals possessing mutant alleles with 7 or more T-A repeats exhibit reduced gene expression of UDP-glucuronosyltransferase and thus decreased glucuronidation of SN-38. This results in a prolongation of SN-38 half-life and an increase in the AUC (Innocenti, 2002; Iyer, 1999) which may explain the observed increase in toxicity.

Iyer et al, noted that in patients possessing the homozygous mutation of 7 repeats, a significant 2.5-fold lower absolute neutrophil count nadir was observed relative to wild-type patients.

In a prospective study of 66 patients, Innocenti et al, demonstrated a 9.3-fold risk of grade 4 leukopenia in homozygous patients compared to wild-type (p=0.001).

Ando et al, showed a 5.2-fold risk of severe toxicity (either grade 4 leukopenia and/or grade 3/4 diarrhea) in patients either heterozygous or homozygous for the mutation.

It should be noted that severe toxicity may develop in individuals who do not carry this allele, indicating other factors are involved in the development of severe irinotecan toxicity.

May Alter Pharmacokinetics of Irinotecan

May Affect Disease Predisposition of Gilbert's syndrome (hyperbilirubinemia), cholelithiasis

Laboratory Evaluation

Commercial testing available: Invader® UGT1A1 Molecular Assay (Third Wave Technologies, Inc.)

Clinical Recommendations Product labeling for irinotecan recommends dose reduction in patients homozygous for the UGT1A1*28 allele. Caution and possible dose reduction is advised for heterozygous patients.

References

Ando Y, Saka H, Ando M, et al, "Polymorphisms of UDP-Glucuronosyltransferase Gene and Irinotecan Toxicity: A Pharmacogenetic Analysis," *Cancer Res*, 2000, 60(24):6921-6.

Innocenti F and Ratain MJ, "Update on Pharmacogenetics in Cancer Chemotherapy," *Eur J Cancer*, 2002, 38(5):639-44.

Innocenti F, Undevia SD, Iyer L, et al, "Genetic Variants in the UDP-Glucuronosyltransferase 1A1 Gene Predict the Risk of Severe Neutropenia of Irinotecan," *J Clin Oncol*, 2004, 22(8):1382-8.

Iyer L, Hall D, Das S, et al, "Phenotype-Genotype Correlation of *in vitro* SN-38 (Active Metabolite of Irinotecan) and Bilirubin Glucuronidation in Human Liver Tissue With UGT1A1 Promoter Polymorphism," *Clin Pharmacol Ther*, 1999, 65(5):576-82.

Lee W, Lockhart AC, Kim RB, et al, "Cancer Pharmacogenomics: Powerful Tools in Cancer Chemotherapy and Drug Development," *Oncologist*, 2005, 10(2):104-11.

McLeod HL and Watters JW, "Irinotecan Pharmacogenetics: Is It Time to Intervene?" *J Clin Oncol*, 2004, 22(8):1356-9.

UDP-Glucuronosyltransferase 1 Family, Polypeptide A7

Synonyms UDP-glucuronosyltransferase 1A7; UDPGT; UGT 1A7; UGT1*7; UGT1G

Chromosome Location 2q37

Clinically-Important Polymorphisms Six nucleotide polymorphisms have been reported in the coding region of exon 1, of which four (T387G, C391A/G392/A, G391A, T622C) are nonsynonymous. These 4 SNPs give rise to amino acid changes of Asn129Lys, Arg131Lys, and Trp208Arg, respectively. The amino acid changes at peptide positions 129 and 131 are in linkage disequilibrium creating four variant alleles: *UGT1A7*1* ($N^{129}R^{131}W^{208}$), *UGT1A7*2* ($K^{129}K^{131}W^{208}$), *UGT1A7*3* ($K^{129}K^{131}R^{208}$), and *UGT1A7*4*($N^{129}R^{131}R^{208}$). The frequencies of these alleles in Caucasian populations have been reported to be 36%, 26%, 36%, and 1.7%, respectively. The variant alleles (ie, *2,

(Continued)

UDP-Glucuronosyltransferase 1 Family, Polypeptide A7 *(Continued)*

*3, *4) encode for proteins with reduced activity (50-73%) compared to the wild-type enzyme (Guillemette, 2000)

Discussion The UDP-glucuronosyltransferase superfamily of enzymes provides critical detoxification of various xenobiotics (McLeod, 2004). A commonly discussed substrate is the active metabolite of irinotecan, SN-38, which requires glucuronidation by UDP enzymes for renal and hepatic clearance. Reduced glucuronidation results in plasma accumulation of the metabolite and increased toxicities, notably grade 3 or 4 neutropenia. Based on its abundance in hepatic and extrahepatic sites, attention has been focused on the contributions of the UGT1A1 subfamily peptides in the metabolism of irinotecan. However, a number of reports cite the importance of additional isozymes, namely the UGT1A7 and UGT1A9 isoforms, in the metabolic clearance of irinotecan, and possibly other compounds (Gagne, 2002; Villeneuve, 2003; Tukey, 2002; Carlini, 2005). In a stable human cell line expressing UGT1A proteins, Gagne et al, evaluated the enzymatic efficiencies (Vmax/Km) of the various isoforms. Compared to other UDP enzymes, UGT1A1, 1A7, and 1A9 were shown to be the most efficient in the glucuronoidation of SN-38 *in vitro*. Unlike the other isoforms, UGT1A7 expression is considered exclusively extrahepatic, with transcripts detected in proximal regions of the GI tract, including the stomach and esophagus (Tukey, 2002; Strassburg, 1997).

Irinotecan:

In a study of 67 patients with metastatic colorectal cancer, patients receiving irinotecan (100 or 125 mg/m^2 I.V. days 1 and 8) in combination with capecitabine (900 or 1,000 mg/m^2 twice daily) were genotyped for variant alleles of *UGT1A1*, *UGT1A7*, *UGT1A9* in association with drug response and toxicity (Carlini, 2005). A significant gene-dose response trend was observed for *UGT1A7*, such that patients with homozygosity for the low activity phenotypes (*UGT1A7*2* or *UGT1A7*3*) demonstrated a high rate of response (85%) compared to heterozygotes (46-50%) and wild-types (33%, $p = 0.017$ for trend). Surprisingly, patients exhibiting the *UGT1A7*2/*2* or *UGT1A7*3/*3* were devoid of toxicity defined as grade 3 or 4 diarrhea or neutropenia, which was highly significant in comparison to all other groups ($p = 0.003$). Interestingly, patients exhibiting the low activity genotypes of *UGT1A1* also demonstrated reduced toxicity, in contrast with previous reports (Ando, 2000; Innocenti, 2004).

Previous studies have suggested that low activity phenotypes predispose patients to systemic toxicity (Ando, 2000; Innocenti, 2004). A developing line of thought suggests that hematologic and gastrointestinal toxicities may occur in a somewhat mutually exclusive manner. Hepatic glucuronidation is known to enhance removal of the drug via the biliary route. Ironically, the presence of intestinal bacterial glucuronidases provide a mechanism of SN-38 regeneration intraluminally, resulting in high localized exposure to SN-38 leading to mucosal lesions (Tukey, 2002; Carlini, 2005). Thus, enhanced systemic detoxification (by increased glucuronidative metabolism) may reduce the occurrence of neutropenia, but conversely increase the incidence of diarrhea simply through biliary shunting of SN-38G (glucuronide).

Another consideration relative to the occurrence of side effects is the dosage regimen employed. Studies documenting grade 3/4 neutropenic episodes have reported on patients receiving higher doses (≥300 mg /m^2), though less frequently administered (Ando, 2000; Iyer, 1999; Innocenti, 2004). In contrast, the dosing schedule reported by Carlini et al, utilized 100-125 mg/m^2 irinotecan given once per week. Toxicity was observed in 19 of 22 patients presenting with grade 3/4 diarrhea, with the remaining 3 patients experiencing severe neutropenia (± diarrhea).

As each of the UGT isozymes has been shown to participate in SN-38 glucuronidation reactions, it is difficult to precisely determine the relative contributions of the different forms of the enzyme to the overall metabolism of irinotecan. As the Carlini study did not quantify protein or drug levels, one cannot determine the strength of association between therapeutic response, toxicity and genotype.

Of course, other factors presumably play a role in the local accumulation of SN-38, including various efflux and transluminal transporter proteins. The contributions of these proteins (and their genetically regulated expression patterns) will need to be considered as well.

May Alter Pharmacokinetics of Irinotecan

Clinical Recommendations Currently, routine clinical assessment of UGT polymorphisms is not recommended.

References

Ando Y, Saka H, Ando M, et al, "Polymorphisms of UDP-Glucuronosyltransferase Gene and Irinotecan Toxicity: A Pharmacogenetic Analysis," *Cancer Res*, 2000, 60(24):6921-6.

Carlini LE, Meropol NJ, Bever J, et al, "UGT1A7 and UGT1A9 Polymorphisms Predict Response and Toxicity in Colorectal Cancer Patients Treated With Capecitabine/Irinotecan," *Clin Cancer Res*, 2005, 11(3):1226-36.

Gagne JF, Montminy V, Belanger P, et al, "Common Human UGT1A Polymorphisms and the Altered Metabolism of Irinotecan Active Metabolite 7-Ethyl-10-Hydroxycamptothecin (SN-38)," *Mol Pharmacol*, 2002, 62(3):608-17.

Guillemette C, Ritter JK, Auyeung DJ, et al, "Structural Heterogeneity at the UDP-Glucuronosyltransferase 1 Locus: Functional Consequences of Three Novel Missense Mutations in the Human UGT1A7 Gene," *Pharmacogenetics*, 2000, 10(7):629-44.

Innocenti F, Undevia SD, Iyer L, et al, "Genetic Variants in the UDP-Glucuronosyltransferase 1A1 Gene Predict the Risk of Severe Neutropenia of Irinotecan," *J Clin Oncol*, 2004, 22(8):1382-8.

Iyer L, Hall D, Das S, et al, "Phenotype-Genotype Correlation of *In Vitro* SN-38 (Active Metabolite of Irinotecan) and Bilirubin Glucuronidation in Human Liver Tissue With UGT1A1 Promoter Polymorphism," *Clin Pharmacol Ther*, 1999, 65(5):576-82.

McLeod HL and Watters JW, "Irinotecan Pharmacogenetics: Is it Time to Intervene?" *J Clin Oncol*, 2004, 22(8):1356-9.

Strassburg CP, Oldhafer K, Manns MP, et al, "Differential Expression of the UGT1A Locus in Human Liver, Biliary, and Gastric Tissue: Identification of UGT1A7 and UGT1A10 Transcripts in Extrahepatic Tissue," *Mol Pharmacol*, 1997, 52(2):212-20.

(Continued)

UDP-Glucuronosyltransferase 1 Family, Polypeptide A7 *(Continued)*

Tukey RH, Strassburg CP, and Mackenzie PI, "Pharmacogenomics of Human UDP-Glucuronosyltransferases and Irinotecan Toxicity," *Mol Pharmacol*, 2002, 62(3):446-50.

Villeneuve L, Girard H, Fortier LC, et al, "Novel Functional Polymorphisms in the UGT1A7 and UGT1A9 Glucuronidating Enzymes in Caucasian and African-American Subjects and Their Impact on the Metabolism of 7-Ethyl-10-Hydroxycamptothecin and Flavopiridol Anticancer Drugs," *J Pharmacol Exp Ther*, 2003, 307(1):117-28.

UDP-Glucuronosyltransferase 1 Family, Polypeptide A9

Synonyms HLUGP4; LUGP4; UDP-glucuronosyltransferase 1A9; UDPGT; UGT 1A9; UGT1AI

Chromosome Location 2q37

Clinically-Important Polymorphisms A common polymorphism within the promoter region of *UGT1A9* gene has been characterized in a small multiethnic population (Yamanaka, 2004). *UGT1A9*22* refers to the insertion of an additional thymidine base in an upstream region (nucleotide -118) of the gene, possibly functioning as the TATA sequence regulating transcriptional efficiency. The wild-type sequence is $A(T)_9AT$; the allelic frequencies of the variant $A(T)_{10}AT$ sequence among a small group of Caucasians (n=50), Japanese (n=87) and African-Americans (n=50) was reported to be 39%, 60% and 44%, respectively. Based on a luciferase assay method, the transcriptional activity of this variant promoter region is 2.6-fold higher than the wild-type gene, suggesting increased cellular protein content.

Discussion The UDP-glucuronosyltransferase superfamily of enzymes provides critical detoxification of various xenobiotics. A commonly discussed substrate is the active metabolite of irinotecan, SN-38, which requires glucuronidation by UDP enzymes for renal and hepatic clearance. Reduced glucuronidation results in plasma accumulation of the metabolite and increased toxicities, notably grade 3 or 4 neutropenia. Based on its abundance in hepatic and extrahepatic sites, attention has been focused on the contributions of the UGT1A1 subfamily peptides in the metabolism of irinotecan. However, a number of reports cite the importance of additional isozymes namely the UGT1A7 and UGT1A9 isoforms, in the metabolic clearance of irinotecan, and possibly other compounds (Gagne, 2002; Villeneuve, 2003; Tukey, 2002; Carlini, 2005). In a stable human cell line expressing UGT1A proteins, Gagne et al, evaluated the enzymatic efficiencies (Vmax/Km) of the various isoforms. Compared to other UDP enzymes, UGT1A1, 1A7, and 1A9 were shown to be the most efficient in the glucuronidation of SN-38 *in vitro*. UGT1A9 is widely expressed in a variety of tissues, including liver, kidney, stomach, small intestine, testis, ovary, and prostate (Burchell, 2001; Albert, 1999).

Irinotecan:

In a study of 67 patients with metastatic colorectal cancer, patients receiving irinotecan (100 or 125 mg/m^2 I.V. days 1 and 8) in combination with capecitabine (900 or 1,000 mg/m^2 twice daily) were evaluated for variant alleles of *UGT1A1*, *UGT1A7*, *UGT1A9* with respect to drug response and toxicity (Carlini, 2005). Presence of 1 or 2 copies of the variant allele was associated with lower responses (49% and 30%, respectively) as compared to the homozygous wild-type patients (74%, $p = 0.033$ for trend). The lower (transcriptional) activity wild-type *UGT1A9* allele showed complete linkage with the lower (metabolic) activity genotypes *UGT1A7*2* or *UGT1A7*3* (likelihood ratio test of association $p < 0.0001$). Thus, it was not surprising that a similar trend was noted for *UGT1A7*, such that patients homozygous for the low activity phenotypes (*UGT1A7*2* or *UGT1A7*3*) demonstrated a higher response rate (85%) compared to heterozygotes (46-50%) and wild-types (33%, $p = 0.017$ for trend). In addition, the incidence of severe toxicity, as defined by grade 3 or 4 diarrhea or neutropenia was significantly lower in the *UGT1A9* wild-type group (5%) compared to carriers of the variant alleles (30-49%).

Previous studies have suggested that low activity phenotypes predispose patients to systemic toxicity (Ando, 2000; Innocenti, 2004). A developing line of thought suggests that hematologic and gastrointestinal toxicities may occur in a somewhat mutually exclusive manner. Hepatic glucuronidation is known to enhance removal of the drug via the biliary route. Ironically, the presence of intestinal bacterial glucuronidases provide a mechanism of SN-38 regeneration intraluminally, resulting in high localized exposure to SN-38 leading to mucosal lesions (Tukey, 2002; Carlini, 2005). Thus, enhanced systemic detoxification (by increased glucuronidative metabolism) may reduce the occurrence of neutropenia, but conversely increase the incidence of diarrhea simply through biliary shunting of SN-38G (glucuronide).

Another consideration relative to the occurrence of side effects is the dosage regimen employed. Studies documenting grade 3/4 neutropenic episodes have reported on patients receiving higher doses (≥300 mg/m^2), though less frequently administered (Ando, 2000; Iyer, 1999; Innocenti, 2004). In contrast, the dosing schedule reported by Carlini et al, utilized 100-125 mg/m^2 irinotecan given once per week. Toxicity was observed in 19 of 22 patients presenting with grade 3/4 diarrhea, with the remaining 3 patients experiencing severe neutropenia (± diarrhea).

As each of the UGT isozymes has been shown to participate in SN-38 glucuronidation reactions, it is difficult to precisely determine the relative contributions of the different forms of the enzyme to the overall metabolism of irinotecan. As the Carlini study did not quantify protein or drug levels, one cannot determine the strength of association between therapeutic response, toxicity and genotype.

(Continued)

UDP-Glucuronosyltransferase 1 Family, Polypeptide A9 *(Continued)*

Importantly, other factors may play a role in the local accumulation of SN-38, including various efflux and transluminal transporter proteins. The contributions of these proteins (and their genetically regulated expression patterns) will need to be considered as well.

May Alter Pharmacokinetics of Irinotecan, mycophenolate

Clinical Recommendations

Currently, routine clinical assessment of UGT polymorphisms (other than the *UGT1A1*28* allele) is not recommended.

References

Albert C, Vallee M, Beaudry G, et al, "The Monkey and Human Uridine Diphosphate-Glucuronosyltransferase UGT1A9, Expressed in Steroid Target Tissues, are Estrogen-Conjugating Enzymes," *Endocrinology*, 1999, 140(7):3292-302.

Ando Y, Saka H, Ando M, et al, "Polymorphisms of UDP-Glucuronosyltransferase Gene and Irinotecan Toxicity: A Pharmacogenetic Analysis," *Cancer Res*, 2000, 60(24):6921-6.

Burchell B, Ethell B, Coffey MJ et al, "Interindividual Variation of UDP-Glucuronosyltransferase and Drug Glucuronidation," *Interindividual Variability in Human Drug Metabolism*, Pacifici GM and Pelkonen A, eds, London: Taylor & Francis, 2001, 358-94.

Carlini LE, Meropol NJ, Bever J, et al, "UGT1A7 and UGT1A9 Polymorphisms Predict Response and Toxicity in Colorectal Cancer Patients Treated With Capecitabine/Irinotecan," *Clin Cancer Res*, 2005, 11(3):1226-36.

Gagne JF, Montminy V, Belanger P, et al, "Common Human UGT1A Polymorphisms and the Altered Metabolism of Irinotecan Active Metabolite 7-Ethyl-10-Hydroxycamptothecin (SN-38)," *Mol Pharmacol*, 2002, 62(3):608-17.

Innocenti F, Undevia SD, Iyer L, et al, "Genetic Variants in the UDP-Glucuronosyltransferase 1A1 Gene Predict the Risk of Severe Neutropenia of Irinotecan," *J Clin Oncol*, 2004, 22(8):1382-8.

Iyer L, Hall D, Das S, et al, "Phenotype-Genotype Correlation of *In Vitro* SN-38 (Active Metabolite of Irinotecan) and Bilirubin Glucuronidation in Human Liver Tissue With UGT1A1 Promoter Polymorphism," *Clin Pharmacol Ther*, 1999, 65(5):576-82.

Tukey RH, Strassburg CP, and Mackenzie PI, "Pharmacogenomics of Human UDP-Glucuronosyltransferases and Irinotecan Toxicity," *Mol Pharmacol*, 2002, 62(3):446-50.

Villeneuve L, Girard H, Fortier LC, et al, "Novel Functional Polymorphisms in the UGT1A7 and UGT1A9 Glucuronidating Enzymes in Caucasian and African-American Subjects and Their Impact on the Metabolism of 7-Ethyl-10-Hydroxycamptothecin and Flavopiridol Anticancer Drugs," *J Pharmacol Exp Ther*, 2003, 307(1):117-28.

Yamanaka H, Nakajima M, Katoh M, et al, "A Novel Polymorphism in the Promoter Region of Human UGT1A9 Gene (UGT1A9*22) and its Effects on the Transcriptional Activity," *Pharmacogenetics*, 2004, 14(5):329-32.

♦ **UDPGT** *see* UDP-Glucuronosyltransferase 1 Family, Polypeptide A1 *on page 322*

♦ **UGT1** *see* UDP-Glucuronosyltransferase 1 Family, Polypeptide A1 *on page 322*

♦ **UGT1*1** *see* UDP-Glucuronosyltransferase 1 Family, Polypeptide A1 *on page 322*

♦ **UGT1*7** *see* UDP-Glucuronosyltransferase 1 Family, Polypeptide A7 *on page 323*

♦ **UGT1A** *see* UDP-Glucuronosyltransferase 1 Family, Polypeptide A1 *on page 322*

- **UGT 1A1** *see* UDP-Glucuronosyltransferase 1 Family, Polypeptide A1 *on page 322*
- **UGT 1A7** *see* UDP-Glucuronosyltransferase 1 Family, Polypeptide A7 *on page 323*
- **UGT 1A9** *see* UDP-Glucuronosyltransferase 1 Family, Polypeptide A9 *on page 326*
- **UGT1AI** *see* UDP-Glucuronosyltransferase 1 Family, Polypeptide A9 *on page 326*
- **UGT1G** *see* UDP-Glucuronosyltransferase 1 Family, Polypeptide A7 *on page 323*
- **UV20** *see* Excision Repair Cross-Complementing Rodent Repair Deficiency, Complementation Group 1 *on page 274*
- **val-COMT** *see* COMT *on page 244*

Vitamin K Epoxide Reductase Complex, Subunit 1

Synonyms VKOR; VKORC1

Chromosome Location 16p11.2

Clinically-Important Polymorphisms Consistent data on the occurrence and location of specific polymorphisms are not available. However, a report by Rieder et al, described 7 noncoding SNPs at positions 381, 3673, 5808, 6484, 6853, 7566, and 9041 that significantly correlated with warfarin dosing.

Discussion Vitamin K epoxide reductase is the enzymatic product of the VKORC1 gene. This enzyme catalyzes the reduction of vitamin K 2,3-epoxide to its active reduced form, enabling the carboxylation of glutamic acid residues required for the function of coagulation factors II, VII, IX, X, proteins C and S. This reductase is the therapeutic target of the vitamin K antagonist warfarin. Several polymorphisms have been described in the promoter, coding, noncoding, and 3' untranslated regions of the gene, with some mutations conferring differential sensitivity to warfarin. Several of the SNPs leading to variant forms of the reductase have been characterized, yet delineation of which individual SNPs or haplotypes are crucial for enzyme function have not been conclusively determined.

Warfarin:

A report by Rieder et al, provides some clarity of this issue by systematically genotyping 186 European-American patients seen at an anticoagulation clinic. From this population, several SNPs were identified which significantly correlated with warfarin dose. Evaluating these SNPs in conjunction with samples from an ethnic diversity panel (DNA samples derived from individuals of European, Asian, and African descent and purchased from the Coriell Cell Repository), allowed for the characterization of 9 distinct haplotypes, of which 5 occurred with a frequency >5%. Analysis of these haplotypes as a function of maintenance warfarin dose allowed for stratification into 2 distinct haplotype groups. These two groups, A (low dose) and B (high dose), thus allowed for 3 potential combinatorial allele pairs: A/A, A/B, or B/B. In this study, there was

(Continued)

Vitamin K Epoxide Reductase Complex, Subunit 1 *(Continued)*

a significant dose/haplotype relationship, such that daily maintenance doses of warfarin discriminated as follows: 2.7±0.2 mg, 4.9±0.2 mg, and 6.2±0.3 mg for the halpotype pairs, respectively ($p<0.001$). In a separate analysis of human liver samples, there was a significantly greater VKORC1 mRNA level detected in B/B tissue samples compared to A/A samples ($p<0.05$) possibly suggesting that this dose effect reflects differential protein expression patterns.

A similar genotype/dose-response relationship was previously evaluated in a group of 147 patients of Italian descent. D'Andrea et al, described patients exhibiting a common 1173C>T SNP (which corresponds to the SNP identified at location 6484 in the Rieder study) occurring with frequencies of 37%, 47%, and 16% for the wild-type (CC), heterozygous (CT), and homozygous (TT) genotypes. Warfarin dosing in this study closely paralleled genotype distribution with mean daily doses of 6.2 mg, 4.8 mg ($p=0.002$ vs wild-type), and 3.5 mg ($p<0.001$ vs wild-type), respectively.

May Alter Pharmacodynamics of Warfarin, vitamin K

May Affect Disease Predisposition of Prophylaxis of venous-or arterial thrombosis

Clinical Recommendations There is no recommendation for prospective genotyping of VKORC1 status at this time.

References

D'Andrea G, D'Ambrosio RL, Di Perna P, et al, "A Polymorphism in the VKORC1 Gene is Associated With an Interindividual Variability in the Dose-Anticoagulant Effect of Warfarin," *Blood*, 2005, 105(2):645-9.

Rieder MJ, Reiner AP, Gage BF, et al, "Effect of VKORC1 Haplotypes on Transcriptional Regulation and Warfarin Dose," *N Engl J Med*, 2005, 352(22):2285-93.

♦ **VKOR** *see* Vitamin K Epoxide Reductase Complex, Subunit 1 *on page 329*

♦ **VKORC1** *see* Vitamin K Epoxide Reductase Complex, Subunit 1 *on page 329*

Xeroderma Pigmentosum, Complementation Group C

Synonyms XP3; XPC; XPCC

Chromosome Location 3p25

Clinically-Important Polymorphisms Exon 15 ($A_{2920}C$, $Lys_{939}Gln$), Intron 11, Intron 9 PAT

Discussion A rare inherited disorder, xeroderma pigmentosum, is associated with a high risk of malignancy. Through the investigation of this syndrome, a number of genes which encode proteins for DNA repair have been identified. Collectively, these are known as the XP genes. The XPC gene encodes a protein which participates in DNA repair following genotoxic events. Two pathways have been described which perform nucleotide excision repair - a transcription-coupled repair pathway and a global genome repair pathway. The XPC protein is part of a protein complex which recognizes distortions in the DNA helix and initiates nucleotide excision repair. It plays an important role in the global nucleotide excision repair pathway. The mRNA and protein products of the XPC gene have been shown to be induced by UV exposure and are regulated by the tumor suppressor protein p53 (Adimoolam, 2002). The distribution of the XPC intron 11 splice acceptor polymorphism when compared with the other two polymorphisms in the XPC gene: a poly(AT) insertion/deletion polymorphism in intron 9 (PAT) and a SNP in XPC exon 15 show that these three markers are in linkage disequilibrium and are consistent with a haplotype of PAT^-/intron 11 C/exon 15 A in ~60% of the donors and PAT^+/ intron 11 A/exon 15 C in ~40% of the donors of normal volunteers.

May Alter Pharmacodynamics of Platinum compounds

May Affect Disease Predisposition of Lung cancer, skin cancer

Clinical Recommendations There is currently no clinically available test for XPC polymorphisms, and XPC polymorphisms as predictors of clinical response to cisplatin have not been prospectively validated. Analysis is not currently recommended for routine use.

References

Adimoolam S and Ford JM, "p53 and DNA Damage-Inducible Expression of the Xeroderma Pigmentosum Group C Gene," *Proc Natl Acad Sci U S A*, 2002, 99(20):12985-90.

Khan SG, Muniz-Medina V, Shahlavi T, et al, "The Human XPC DNA Repair Gene: Arrangement, Splice Site Information Content and Influence of a Single Nucleotide Polymorphism in a Splice Acceptor Site on Alternative Splicing and Function," *Nucleic Acids Research*, 2002, 30(16):3624-31.

Vodicka P, Kumar R, Stetina R, et al, "Genetic Polymorphisms in DNA Repair Genes and Possible Links With DNA Repair Rates, Chromosomal Aberrations and Single-strand Breaks in DNA," *Carcinogenesis*, 2004, 25(5):757-63.

♦ **xeroderma pigmentosum group D** *see* Excision Repair Cross-Complementing Rodent Repair Deficiency, Complementation Group 2 *on page 277*

♦ **XP3** *see* Xeroderma Pigmentosum, Complementation Group C *on page 330*

♦ **XPC** *see* Xeroderma Pigmentosum, Complementation Group C *on page 330*

♦ **XPCC** *see* Xeroderma Pigmentosum, Complementation Group C *on page 330*

♦ **XPD** *see* Excision Repair Cross-Complementing Rodent Repair Deficiency, Complementation Group 2 *on page 277*

♦ **X-ray Repair Complementing Defective Repair in Chinese Hamster Cells 1** *see* XRCC1 *on page 331*

XRCC1

Synonyms RCC; X-ray Repair Complementing Defective Repair in Chinese Hamster Cells 1

Clinically-Important Polymorphisms Arg399Gly

Discussion The protein encoded by the XRCC1 gene is involved in the efficient repair of DNA single-strand breaks. This protein interacts with a number of other enzymes in the base excision repair pathway, and plays an important role in repairing DNA damage from exposure to ionizing radiation and alkylating agents. A deficiency in DNA repair

(Continued)

XRCC1 *(Continued)*

pathways has been associated with resistance to some chemotherapeutic agents. The *Arg399Gly* substitution in the XRCC1 gene is associated with increased levels of markers of DNA damage. This SNP in exon 10 of the gene, has been linked to functional changes and cancer risk. The polymorphism is common, with a variant frequency of approximately 30% in patients with NSCLC.

Cisplatin:

In an evaluation of more than 1000 subjects with NSCLC treated with cisplatin, Gurubhagavatula and collegues showed that the XRCC1 *Gly* polymorphism predicted poorer overall survival. Individuals who were wild-type or heterozygous had a median survival of 11.4-17.3 months compared to individuals homozygous for the *Asn* allele with a median survival of 7.7 months.

Oxaliplatin and 5-FU:

A polymorphism of XRCC1 gene was evaluated as a predictor of response and survival in patients with metastatic colorectal cancer following treatment with oxaliplatin and 5-FU. In this population, 66% (33/50) of nonresponders carried at least one mutant allele (a *Gln/Gln* or *Gln/Arg* genotype). The mutant allele was associated with a more than 5-fold increase in the risk of chemotherapy failure.

May Alter Pharmacodynamics of Platinum-derivative chemotherapy

May Affect Disease Predisposition of Mutations of CRCC1 have been associated with a variety of cancer types

References

Gurubhagavatula S, Lin G, Park S, et al, "XPD and ERCC1 Genetic Polymorphisms Are Prognostic Indicators in Advanced Nonsmall-cell Lung Cancer Patients Treated With Platinum Chemotherapy," *J Clin Oncol*, 2004, 22:2594-601.

Stoehlmacher J, Ghaderi V, Iobal S, et al, "A Polymorphism of the XRCC1 Gene Predicts for Response to Platinum-Based Treatment in Advanced Colorectal Cancer," *Anticancer Res*, 2001, 21(4B):3075-9.

POLYMORPHISM AND DRUGS POTENTIALLY AFFECTED INDEX

Adipocyte-Derived Leucine Aminopeptidase

Aldosterone Synthase

$Alpha_1$-Adrenergic Receptor

Alpha-Adducin

Angiotensin II Type 1 Receptor

Angiotensin-Converting Enzyme

Angiotensinogen

ATP-Binding Cassette, Sub-Family B, Member 1 *(Continued)*

Beta$_1$-Adrenergic Receptor

BRCA Genes

Cardiac Potassium Ion Channel

Cardiac Sodium Channel

Cholesteryl Ester Transfer Protein

COMT

CYP1A2

CYP2C8

CYP2C9

(Continued)

CYP2C9 *(Continued)*

CYP2C19

CYP2D6

CYP3A4

(Continued)

CYP3A4 *(Continued)*

D_2 Receptor

D_3 Receptor

D_4 Receptor

Dihydropyrimidine Dehydrogenase

Glucose-6-Phosphate Dehydrogenase *(Continued)*

Glutathione-S-Transferase

Glutathione-S-Transferase Alpha 1

Glutathione-S-Transferase Pi

Glycoprotein IIIa Receptor

G-Protein Beta$_3$ Subunit

Gs Protein Alpha-Subunit

(Continued)

ALPHABETICAL INDEX

ALPHABETICAL INDEX

NOTES

Other Products Offered by LEXI-COMP®

MENTAL HEALTH SERIES™

Drug Information Handbook for Psychiatry
Psychotropic Drug Information Handbook
Rating Scales in Mental Health
A Patient Guide to Mental Health Issues - Flip chart

DENTAL REFERENCE LIBRARY™

Clinician's Endodontic Handbook
Dental Insurance And Reimbursement
Dental Office Medical Emergencies
Employee Embezzlement And Fraud In The Dental Office
Illustrated Handbook of Clinical Dentistry
Little Dental Drug Booklet
Manual of Clinical Periodontics
Manual of Dental Implants
Oral Hard Tissue Diseases
Oral Soft Tissue Diseases
Patient Guide to Dental Implants - Flip chart & Booklet
Patient Guide to Periodontal Disease - Flip chart
Patient Guide to Root Canal Therapy - Flip chart
Your Roadmap To Financial Integrity In The Dental Office

OTHER

Medical Abbreviations by Neil Davis